THE AUDUBON
NATURE
ENCYCLOPEDIA

THE AUDUBON
NATURE
ENCYCLOPEDIA

SPONSORED BY THE NATIONAL AUDUBON SOCIETY

VOLUME 11

TE-WE

CURTIS BOOKS
A division of
The Curtis Publishing Company
Philadelphia — New York

CREATED AND PRODUCED BY
COPYLAB PUBLISHING COUNSEL, INC., NEW YORK

Copyright © 1965
by
National Audubon Society, Inc.

Published simultaneously in Canada by
Curtis Distributing Company, Ltd., Toronto.

Printed in the United States of America

PICTORIAL ACKNOWLEDGEMENTS, Volume 11

Allan D. Cruickshank*, VIII, 1994, 1995 top, 2008, 2009, 2011, 2015, 2016-17, 2020, 2023, 2032, 2040, 2074, 2079, 2105, 2106, 2111, 2112, 2120, 2121, 2130, 2174-75 —John K. Terres, 1993, 2006 —National Park Service, 1995 bottom —Girl Scouts of the United States, 1996 —Brooklyn Botanic Garden, 1997 —Edward Hill*, 2000 —Roger T. Peterson*, 2003, 2010, 2013, 2031 bottom —Allan Brooks, 2012, 2113, 2114, 2115, 2116, 2133, 2134, 2135, 2136, 2137, 2138, 2139, 2140, 2141 —Dade Thornton*, 2025 —George Porter*, 2026, 2028, 2029, 2063, 2064 top and right, 2123 —Lena Scott Harris, 2030, 2031 top, 2067 top, 2109 —Cleveland Press, 2035 —United States Department of Agriculture, 2038, 2153, 2155, 2168, 2169, 2172 —E. Peterson, 2041 —John H. Gerard*, 2042, 2058, 2080 —John W. Thomson, 2048-49, 2050-51, 2054 —National Audubon Society, 2056 —Charles E. Mohr*, 2061, 2064 bottom left —Lee Adams, 2065, 2066, 2110 —George M. Sutton, 2067 bottom —The New York State Conservationist, 2069, 2072-73, 2077, 2147 —Michael H. Bevans, 2071, 2125 —Zoological Society of Philadelphia, 2075, 2081 —A. Starkey, 2082 —Dur Morton*, 2083 —Lucylle Lamb, 2108 —Hal Harrison*, 2117 —A. Sprunt*, 2118 —R. Bruce Horsfall, 2119 —R.D. Muir*, 2122 —William Sholes, 2126 (courtesy of the United States Department of the Interior, Fish and Wildlife Service) —Lynwood M. Chace*, 2145 —Howard E. Evans, 2143 —United States Soil Conservation Service, 2157 —United States Forest Service, 2158 —United States Department of Health Education and Welfare, 2164 —United States Army Engineering Division, North Pacific, 2165 —United States Fish and Wildlife Service, 2176-77 —Walter Ferguson, 2178-79 —Roland C. Clement, 2181 —G. Ronald Austing*, 2182 —Audubon's Elephant Folio, 2184 —W.D. Berry, 2186 —United States Weather Bureau, 2187, 2192 —Roy Kligfield, 2089 —Verna Johnston*, 2095 —C. H. Baynes, 2101 —United States Forest Service, 2170

*Photographs from Photo-Film Department of National Audubon Society

A least tern settles down on her two speckled eggs laid in a shallow depression

TERN

Of the 13 terns that occur north of Mexico, 8 species are fairly common on both coasts, and some occur on inland lakes and rivers.

The largest of these is the Caspian tern, *Hydroprogne caspia*, breeding on both coasts and the Great Lakes. It has a shaggy crest, a blood-red bill, and a slightly forked tail. Nearest to it is the slightly smaller royal tern, *Thalasseus maximus*, with an orange bill and a more deeply forked tail. The royal tern is more of a southern bird ranging from Virginia and from San Francisco Bay south.

The gull-billed, Forster's, and arctic terns are of about the same size as the common tern *Sterna hirundo*. The gull-billed tern, *Gelochelidon nilotica*, is the only tern with a heavy, black, gull-like bill. Forster's tern, *Sterna forsteri*, has whiter wing tips than the common tern, and in winter the black eyeline does not reach around the head; it is more of a marshbird than the common tern. The arctic tern, *Sterna paradisaea*, has a whiter area below the black cap than the rest of the face; its legs are very short; and at rest, the long tail projects beyond the folded wings. The bill is a blood-red. This bird is difficult to separate from the common tern. It is an arctic nester, and is seldom seen along the southern coasts of the United States, as it usually migrates offshore on its way to South America and back.

The two smallest terns are the least and the black. The least tern, *Sterna albifrons*, between 8½ to 9½ inches, is white and pale gray, with a black cap and yellow bill and feet. It nests from Massachusetts and from central California south, and along the major river systems. The black tern, *Chlidonias niger*, in spring, is all black and gray; from midsummer through late winter it is irregularly mottled. It breeds on small lakes and ponds from southern Canada through the northeastern and central United States and migrates both inland and along the coast.

Of the five less common terns, one, the sandwich tern, *Thalasseus sandvicensis*, with its long, slender, black bill with a yellow tip, is coastal, from Virginia to Texas. The elegant tern, *T. elegans*, is a tropical species—smaller than the royal tern but larger than the Forster's tern—that occasionally is seen along the Pacific Coast south of San Francisco. The roseate tern, *Sterna dougallii*, occurs sparingly along the Atlantic Coast from Nova Scotia to Texas; it has a very long, deeply forked tail and a black bill. The two remaining terns, the sooty tern, *Sterna fuscata*, and the noddy terns, *Anous stolidus*, are birds of the tropical oceans, that maintain one nesting colony at the extreme tip of South Florida, in the Dry Tortugas Islands. —G.B.S.

Royal tern

When fishing, the common tern flies with its long bill pointed slightly downward

Common Tern
Other Common Names — Medrick, striker, sea swallow, mackerel gull, redshank
Scientific Name — *Sterna hirundo*
Family — Laridae (gulls and terns)
Order — Charadriiformes
Size — Length, 15 inches
Range — Breeds in North America from Great Slave Lake, central Keewatin. southern Ungava, south to northern North Dakota, northern Ohio, and along coast to North Carolina. Winters from Florida to Brazil. In Old World from Scandinavia, British Isles, northern Russia, and central Siberia south to Mediterranean, central Asia, and Africa

These birds, although occurring inland, are associated in many minds with coastal islands, with salt spray, and resounding beaches where the sea winds have full sway, They have very appropriately been called sea swallows on account of their narrow, pointed wings, and graceful flight. They are known also as medricks in Maine, and as strikers in Virginia and the Carolinas on account of their method of procuring food. Poising a moment on beating wings above a school of small fishes they will descend with arrowlike swiftness, piercing the water with their sharp beaks and usually emerging with their finny prey. When a school of small fry is discovered they show great excitement, repeatedly ascending and plunging into the water, all the while accompanying their movements with piercing cries. In addition to fishes, which consist almost entirely of unmarketable species, they also eat aquatic worms and insects.

In summer they gather in colonies on islands or beaches. The nest is sometimes a shallow depression in the bare sand or among broken shells, or again in windrows of stranded eelgrass. From three to four eggs are laid. These are variable in color, olive-gray or buff, heavily marked with chocolate.

The sooty tern (above) makes no attempt to build a nest, but lays it eggs in a shallow depression. The noddy tern (below) places its single egg in a nest of sticks and seaweed built on a grass tussock, or in a low bush. Both birds nest in colonies

TERRARIUM
A Wildlife Home Under Glass

The study of living plants and animals is an important part of every course in nature study, and the terrarium, or "garden under glass," provides a place where wild or cultivated plants can be grown successfully the year round, and where many kinds of animals can be housed. It also provides a background for the study of that important subject, conservation. Terraria (terrariums) are miniature habitats. Each displays living plants and animals typical of one environment and gives one an opportunity to observe adaptations and interrelationships existing among some of the living things that make up a natural habitat. Strictly, the terrarium used as a native habitat containing living animals should be termed a "vivarium."

The first garden under glass was the Wardian case developed more than a hundred years ago by Nathaniel Ward, an English physician. Interested in a chrysalis of a butterfly, he placed it on moist earth in a glass jar. Soon he observed a small fern growing in the soil. From this accidental beginning, Ward developed a practical method of transporting rare plants from far ports in the days of slow sailing vessels. Conservation of moisture, protection against sudden changes of temperature, and provision for light are the basic principles of this indoor garden. It may be a decorative landscape for the home or schoolroom or a bit of outdoors brought indoors for the study of plants and as a habitat for living creatures.

The terrarium may vary in size from a tiny jar containing small ferns and bits of moss to a three-or four-foot container in which larger plants and animals live. Small terraria can be used for rearing insects (see Insect: Insects in the Classroom) and their relatives, or small frogs, toads, and salamanders. Large terraria make possible such plant associations as the woodland, the bog, the meadow,

Terrariums can be used to house wild animals such as toads and lizards. A variety of habitats can be simulated by varying moisture, light, and soil

or the desert. In these, frogs, toads, salamanders, turtles, and lizards can be kept in their native habitats. But a word of caution. Some of these animals are cannibalistic and large specimens should not be housed with small ones (See under Frog; and under Lizard).

Containers

The most satisfactory containers for terraria are straight-sided tanks such as are used for aquaria (see Aquarium), although any glass container may be used. The rectangular tanks are easy to plant and to care for; they provide sufficient air space; and they permit an undistorted view of the plants and animals.

Simple, inexpensive containers may be constructed in the schoolroom by using panes of single strength window glass taped together to form a glass box, or a miniature greenhouse. One kind has the sides taped together and set in mixed Plaster of Paris in a baking pan. This makes a more substantial container than the all-glass one. Neither need be larger than 10 by 12 inches. Join the edge of the glass with adhesive tape, Mystic or Scotch tape or use Lemil adhesive (a milky fluid adhesive that dries clear and is very strong). Most hardware stores carry some form of this. Have two pieces of glass cut so that they fit the long dimension of the bottom of the pan by 10 inches high. Then have shorter pieces cut to fit between the long pieces, and also 10 inches high; locate them one at each end of the pan. (These two shorter pieces will be substantially equal to the width of the bottom of the pan minus twice the thickness of the glass used.) Make a rectangle by taping the four pieces of glass at the corners. Fill the pan two-thirds full of Plaster of Paris and put in the rectangle of taped glass. Allow the plaster to harden. For a cover use a piece of glass slightly larger than the opening so that it will not fall in and damage the plants and animals.

Among the odd-shaped glass containers used for decorative gardens, the bell jar of Victorian vintage is best adapted to this purpose and is the loveliest. Upon the base of wood, which comes with the bell, place a waterproof dish or metal pan, preferably copper, in which to make the planting. This should be so arranged that the leaves do not touch the glass.

A simple arrangement of a few plants, giving prominence to a high fern or tree seedling, is most effective. This garden requires special care because there is no opening for ventilation. The glass jar itself must be removed and wiped daily and the planting must be such that the bell can be removed and replaced without striking the leaves.

Large-mouthed glass gallon jars such as mayonnaise, pickles, or apple butter come in, may be turned on the side to form a good terrarium. To keep the jar from rolling, make a simple frame to hold it. Use a board for the base and erect two small boards each with an arc cut out along its top curved to fit the jar. Another attractive terrarium similar to the bell jar type uses a plastic cake dish. Plant the garden in an aluminum baking pan of suitable size and place the plastic cake dish cover over it.

Collecting and Conservation

To comply with the laws and principles of conservation, a person doing his own collecting of wild plants should acquaint himself with the laws in the area and must have a permit from the owner of the land on which he collects. The very plants that are adaptable to terrarium planting are not only often rare but play an important part in soil conservation. They form the forest ground cover that, by holding moisture and binding the soil, prevents the quick run-off of water with its accompanying floods and erosion.

Plants collected in the fall after cold weather has come prove to make a more satisfactory growth. Dig each plant carefully with soil surrounding the roots and wrap in cornucopia of paper to protect the stems and leave. Mosses (*see under Mosses and Liverworts*) may be rolled or packed in layers of paper. Wild plants, collected by licensed nurserymen, are available at some florist shops.

Aquariums make good terrariums. Here, an eastern woodland habitat has been created with tiny pines, ferns, and mosses

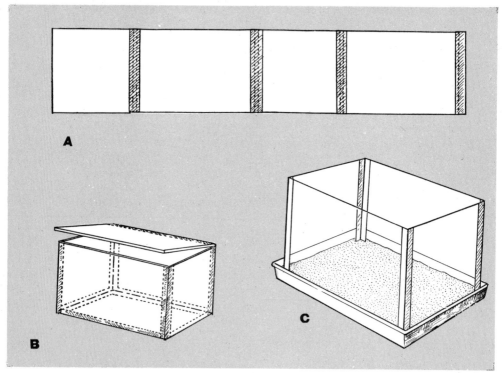

A terrarium can be made by taping panes of window glass together (A) to form a box (B) that can be further strengthened by placing its base in plaster-of-Paris (C)

The Woodland Garden

The wild garden reproduces a natural scene in miniature by using native plants and rocks; the cultivated garden is made by using cultivated plants. Native and cultivated plants should never be combined. Artificial figures and specimens of minerals are definitely out of character with the woodland landscape.

Before starting any terrarium, be sure the container is clean. The foundation of the garden should be established with care. Place clean gravel or bits of broken flower pot in the container and cover with sand to a depth of one or two inches for drainage. Charcoal may be pressed into the sand. Cover the drainage material with one to two inches of slightly sandy garden soil, well sifted and dampened. If the soil will hold together when squeezed together in the hand, it is wet enough. Spread leaf mold over the soil. At this time the general plan is developed by building up the soil in places, towards the back or sides for hills, leveling off in spots, and dipping down to form valleys. One or two rocks may be firmly set in the soil for cliffs and ledges. Choose weathered or lichen-covered rocks to give a natural and aged appearance to the scene.

A glass dish or enameled pan makes a good pool. Sink it in the soil and edge it with pebbles so that the moss will not absorb the water. Pebbles and tiny water plants add interest to the pool. After the general contour plan has been worked out, plant tiny ferns at the base of the cliff or in soil pockets in the rocks, seedling trees high on a hill, and other plants, preferably evergreen, spaced in a naturalistic manner. Be careful that the leaves do not touch the glass. Dampen the moss and press it firmly over the bare places. The plants are most ef-

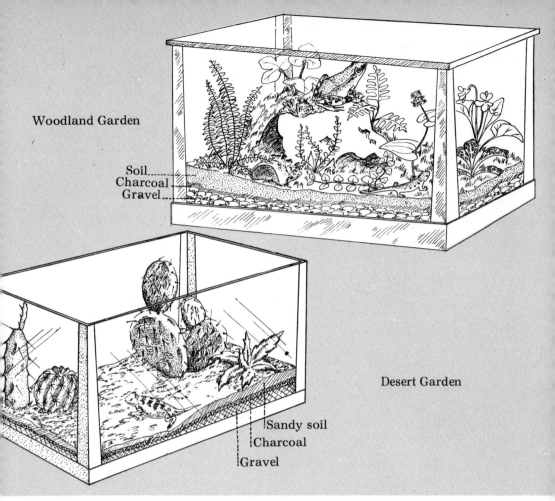

Woodland Garden

Soil
Charcoal
Gravel

Desert Garden

Sandy soil
Charcoal
Gravel

fective and thrive when well spaced.

Hemlock, spruce, and laurel seedlings, pipsissewa, spotted wintergreen, wintergreen, ebony spleenwort, polypody, Christmas fern, club mosses, rattlesnake plantain, and partridgeberry—all serve as excellent material for the wild woodland garden. Blueberry, maple, tulip, and sassafras seedlings will be rewarding with their unfolding leaf buds. Although the evergreen species are surer of success, definitely so in a vivarium, some of the flowering plants are satisfactory. Violets, hepatica, bloodroot, the picot-edged rosette of the saxifrage, cinquefoil, and wild strawberry are among the best of these. Sprouting acorns, moss or lichen covered twigs, and hemlock cones add a touch of the deep woods. Lichens and fungi give color and contrast to the garden but should be placed on ledges and watched for mold.

Care of the Garden

After the garden is planted, wet it well with a bulb spray but do not saturate it. Clean the container and cover with glass to prevent evaporation and to preserve a more even temperature. The cover should fit loosely enough to allow air to circulate. Terraria other than those with desert plants and animals are best kept in a cool place in good light but not direct sunlight. Keep the glass clean and remove yellowing leaves and dying fern fronds. If much condensation appears on the glass in the mornings, lift the cover for an hour or two. When the plants take on a dry appearance and little condensation appears, the garden needs a thorough spraying. For a well established terrarium a monthly spraying is sufficient. However, each garden is individual and demands individual attention.

A terrarium providing a small pool and a woodland or swampy habitat makes a suitable home for a spring peeper

The Cultivated Garden

Since it is difficult for the city dweller to obtain wild plants, cultivated plants purchased from the florist or the ten cent store can be used effectively in a terrarium. In fact, many of these plants will thrive better sheltered in a covered garden than exposed to the drying atmosphere of a steam-heated apartment. Establish the drainage base as in the woodland garden but use potting soil for the planting. If the tiny plants are potted, keep the soil around the roots when transferring to the terrarium. Creeping plants make a good ground cover. Small plants and slips of the following are successful: *Begonia, Croton,* ferns (Pteris group), *Fittonia, Maranta, Peperomia,* African violet, strawberry saxifrage, *Philodendron.* For ground cover and vines use: baby-tears (*Helxine*), *Oxalis, Selaginella,* grape ivy, *Ficus repens,* myrtle, and moneywort. The terrarium makes an excellent container for the propagation of seeds and slips. (*See under Plant: Indoor Plants*).

The Bog Garden

The bog garden (*see under Bog*) should be planted in a fairly large container. Place the drainage as in the woodland garden but use acid soil for this garden. For interest, the plan may include the sloping side of a bog or a cliff with overhanging hemlocks. Pitcher plants should be rooted deeply in the soil and surrounded by sphagnum moss. Sundews, also insectivorous plants, do very well on higher ground. Sheep laurel, hemlock, swamp blueberry seedlings, and cranberry are satisfactory bog garden plants. This garden must have more water than the woodland garden and should be kept in a cool location. A very attractive and interesting garden is the combination one of bog and woodland, each with its typical plants.

The Desert Garden

Although the desert garden is easy to establish, it is more difficult to maintain in growing condition than the woodland garden. There are two methods of planting. Cover a two- or three-inch-deep drainage base of pebbles and dry sand with three or four inches of a sandy potting mixture. A rolling contour is more interesting and natural than a flat surface; even an arroyo, or "dry wash," may be incorporated into the scene. Use tiny potted succulents and cacti (*see Cactus*); remove from the pots, keeping the soil around the roots, and plant. The ground cover should be fine white or light-colored sand. A more successful growth results if the plants are kept in the pots buried in the sand. Spray the soil around the plants once a week, taking care not to wet the rest of the sand or the plants themselves. Keep the garden in a warm sunny location. This method is especially recommended if horned toads and other lizards (*see under Lizard*) are kept in the garden because most reptiles thrive in a warm, dry habitat. However, the American chameleon, a lizard frequently kept in nature rooms, needs a semi-tropical habitat, not a desert back-tround. A correct habitat for the horned toad, a native of our Southwest, is a desert with native American cacti such as prickly pear, cardinal's cap, old man, and *Echinopsis.* Other plants easy to grow and obtainable in most florist shops are various cacti, aloes, sedums, *Stapelias,* and *Crassulas* (*See under Desert Plants*).

The Weed Garden

Unnoticed in winter are the evergreen rosettes of many of our common weeds and some of our more spectacular summer flowering plants that are supposed to die with the first touch of frost. The leaves of these rosettes, often quite different from the upper or stem leaves, form in the fall and make tight whorls close to the ground. For the study of immigrant plants a weed garden is helpful and interesting since most of our common weeds were introduced accidentally from abroad and have made themselves at home, especially in the cities. The growth of these plants, when brought indoors, is rapid and will prove interesting, if not of long duration.

Plants that reproduce themselves from their roots from year to year are called perennials. Some form their basal leaves in the shape of rosettes in the fall to be in readiness to send up central shoots in the spring. Of these the asters, goldenrods, Indian tobacco, *Lobelia inflata,* and some hawkweeds are native. The tawny hawkweed, tansy, common plantain, sheep sorrel, and tall field buttercup are migrants from Europe; English plantain, oxeye daisy, and dandelion are from Eurasia. Plants of two years duration, occupying the first year of their lives in perfecting a rosette or set of root leaves, and the next year in producing flower-bearing stocks, are called biennials. Of these, the evening primrose and black-eyed susan are native; great mullein, common thistle, and burdock are from Europe.

The weed garden is set up in the same manner as the cultivated garden. However, it will be unnecessary to use much extra soil because the fine roots of these plants, when collected, will

Terrariums are valuable educational exhibits in classrooms or nature centers

hold a sufficient amount. Since the rosette form is an adaptation against excessive loss of water during the winter, this garden will need little spraying after it is established.

Housing of Animals in the Terrarium

A small case is useful for spiders and insects such as crickets, grasshoppers, praying mantids, and caterpillars. Cover the bottom of the cage with sand and then with a layer of loam. To provide moisture, spray sparingly once a day. Keep cocoons in a mossy garden through the winter but remove them to larger quarters toward spring so that the moths will have room to spread their wings when they emerge. Feed young mantids on fruit flies or their larvae until they are able to manage bluebottle flies, mealworms, grasshoppers, or roaches. Feed caterpillars the particular plant on which they were found, or consult a manual on insects for a satisfactory substitute food plant. Crickets and grasshoppers do well on apple, lettuce, and moist bread. Frogs, toads and salamanders thrive in the woodland and swamp gardens. Small turtles frequently burrow in for the winter and ruin the appearance of the garden. Soil or sod provides a better home for them.

The American chameleon needs a moist garden of tropical plants that can stand several hours of sunshine daily. Spray the plants twice daily, for the chameleon does not drink from a dish but laps water from the vegetation. The horned toad lives best in a desert garden in good warm sunlight. Give it water from a medicine dropper, or place a shallow dish of water in the sand. Adult lizards, frogs, toads, and large salamanders may be fed roaches, mealworms and earthworms. Try to induce them to eat bits of raw beef or liver by moving the meat on the end of a broom straw. Red efts eat white worms, small earthworms, and small mealworms (*See under Amphibian; and under Newt*).

Garden snails and slugs grow well in a terrarium and are interesting to watch. To keep them from wandering too far over the glass and plants and leaving sticky trails behind them, make it easy for them to find food. Place a small piece of lettuce in the terrarium every day. Snails and slugs are very fond of lettuce. Try watching the eating process through a reading glass and seeing the tiny tongue with teeth on it as it rips the lettuce leaf. Garden snails often lay eggs in the terrarium. They are white and about the size of small pearls. It is interesting to watch the little snails that emerge and to see their shells grow (*See under Snail: Snails and Slugs*).
—J.H.T.

Recommended Reading

Aubudon Nature Bulletins—Published by National Audubon Society, New York.—*Caterpillars; Live Insects in the Classrooms; Turtles; Snakes; Frogs and Toads; Salamander; Lichens; Mosses; Club Mosses; Fungi; Ferns.*
Book of Nature Activities—William Hillcourt. G.P. Putnam's Sons, New York.
Book of Nature Hobbies—Ted Pettit. Didier Publishing Company, New York.
The Book of Wild Pets—C.B. Moore. Charles T. Branford Company, Boston.
Dish Gardens, Terrariums and Novelty Planters —Walter Singer. *The Garden Journal*, The New York Botanical Garden, New York. Jan.-Feb. and Mar.-Apr. 1959 issues.

TEXAS BIRDS

It is safe to say that in no place in the United States can so many birds be seen with so little effort as in the Rio Grande valley of southern Texas. Here eastern birds and western birds are often seen together with typical Mexican species. There is a great variety of habitats— sea beaches, coastal prairie, arid scrublands dominated by cacti and mesquite, elm and hackberry woodlands festooned with hanging moss, rich resacas where the old river beds used to be, and a number of other wildlife habitats. Each one has different birds.

Some of the common birds of southern Texas are listed below. The number beside each entry refers to the number accompanying the pictures (*opposite*).

1. Green jay. There are a number of blue jays in different parts of the United States, but the Rio Grande valley boasts the only green one—a gorgeous bird, which in Mexico is called *Pajaro verde* or "green bird." The stout nest of thorny twigs is hidden in a thicket or dense tree. It usually holds four spotted grayish or greenish eggs.

2. Sennett's oriole. Male. This, the commonest one of its family, can be told from any other oriole by the orange crown of the head. All other male orioles have black crowns. The female is duller olive-colored above, yellow below. The basketlike nest is usually made of palm leaf fibers (very frequently in a palm tree) or hanging in a tuft of moss in an elm or in some vine. The three to five white eggs are spotted and scratched with dark marks.

3. Audubon's oriole. This large yellow oriole with the black head was named in honor of John James Audubon, the great naturalist. The song has odd half-tones, and sounds like a small boy who had just learned to whistle. The hammocklike nest of fine grasses is usually built in mesquite.

4. Pyrrhuloxia. Male. This beautiful gray and rose bird likes the mesquite thickets of the more arid sections. It is

Eighteen birds of the lower Rio Grande Valley, Texas (referred to in the text)

really a type of cardinal, but its calls are thinner. From a bush top or wire, the male sings *quink quink quink quink* or *what-cheer, what-cheer.* Its bulky nest in the mesquite usually contains three to five speckled eggs.

5. Sennett's thrasher. The two breeding thrashers are long-tailed strong-legged birds that rummage about on the ground. This species is much browner than the other, with heavy breast streakings. Its song and nest are similar to the Brownsville thrasher.

6. Brownsville thrasher. A race of the curve-billed thrasher. It is common in the thorny brush country, where it builds its nest among the cactus or mesquite. The eggs are pale bluish-green, finely speckled with brown. Both thrashers have fine songs. The call note of this species is a sharp two-noted whistle *whit wheet!* that sounds like some unfriendly landowner calling the attention of a trespasser.

7. Sennett's warbler. Male. This little bird reaches its northern limit in the woodlands of the Rio Grande valley, where it builds its oriole-like nest in a hanging piece of Spanish moss. The bluish upperparts and clear yellow breast are good marks. The song is a buzzy trill which runs up the scale and tips over at the top.

8. Texas kingfisher. Male. This little fellow, hardly larger than a sparrow, not only catches tiny fishes but insects, too. It had a sharp note, instead of the loud rattle of its bigger cousin, the belted kingfisher. The female, which does not have the rusty breast band, lays her eggs at the end of a burrow in a bank.

9. Texas wren. The Texas wren can be told from the Lomita wren by its grayer color and white-tipped tail. Its lively musical song is characteristic of both mesquite lands and dry brushy places. The four to seven white eggs are laid in an old woodpecker hole, hollow stump or bird box.

10. Black-crested titmouse. A perky little bird that whistles *peter peter peter peter* or *petee petee petee petee.* In winter it is very fond of seeds and will eat pecans and sunflower seeds that are put out for it. The nest is in a woodpecker hole or other cavity.

11. Texas woodpecker. Male. The little "speckle-back" woodpecker announces itself with a sharp thin note. Where trees are scarce it hammers on the stalks of the yucca and cacti for its food of grubs and borers. Only the male has the red crown. The nest excavation is made in a fence post or low trunk or stalk.

12. Golden-fronted woodpecker. Male. This is indeed a common bird, both in the cities and outside. Its round nesting hole in telephone poles and tree trunks is a familiar sight. Besides a large number of borers and other insects this handsome bird eats some wild berries. Only the male has the red crown.

13. Inca dove. A small dove about 8 inches long. Its rather long, double-rounded tail identifies it from the even smaller Mexican ground dove which has a stubby black tail. It is a lover of cities and barnyards where its cooing tells of its presence—two notes of about even emphasis, *coo-oo* or *coe-coo*. The two white eggs are laid in a nest which is a little better built than other doves'.

14. White-winged dove. Some woodlands and mesquite thickets seem alive with doves. The white-wing has a hard, vigorous cooing, *whoo-whoo, hu-whoo* or *who cooks for you?* The nest is a flimsy platform of twigs. Sometimes this dove nests in colonies. White-winged doves are gamebirds, but regulation is required if they are to maintain their numbers.

15. Texas sparrow. At one time this sober little bird was called "green finch." Its song is frequently heard in brushy places, a dry *chip chip chip chip chip chip chip* starting deliberately and accelerating into a chippery rattle. The well made nest, hidden in a thicket, is built of grass and lined with hair.

16. Sharpe's seedeater. Male. This tiny little finch sits in a tree top or on a wire and sings its bright song which sounds like *sweet sweet sweet sweet, cheer cheer.* It is the smallest of the finches, with an exceptionally stubby bill, well adapted for cracking small seeds. The nest is a small well-made cup attached to the stalks of tall weeds.

17. Derby flycatcher. The big, handsome derby flycatcher often departs from the ways of other flycatchers and catches little frogs, minnows and sometimes lizards around the pools and resacas. Its call is a loud *git-ta-hear!* The domed nest is built among the branches of trees, *twenty-five* or *thirty* feet from the ground. The five eggs are a light cream color with small specks.

18. Couch's kingbird. Most of the Couch's kingbirds arrive in March. Like most flycatchers, they sit still on an exposed twig or wire until they spot a passing insect, which they dash out to catch. The note is a nasal *queer*, or *che-queer*. The nest, made of hanging mosses and twigs, is supported by a horizontal branch or crotch.

19. Florida gallinule. A gray ducklike bird with a red bill can be safely called this species. When swimming, the white powder puff undertail coverts are noticeable. It seems to be half duck and half chicken, swimming well, and clucking excitedly when disturbed. The nest is similar to the coot's with a short runway leading to it from the water.

20. Coot. This slate-colored ducklike bird with the black head and white bill lives on freshwater ponds and resacas. Abundant in winter, quite a few coots stay to breed and build their platform nests in the wetter parts of the marsh. Eight to twelve finely speckled eggs are laid.

21. Mesquite grackle. This is the common, large blackbird with the big tail. It is a race of the boat-tailed grackle which lives father east. Females are considerably smaller, and brown, not black. The "jackdaw," as it is called in some places, is a very abundant bird all the year round, and sometimes nests in colonies. A large flock sounds like a bedlam, with loud whistles, wheezy notes and harsh clucks. The nest is built in bushes or thick trees.

—R.T.P.

Common thistle blossoms are not often picked because of their protective spines

THISTLE
Common Thistle
Other Common Names — Bull thistle
Scientific Name — *Circium vulgare*
Family — Compositae (composite family)
Range — Newfoundland to British Columbia, south to Georgia
Habitat — Clearings, pastures, and roadsides.
Time of Blooming — June to September

This plant with its large showy head of purple flowers is not often molested by flower gatherers or mammals, as the extremely spiny foliage and stem give effective protection. The leaves are white underneath and the plant may reach a height of five feet. As with all members of the composite family the thistle has a compact group of tiny flowers attached to the end of the stem. Each flower head produces a large number of silky-haired seeds that ripen during the sum-

mer, and are then dispersed by the wind. The goldfinch uses the "down" from the thistle seeds in making its nest. The down is available by late June and July when the goldfinch, one of the last to nest, starts to build.

The flowers of the common thistle are quite fragrant and bees and butterflies congregate in numbers on a single head of flowers to gather nectar and inadvertantly bring about cross-fertilization. The bumblebee is said to often become intoxicated on the nectar of the common thistle (*See Pollination*).

This plant is a naturalized "citizen" whose home was Europe. It also grows in Asia. Since it was introduced into this country it has extended its range to most cultivated areas of United States and Canada. Native species of thistle are far less common than several that have been introduced from other countries.

THRASHER

Eight species of thrashers inhabit North America. They are closely related to the mockingbirds and are primarily ground-feeding birds that scratch up insects from the floor of the forest or shrubby undergrowth of more arid regions.

Only the brown thrasher, *Toxostoma rufum*, inhabits the eastern part of North America, ranging from southern Canada south to the Gulf Coast and Florida, and west to the eastern slope of the Rocky Mountains.

In the brushy valley and foothills of California, the California thrasher, *T. redivivum*, is the dominant species. This large thrasher makes holes in the ground with its long downcurved bill and then watches them until an insect emerges. As soon as this happens the bird quickly snaps up its prey.

Six other thrashers occur in the arid lands of the American Southwest. Two of them, the long-billed thrasher, *T. longirostre*, and the sage thrasher, *Oreoscoptes montanus*, are similar to the brown thrasher. The long-billed thrasher has black streaks on the underparts, and less red in the back. The sage thrasher is smaller, with a short tail with white corners; it is more gray than rufous. Bendire's thrasher, *T. bendirei*, has faint, cloudy spotting underneath, where the others are streaked, and it is pale, almost clay colored.

The remaining three western thrashers resemble the California thrasher; they are of about the same size, and have the long, downcurved bill of that bird. LeConte's thrasher, *T. lecontei*, is pale, with no spotting on the breast. The curved-billed thrasher, *T. curvirostre*, is dull gray-brown above, cinnamon below, with faint spotting on the breast. The crissal thrasher, *T. dorsale*, can be identified by the rich chestnut color on its under-tail coverts. A shy bird of the Southwestern deserts, it lives in thick brush along creek bottoms.   —G.B.S.

Brown Thrasher

Other Common Names — Brown thrush, sandy mocker, planting bird
Scientific Name — *Toxostoma rufum*
Family — Mimidae (mockingbirds and thrashers)
Order — Passeriformes
Size — Length, 10½ to 12 inches
Range — Breeds from southern Alberta, southern Manitoba, northern Michigan, southeastern Ontario, southwestern Quebec, and northern Maine, south to Florida, Alabama, Mississippi, and Texas. It lives from the Atlantic Coast west to the eastern slope of the Rocky Mountains in Montana, Wyoming, and Colorado. Winters in the southern tier of states and north to Missouri and North Carolina. Occasionally, individuals will stay as far north as New York and southern New England

The brown thrasher has a brown back and a streaked breast. It resembles a thrush, but its tail is much longer, and its eyes are pale and yellow, not dark. It has a long slightly downcurved beak. Like a catbird and the mockingbird, it belongs to a family that some ornithologists call the mimic thrushes. The mockingbird is by far the best mimic of the three. The easiest way to remember the songs of this family is that the catbird warbles and wheezes along without any repetition of its notes. The brown thrasher almost always repeats everything twice. The mockingbird repeats each note or phrase half a dozen times or more.

The brown thrasher usually arrives in the North well along toward late April. It does not arrive in great waves as warblers do. It seems to make the journey northward by short flights from bush to bush, reaching its destination silently and unheralded. After several days of rest, the thrasher starts to call and sing from a high perch. Its song grows more fluent as the warm days of May lengthen. Some farmers say it sings *drop it, drop it; cover it cover it; pull*

Brown thrasher

Under watchful eyes, fledgling brown thrashers feather out in a nest of grasses

it up, pull it up. They call it the planting bird. It sings throughout the day, with brief pauses for food and water.

The brown thrasher prefers to nest in tangles of thorny shrubs and vines that are almost impossible to penetrate. The nest is placed in low growth within a few feet of the ground—a bulky structure of twigs, leaves, and strips of bark. Inside, it is lined with rootlets. Sometimes nests are built on the ground, but the more usual place is in the thorny undergrowth.

The three to six eggs are white—or green-white—finely dotted with brown. The incubation period is 12 to 14 days. Both birds take part in the brooding. The thick twigs and thorns about the nest help protect against predators, but if the thicket is invaded, the thrasher will defend its young.

The baby birds stay in the nest 10 or 12 days. They are fed all sorts of berries and wild fruits, which, at that season, are to be found everywhere. Over two-thirds of the food of the brown thrasher is made up of animal matter, such as grasshoppers, caterpillars, ants, grubs, and once in a while, such items as lizards, snails, small frogs, and snakes.

Most birds that live on insects are migratory, and the brown thrasher is no exception. Although many thrashers leave about the same time as the catbirds, along in September or October, a few linger until the long nights and shortening days force them to move. Every now and than a thrasher tries to spend the winter in the North, even as far as New York State and the Great Lakes region, but the majority migrate to the southern United States. —A.B., Jr.

The California thrasher uses its curved bill to probe the soil for insects

California Thrasher
Other Common Names—None
Scientific Name—*Toxostoma redivivum*
Family—Mimidae (mockingbirds and thrashers)
Order—Passeriformes
Size—Length, 11½ to 13 inches
Range—Resident bird from northern California south to northern Baja California

The California thrasher lives in the same sort of brushy places that towhees frequent. Using its long curved bill as a hoe, it scratches up all sorts of interesting things from among the leaf mold and dead twigs. Surprised at its work, it lifts its tail and sprints for the darkest shadows. There are half a dozen kinds of thrashers in the Southwest, but the others are more partial to the arid lands and desert. Only this one, the largest, holds dominion over the brushy valleys and foothills of most of California.

Its song is a long series of notes and phrases, some harsh and some musical, similar to a mockingbird's, but lower pitched and more leisurely, each phrase being repeated only 2 or 3 times. Its most used call note is a loud *plik*.

"THRESHOLD OF SECURITY" (*See under Predation: A Closer Look at the Killers*)

THRUSH
Medium-sized perching birds that live on berries, fruit, and insects, thrushes include some of the sweetest singers among birds. The nightingale of Europe and Asia is a thrush; and, in the New World, the hermit thrush and the wood thrush each have strong support among bird lovers for the title of "best songster."

The best known thrush in North America is the robin, *Turdus migratorius*. It nests in every Canadian province and every state except Hawaii. At 10½ inches, it is the largest of the North American thrushes, chunkier than the others, with a typical, rather stout thrush bill. Like other thrushes, it feeds on the ground to a large extent and nests in trees. It is more tolerant of the human race than other thrushes, and often nests near or even on human habitations. The eggs are bluish-green, as are all thrush eggs except those of the solitaire (*See also Robin*).

The varied thrush, *Ixoreus naevius*, is slightly smaller, with orange face marks and wing bars, and a band across its chest that is black in the male and gray in the female. It is a bird of the deep, wet woodlands of the Pacific Coast.

A wood thrush tends its young in a nest of grasses covered with paper napkins

Hermit thrush

The three bluebirds prefer open areas with scattered trees, and will accept nest boxes as substitutes for abandoned woodpecker holes. The eastern bluebird *Sialia sialis*, that lives east of the Rocky Mountains is completely blue on the back, and reddish underneath up to the bill. The western bluebird, *S. mexicana*, that lives west of the Rocky Mountains has a reddish patch on the back, over the shoulders, and is blue on the throat. The male mountain bluebird, *S. currucoides*, of the Sierra Nevada and Rocky Mountains is all blue with some white on its underparts but never any red. The females are duller; the eastern bluebird slightly so, the western blue-

bird with hardly any red, and the mountain bluebird with none. The young are speckled, with a few bluish patches (*See also Bluebird*).

The five brownish or grayish woodland thrushes are the wood thrush, hermit thrush, Swainson's thrush, gray-cheeked thrush, and the veery. The wood thrush, *Hylocichla mustelina*, is eastern, breeding west to the Dakotas; the United States, and in the Rocky Mountains and the Appalachians to Virginia, except the gray-cheeked thrush's southern unit is New York. The wood thrush has the reddest head and the largest spots. The hermit thrush, *H. guttata*, combines a reddish tail with a gray back. The veery *H. fuscescens*, is rusty from head to tail, with a few, small spots on the throat and breast. Swainson's thrush, *H. ustulata*, and the gray-cheeked thrush, *H. minima*, are much alike, but Swainson's thrush has an eye-ring and a buffy face and breast; the gray-cheeked thrush lacks the eye-ring, and is gray on face and breast.

Townsend's solitaire, *Myadestes townsendi*, is slim and gray, with a rather long tail. The white outer tail feathers give it the appearance of a short-billed mockingbird, but the wing patches are buff, not white. A bird of deep forest, it is shy and not easily found except when singing. It ranges from Alaska to New Mexico in summer, in the mountains (*See also Solitaire*).   —G.B.S.

Hermit Thrush
Other Common Names—American nightingale, solitary thrush
Scientific Name—*Hylocichla guttata*
Family—Turdidae (thrushes, solitaires, and bluebirds)
Order—Passeriformes
Size—Length, 6½ to 7½ inches
Range—Nests from Alaska south to Mackenzie and east through southern Canada to Labrador and Newfoundland, south to central Wisconsin and Maryland. In the West from southern Canada

Swainson's thrush

south to southern California and northern New Mexico. Winters south to Baja California, Gulf of Mexico, and southern Florida

The hermit thrush is the earliest thrush to arrive in the spring, for it comes while the trees are still leafless, and lingers in the autumn until the woods are quite bare. At such times it may be seen quickly and silently flitting through the forest aisles, sometimes alighting on the ground and again on some low perch. If approached too closely it again takes flight, its shadowy, elusive form blending in with the russet autumn leaves and the thicket's dusky tones.

The call note of the hermit thrush is a scarcely audible, low *chuck*. Its song, however, is a notable performance, and poets and naturalists alike have vied with one another in attempts to do it justice. When heard at dusk in the quiet solitudes of the northern hemlock forests it possesses a serene clearness and sweet tranquility of tone that will scarcely brook comparison with other bird songs.

The nest is on the ground, of mosses, coarse grasses, and leaves, lined with pine needles and rootlets. From three to four greenish-blue eggs are laid.

Swainson's Thrush
Other Common Names — Russet-back, russet-backed thrush, olive-backed thrush
Scientific Name — *Hylocichla ustulata*
Family — Turdidae (thrushes, solitaires, and bluebirds)
Order — Passeriformes
Size — Length, 6½ to 7½ inches
Range — Nests from Alaska south in Canada to Manitoba and east to Labrador and Newfoundland. In western United States from California to Colorado and Great Lakes south in mountains to West Virginia. Winters from southern Mexico to South America

In somber fern-carpeted forests in the Northwest, in tangles of dogwood and bracken, or in willow thickets, the breezy flutelike phrases of the Swainson's thrush make cathedral-like music. Each vibrant phrase ascends in a sequence. Its commonest call notes are a soft, low *whit* and a louder, rising *whee*. The hermit thrush, another wide-eyed chorister of the shadows, shows a rusty red tail when it flies away, but the Swainson's thrush is cloaked from head to tail with a dull, even brown.

In the South, these two thrushes scarcely overlap in dates, the Swainson's thrush arriving in late April just as the last wintering hermit thrushes are leavings, but in the northwest both live where dense conifers and streamside thickets occur together. All over the East and the western and southern parts of California the species is often very abundant as an overhead night migrant in April and May and in September, its frequently uttered call notes identifying it in the dark.

Wood Thrush
Other Common Names — Wood robin
Scientific Name — *Hylocichla mustelina*

Family—Turdidae (thrushes, solitaires, and bluebirds)
Order—Passeriformes
Size—Length, 7½ to 8½ inches
Range—Breeds from the Gulf States—eastern Texas, Louisiana, and northern Florida—north to southern South Dakota, central Minnesota, southern Ontario, and southern Quebec. Winters occasionally in Florida, but chiefly from southern Texas to Panama

Like many other woodland birds, the wood thrush is heard more often than it is seen. Occasionally, it can be seen walking over the forest floor—a plump-looking bird, with strong legs, that give it a robinlike appearance; in fact, it is called the wood robin in some places, especially in the South. It walks or hops along, flits its wings nervously, cocks its head, and turns over leaves and litter with its bill, much like robins do.

The thrushes are long-legged and big-eyed. They are readily identified by their spotted breasts, at least the brown-backed woodland species are. One would not suspect the robin and bluebird to be thrushes, if it were not for their speckle-breasted young (*See, Bluebird*). The wood thrush may easily be distinguished from the others by the bright rusty red color around its head and shoulders.

In Canada the wood thrush is not as well known as most of the other thrushes. One reason is that its range is almost entirely confined to the southern parts of Ontario and Quebec where it seeks the wilder woodlands and seldom, if ever, frequents sites close to human habitations. In the United States it is perhaps the best-known thrush. It has a much wider range than the others and often lives close to houses, even in city parks. It is the typical thrush of the eastern hardwood forest. In the northern states, where the evergreens mix in with the hardwoods, the hermit thrush lives. The most boreal of all is the gray-cheeked thrush, which prefers pure stands of spruce.

The song of the wood thrush has been described as one of the most beautiful sounds in nature. Its well measured phrases are flutelike, and ripple out in sweet tones. Some people contend that the hermit thrush has the most beautiful song of all the thrushes; others believe the wood thrush has. Actually, most amateurs can hardly tell one song from the other until the differences are pointed out.

Every bird in a woodland fits some particular ecological niche. Some live near the ground, others in the shrubbery, some in the treetops. The wood thrush hunts for its food on the ground. Most of its diet is made up of the small insects, snails, and spiders which it finds among the roots and fallen logs. But when berries are available, they are eaten, too—mulberries, blackberries, chokeberries, elderberries, and dogwood berries.

Although the wood thrush spends most of its time on the ground, it nests in a bush or a low tree, anwhere from 3 to 12 feet up. The nest is very easy to identify, because it is robinlike—a well made bowl, with many dead leaves on the outside, or even large pieces of paper. The muddy-looking substance, which is used to bind the walls, is really wet leaf mold, not mud. It is lined with fine rootlets.

The four eggs are blue-green. Incubation takes a little less than two weeks, and if all goes well, the young are able to fly in another 8 to 10 days. This is a very short period in which to reach the flying stage. Most small birds take a bit longer. Sometimes a second brood is attempted, especially if something has happened to the first set of eggs or the young.

By mid-July the clear, beautiful strains of the male are no longer heard, but he, or one of his family, can be seen

In eastern woods, the wood thrush spends most of its time on the forest floor

occasionally in the woodlands, a quick flash of brown wings disappearing into the shadows.

On clear, calm August nights, the notes of southbound thrushes can be heard from the starlit sky. Some of these are undoubtedly wood thrushes, but probably most wood thrushes make their journey in September. A few do not make the hazardous hop over the Gulf of Mexico, but stay in Florida through the winter. Most of them, however, go to southern Mexico or Panama. By the following March, wood thrushes are again singing in Carolina woodlands; by late April or early May, they have reached the Great Lakes and New England.   —A.B., Jr.

TIDAL POOL

[Editor's Note: A tidal pool, or tide pool
is a basin of water left in a hollow along
a beach or other shore by the ebbing
tide. Such pools are often filled with
interesting kinds of animals that live in
a watery environment. The following
account is the story of one of these
tidal pools along the coast of Maine.]

The Pool on Frenchman's Bay

Across Frenchman's Bay the mountains of Mt. Desert Island (*see Acadia
National Park*) rise abruptly from the
surrounding water. Cadillac—with an
elevation of more than 1,500 feet—is
the highest point within 20 miles of the
Atlantic coastline, and each morning
its peak is the first place in the United
States to be touched by the light of the
new day. On either side of it, the mountains descend to the sea—to the west
in gentle rolls and to the east, in a series
of rugged, granite outcroppings.

All day long the slopes of the mountains, dotted with woods and rocks and
still scarred by the forest fire of a few
years ago, catch the passing shadows.
At one moment they lie in brilliant sunshine. At the next, a rainstorm blowing
in from the southeast shrouds them in
gray mist. Then a northwest wind, with
the vigor of a farmwife with her broom,
sweeps away the clouds again and
restores the mountains to their natural
color.

Dramatic as this sight may be, one's
attention often passes from it and
centers on a small pocket in the igneous rock that lies along the shore almost
at one's feet. For there, twice each day,
the tide rolls back and lets one read,
within a space of only 20 square feet,
millions of years of history and reveals
an intimate, closeup view of life's struggle to survive.

The rock—forced, many years ago,
in a molten state through softer layers
of sedimentary material—juts into the
bay like a small breakwater for a distance of 50 feet at low tide. Through

An algae-laden tidal pool

it run tiny fissures that provide footholds for the erosive forces of ice, lichens, and waves. At the seaward end, where the tidal pool lies, the waves have gradually torn away great blocks of stone, fashioning a passage from one side of the point to the other. In this passageway a small hollow has been created that catches water from each retreating tide and so makes up the pool.

There, on a warm summer's day, one can watch the graceful fronds of the seaweed swaying gently, while a breeze ripples the surface. Orange-and-purple starfishes slowly extend their legs and draw themselves over the stones that line the bottom of the pool; mussels in their deep blue shells cling to the rocks with their yellow cords; and brown-gray snails, moving quietly on their single feet, wander from one end of this tiny world to the other.

This peaceful appearance is deceiving, for living conditions within the pool are harsh and severe. The waves, powerful enough to tear the granite apart block by block, can exert pressures measuring many thousands of pounds on each square foot, enough to crush and destroy many forms of living tissue. The temperature, instead of remaining relatively constant as it does in the open ocean, rises and falls with the tide. Within a few hours after the tide has gone out, the water in the pool can leap from a cool 50° F. to a tepid 75°, while the rocks around it can easily reach 90°. Evaporation is also a hazard—a hazard against which most sea life has no protection. A piece of glass immersed in the water and laid on surrounding rocks can lose 10 degrees of temperature within a minute, as a gentle breeze dries its surface.

Beside creating temperature changes, evaporation also increases the salinity of the water, a factor to which many sea plants and animals are sensitive. A freshwater plant placed in a bucket of seawater quickly withers and dries up, because it is designed to absorb fresh water by the process of osmosis. In the denser salt water, the osmosis reverses itself, and the fluids in the plant are drained away from it. A saltwater plant placed in fresh water also is affected, but from a different cause. The saltwater plant is designed to live in heavy solutions, and the less dense fresh water rushes into it with such force that its cells may be crushed. Among sea life, there are varying degrees of sensitivity to salinity. For example, an octopus can be driven from the dark crevices where it likes to hide by adding salt to the nearby water. Obviously, such sensitivity cannot be afforded by the animals and plants in a tidal pool.

In addition to this adaptation which is common to all the life in a brackish tidal pool, many other adaptations are needed for survival, and each plant or animal has developed its own. Some are illustrated by the seaweeds, both bladderwrack and rockweed, that grow in abundance (*See under Kelp*). Their roots, unlike those of land plants, do not furnish nourishment, but instead act like anchors, clinging to the rocks in all but the worst of storms. Seaweeds have limp stalks that permit them to bend with the pressure of the onrushing waves, and when the tide is out to collapse in a heap, thus preserving their moisture against the threat of evaporation. To help restore them to full stature when the tide is in, the fronds contain air bladders, which give them greater buoyancy.

Although the seaweeds do not play the same role as plants on land (few animals feed directly on them) they are an essential part of a tidal pool community, because of the cover they provide. Especially when the tide has gone out, many a crab or starfish or other animal has found safe refuge under the bladders of the seaweed. So delicate is the balance of existence within a tidal pool that the seaweed has even taken the hazard of evaporation and turned it to its own advantage. As its tissues dry, they also shrink, and this helps eject its seeds of the next generation.

Near the waving branches of the seaweed lie clusters of blue-shelled mussels, which have also adjusted to the extreme conditions within the pool. These animals are so insensitive to changes in salinity that they can survive a decrease of 50 percent, provided that the change is made slowly enough. Like the seaweeds, they anchor themselves firmly to the rocks; but instead of roots, they use a plasticlike material that they extrude from their feet. On contact with either air or water, it hardens, making it possible for the mussels to attach themselves by a series of guy ropes. Since the shell itself cannot be soft and pliant like the stem of the seaweed, it is designed to present the least possible resistance to the waves, being gently curved with a knife-edge on one side. While the tide is in, the mussel is impervious to the action of the waves and filters water through its gills, extracting food particles from as much as two pints of water an hour. When the tide is out, it clamps its shells tight and thus can remain moist even in the blazing sun (*See under Bivalve; and under Mollusk*).

Sometimes the mussel has a tiny, visitor, the pea crab. This small crab slips between the shells of the mussel and sits down on the mussel's gills. There, it can sweep up some of the food that the mussel has taken from the water, enough to feed itself but not enough to damage the mussel.

At first glance, the barnacles that cluster on the rocks, cutting the feet of barefoot children and swimmers, seem to resemble the mussels. Actually, they are an entirely different form of life, which through a series of adjustment, have been able to find a home for themselves in the tidal pool. For the barnacles, in spite of their outward appearance, are crustaceans and relatives of the crabs and lobsters (*See under Barnacle*). In their younger stages,

they still look like crabs; but when they drift against a hard surface, they attach themselves. In fact, no surface has ever been discovered that is sufficiently slippery to resist them. When they find a permanent home on the rocks, they in effect turn over on their backs and surround themselves with a white, lime shell that is jointed—the joints being a sign of their relationship to the other crustaceans. When the tide is in, they open their shells and wave their feet in the water, drawing in food particles. When the water has gone again with the receding tide, they shut their shells tightly to protect themselves against evaporation.

Some of the most beautiful animals in the tidal pool are the purple-and-orange starfishes (*See under Starfish*). Seen from above, their brilliant backs and five waving legs create a handsome pattern in the water; but to many of the other occupants of the pool, they are a Jules Verne instrument of destruction. In each of its five legs the starfish has suction cups that operate by what amounts to an internal hydraulic system. Taking a firm grip on each side of a mussle, it arches its back and slowly forces the mussel's shell open. Once the mussel's body is exposed, an extraordinary event takes place. Instead of putting the mussel into its mouth, the starfish puts its stomach into the mussel. This unusual method of eating is accomplished by disgorging its stomach, wrapping it around the mussel, and then allowing the stomach acids to dissolve the helpless victim (*See under Echinoderm*).

The starfish has several other peculiarities. For one, it has a perfect defense against barnacles. Should a young barnacle ever settle on the back of a slow-moving starfish, it will be crushed immediately. For the starfish's body is covered with tiny pincers, adapted, or evolved, for just this purpose. Another peculiarity is the fact that the starfish can never walk backward.

It can reverse its direction any time that it wants to, but since all five legs are exactly the same, it always has to be moving forward. The starfish, in spite of its adaptation to life in the pool, also has animals about that destroy it. Often, herring gulls will drive their bills into the masses of seaweed and emerge holding a starfish, which they swallow in one gulp.

The ability of the starfish to disgorge its stomach is duplicated by its relatives, some of the sea cucumbers, but for a different reason. The sea cucumber (*see under Echinoderm*), which vaguely resembles a real cucumber in shape and color and sometimes visits the tidal pool, can extend its insides out through the anal opening, when it is attacked by a predator. These are devoured by

Tidal pools are a special ecological niche for several marine plants and animals

the enemy, while the sea cucumber slips away and grows new internal organs.

Other inhabitants of the pool also show remarkable variety in their adaptations to life between the tides. The limpet, whose shell so many children have used for toy rowboats, crawls along the surface of seaweeds and rocks, scraping off bits of food. Its shell is so built that when it nestles in a depression in the rocks, the waves cannot hurt it (*See under Gastropod*).

The brown-gray snails—the common periwinkles—are an accidental import from Europe. So well adapted are they to life on our shores that, since 1857 when the first one was discovered in Nova Scotia, they have earned the prefix *common* in front of their popular name. Even the sea urchin, looking like an undersized green tennis ball with spines on it, can survive by clinging to the rocks with its own hydraulic system, which in some respects resembles that of the urchin's relative, the starfish.

Looking at the strange animals and plants that have equipped themselves to live in a tidal pool, one begins to realize the efforts that living things will make to succeed. Just as the physicist says that "nature abhors a vacuum," so can the biologist remark that "life abhors any unoccupied niche on the earth, whether it is a desert, a mountaintop, or a rockbound coast." Like the great tides that sweep along the shore, life is always trying to flow into every corner, regardless of the price exacted. Only this impelling force could make life succeed under the arduous conditions present in the tidal pool.

The pool teaches another lesson beside the determination of life to succeed. Life must not succeed too well. If all the young barnacles and mussels in the water survived for several generations, there would be room for nothing else along the coast. The prodigality of life in the sea was brought home to an observer one day, as he watched numerous moon jellyfishes floating past the shore. By estimating the number in an average square foot of water and by plotting their extent on a nautical chart, he was able to determine that more than one million jellyfishes drifted by his shore in that single afternoon. The sight of these jellyfishes helped him to understand the horrors that might be in store for bathers, if natural forces such as predators and the swirling waves did not exact their usual toll (*See Predation*). Left unmolested, one form of life might crowd out all the others in the tidal pool—in the entire bay, in fact. Then, in the end, even the apparently successful form would suffer. One biologist has noted that the price of thinking is death, because no organism complicated enough to think can perpetuate itself by simple division. At a tidal pool one sees this principle expanded. Looking into the quiet waters, he finds that death is the necessary price of life itself.

The pool also shows how life has changed over the years. At times, one might drag the bay with a net, collecting plankton, the microscopic animals and plants that are the basic source of life in the sea (*See Plankton*). Looking through the microscope, one sees this weird community of outlandish plants and animals, their shapes reminding one of the outpourings of some mad artist's imagination. Most important of these are the diatoms, tiny plants encased in silica shells which fill the role that grasses play on land. On them feed many other members of the plankton, as well as larger animals, including the great baleen whales. Remove the diatoms from the ocean, and the first link of the food chain leading to many higher varieties of life would be broken (*See Food Chain*).

Sometimes in the evenings one living along the coast can perform another experiment with the plankton, one requiring much less equipment. Take a bucket of water from the pool and add a dash of household ammonia. Then, when one swirls the water with his hands, any luminescent plankton reveal their presence immediately in a glow of cold, white light. As darkness begins to envelop the tidal world, one thinks of these tiny creatures and compares them with the larger inhabitants of the pool that he has seen during the daytime. Immediately he becomes aware of the many changes that life has brought about within itself. From single-celled plants and animals, it has surged forth into infinite variety—from the pea crab to its host, the mussel; from the barnacle that has surrendered its freedom to lie attached to the rocks to the starfish with its powerful hydraulic system.

But change is not limited to living things. The tilting beds of igneous rock tell that the rocks that make up the tidal pool once reached high above the water. Today, worn and broken by erosion, they lie at the water's edge, and sometime in the future, as the waves continue their work, they will disappear, swallowed in the immensity of the bay.

The sunlight shadows disappear from the slopes of the mountains on Mt. Desert Island, and the valleys are dark where the moonlight has not yet reached them. Below one the tide has come in; and he thinks again of the tidal pool, now under six feet of cool salt water. Its inhabitants, with all they have to teach, are now separated from the human observer by a barrier of water that one cannot penetrate. They have returned to the environment from which they came—the environment from which man came, too, but which he has left so far behind that he cannot reenter it. At this point, they seem a long distance from mankind but in spite of man's differences, he shares with them a common bond in the business of living, of adapting, and therefore of coping successfully, day after day, with the environment of life.   —A.B.A.

TIDAL ZONE (*See under Seashore: Life of the Seashore*)

TIMBERLINE (*See Arctic-Alpine*)

TITMOUSE

The tufted titmouse has three western relatives. The black-crested titmouse, *Parus atricristatus*, ranges east from Mexico along the Rio Grande River almost to Louisiana; it has a black crest and a white forehead. The plain titmouse, *Parus inornatus*, is all gray; it is the only one of the group to be found in most of the West and is most common in oak woodlands, or pinyon pine and juniper scrub. The bridled titmouse *Parus wollweberi*, has a white face with black markings; it occurs only in the mountains of southern Arizona and New Mexico and southward.   —G.B.S.

Tufted Titmouse
Other Common Names—Tomtit
Scientific Name—*Parus bicolor*
Family—Paridae (titmice, verdins, bushtits)
Order—Passeriformes
Size—Length, six inches
Range—From southern Ontario, Canada, through South Dakota, southeastern Nebraska, Minnesota, southern Michigan and Wisconsin, eastern and central Iowa, northwestern Pennsylvania, northern Ohio, southwestern Connecticut, and southern New York, eastern Oklahoma, Kansas and Texas, southern Alabama, Louisiana, Mississippi, Georgia, and central Florida

In spring, when the arbutus and the jessamine bloom in the South, the voices of the trio to which the tufted titmouse belongs—cardinal, Carolina wren, and titmouse—keep the woods ringing with their songs. When heard for the first time in their daybreak or late-afternoon chorus, it may well puzzle one to tell which songster is which. But the characteristic note of the tufted

A tufted titmouse perches upon a pine con

titmouse is the two-syllabled *pe-to, pe-to,* or *pe-ter, pe-ter.*

The titmouse examines leaves, and cracks and crannies of tree bark with microscopic care, searching for insects or their eggs or larvae. When not hunting insect eggs like a chickadee, the tufted titmouse may be cracking nuts like a blue jay, hammering away at one held firmly under its foot. Beechnuts, hazelnuts, chinquapins, or even acorns, the titmouse accepts cheerfully. Wild berries, such as those of dogwood and Virginia creeper, are also taken in their turn; and, in their proper season grasshoppers, beetles, cutworms, and caterpillars form a large part of the titmouse's diet. Boll weevils and scale insects, two of the worst plant pests, are sometimes eaten by it.

The nest of the tufted titmouse is almost always in a ready-made hollow, very often in a deserted woodpecker's nest, especially in that of the red-bellied woodpecker. On rare occasions it excavates its own nest cavity. To line the hollows the titmice carry in a variety of material. For the foundation they sometimes use grasses, strips of bark, and Spanish moss, filling in with a lining of soft materials such as feathers and hair. The eggs of the tufted titmouse vary from five to eight and are white, marked with brown.

Not only do the titmice need holes to nest in in summer, but to roost in in winter, for unlike many birds, these hardy little creatures do not go south in the autumn, but spend the winter where they have passed the summer. —F.M.B.

TOAD

Toads are amphibians and are related to the frogs and salamanders (*See under Amphibian*). Toads are members of the family Bufonidae. The name toad, however, is applied also to certain other members of the order Salienta, such as tree frogs, sometimes called tree toads, which are members of another family, the Hylidae, and to spadefoot toads, which are classified in the family Pelobatidae.

One of the most commonly asked questions is. "What is the difference between a frog and a toad?" Actually toads differ greatly from their relatives the frogs (*See under Frog*). Toads have short legs and are slow movers as compared to the long-legged, fast-moving frogs. Further, toads have dry, rough, and warty skin with prominent paratoid glands, while the skin of true frogs, and most other frogs, is moist and smooth, and paratoid glands are never present. Although toads do have warty skin there is no truth to the old superstition that toads can give warts to humans. When a toad is attacked, however, it is capable of excreting a fluid from its paratoid glands which, in some species, is highly toxic and may cause many an attacking animal to release its prey speedily. It has been observed that dogs that at any one time have tried to devour a toad, received such an unpleasant experience that they never tried it again. Many animals however—notably snakes —are able to feed on toads. The American toad, *Bufo americanus,* is the favorite food of the hognose snake(*See under Snake; and under Reptile*).

Male toads have single external vocal pouches and during the breeding season their trill-like calls are one of the most beautiful sounds in nature. Toads are extremely prolific, the females of some species laying tens of thousands of eggs each. As in other Salienta, the male, by virtue of its clasping thumb, extrudes the eggs from the female and then fertilizes them externally. The eggs of most toads are laid in long gelatinous strings and deposited in shallow waters, often in temporary roadside ditches, and tadpoles emerge rapidly. Shortly after breeding has taken place it is a common sight to find breeding ponds black with a wriggling mass of thousands and thousands of newly hatched tadpoles. After weeks as tadpoles and final transformation into tiny toadlets, they emerge

The skin gland secretions of the giant toad are toxic to dogs and other animals

Digging with its hind feet, a spadefoot toad can disappear in seconds

from the water. At this time the banks of the breeding pools are virtually alive with the tiny hopping creatures seeking to take up life out of the water. Despite their great numbers as tadpoles and then toadlets only a very few reach maturity, for in this early period of their lives they are heavily preyed upon by many creatures. The adult toads are land-dwellers, and return to the water only for the purpose of breeding. In size, toads range from the tiny oak toad, *Bufo quercicus,* about one inch in length, to the giant toad, *Bufo marinus,* which has been known to attain a length of more than nine inches.

Just before the onset of winter, toads go into hibernation, usually burying themselves deep in the ground. During hot and dry summer months they some-times go underground in estivation, or "summer sleep" as it is sometimes called (*See Hibernation*).

Toads are highly beneficial to man, for they feed largely on beetles and other insects. One species, the giant toad, *Bufo marinus,* because of its ability to devour large numbers of sugar beetles, has been introduced into regions, especially Louisiana in the United States, where sugar is raised. The feeding habits of this toad are said to help protect the sugar crop (*See Balance of Nature; and Biological Control*).

Toads thrive extremely well in cap-tivity and make very interesting pets. They should be kept in a terrarium (*see Terrarium*), filled with earth, with a few logs or pieces of bark for them to hide under. Also, as toads drink by absorbing water through their skins, a water dish large enough for a toad to sit in should be provided. Toads feed only on moving objects, so they should be fed live food such as mealworms, earthworms, and small insects. During any temporary absence of live food, toads may be fed small pellets of very lean, raw chopped beef, which should be moved at the end of a broom straw

in front of the toad's nose, to simulate a live creature.

Spadefoot Toads

Spadefoot toads, family Pelobatodae, order Salienta, are in appearance some-what similiar to the true toads, family Bufonidae. They do, however, have a smooth skin; none, or only indistinct, paratoid glands; and elliptic pupils, in contrast to the true toad, whose pupils are vertical. The eyes of all toads are notable for their beauty.

The main characteristic of the spade-foot toad is a sharp-edged, spadelike tubercle on each hind foot, with which they dig themselves into the ground. Place a spadefoot toad on the top of loose soil and one will see the animal immediately begin to dig itself in, turn-ing around and around in the process. Within a few seconds it will be almost completely buried, with only one eye showing. Then comes the final twist, the animal has disappeared, and there is no sign of the presence of a toad, or of a hole.

Small animals, about two inches long, spadefoot toads are strictly nocturnal, and spend most of their adult lives underground. During the breeding season, following a warm spring rain, they appear seemingly out of nowhere, and migrate in large numbers to the breeding ponds, on the way frequently crossing highways where thousands of them are killed yearly by automobiles. Nevertheless many of them complete their journeys to the breeding pools, where the females lay their eggs in gelatinous strings on water plants. The emerging tadpoles are extremely under-developed. After three months the tad-poles complete their metamorphosis, at which time they leave the water not to return until they themselves are ready to breed.

Owing to their underground lives, the spadefoot toads do not lend themselves well to captivity. —G.P.

American Toad
Other Common Names—Hop toad, common toad
Scientific Name—*Bufo americanus*
Family—Bufonidae (true toads)
Order—Salienta
Size—Length, two to four inches
Range—Maritime Provinces and most of northeastern and Atlantic seaboard, southeast to Mississippi and west to Kansas

This is the most common toad within its range. It lives in a great variety of habitats—in forests, meadows, gardens, and near, or in, houses. The only time that it may be found in water is during the breeding season, which, depending on latitude, ranges from March to July. The American toad is usually brownish-olive, but there are wide variations in its color. During the breeding season, particularly, this usually quite drab animal may take on a rather bright color-

ing, especially noticeable in the female.

The call of the male is a melodious, long trill, which is one of the most beautiful sounds of spring. During the breeding season toads may be found in very large congregations in all types of bodies of shallow waters, where, by their sheer numbers, they create a turbulence. The female lays between 4,000 and 8,000 eggs in long, gelatinous strings. Under favorable conditions the tadpoles may emerge as early as three days after the egg-laying. Transformation takes approximately two months, at which time thousands of the toadlets, one-quarter inch in length, may be found teeming on the banks of the waters from which they emerged. To the untrained eye they may appear like masses of small, hopping insects. They are now ready to take up their terrestrial habitat and will return to the water only after they have reached maturity and are ready to breed.   —G.P.

The American toad lives in a variety of habitats, entering the water only to breed

A Fowler's toad usually has three or more warts in each dark spot on its body

Fowler's Toad

Other Common Names—None
Scientific Name—*Bufo woodhousei fowleri*
Family—Bufonidae (true toads)
Order—Salienta
Size—Length, two to three inches
Range—Central New England, Middle Atlantic States, west to Michigan, south to Louisiana

The range of the Fowler's toad overlaps that of the American toad in great part, and, therefore, both species may frequently be found in the same area, and have been known to hybridize. While, in many respects, the two species are quite similar in appearance, each toad has its own distinctive identification marks which makes differentiation relatively easy, unless the specific animal is a hybrid and therefore may carry identification marks of either or both species.

The Fowler's toad is smaller and more compact in build than the American toad, and in color is usually bright gray with a distinct mid-dorsal stripe. The best way to visually separate these two species is by the number of warts in the dark spots on their backs. The Fowler's toad has at least three small warts in each spot, whereas the American toad has usually only one large wart or, at most, two. Also the chest and belly of the Fowler's toad is unspotted, whereas the American Toad has a spotted chest. While there are certain other visual features that differentiate the two species of toads, the surest way to tell one species from the other is by listening to their calls. Contrary to the American toad, whose call is a long, melodious trill, the call of the Fowler's toad is a short scream or bleat.

In the same location Fowler's toads usually breed later than American toads, which prevents hybridizing on a larger scale.   —G.P.

TOADSTOOL (*See under Fungus*)

Tollon, or Christmas berry

TOLLON
Christmas Berry
Other Common Names — California holly;
Tollon or Toyon
Scientific Name — *Heteromeles arbutifolia*
Family — Rosaceae (rose family)
Range — California from Humboldt and
Shasta counties to Mariposa County and
and in the Coast Ranges to northern
Baja California
Habitat — Hillsides and canyons; at its
best in rich soils, mainly Upper Sonoran
Zone
Time of Blooming — April to July

Much of the Christmas decoration in
California is made from the so-called
California holly. This is an evergreen
shrub (toyon) in spring bearing lacy
white heads of blossoms which later
produce the brilliant red berries somewhat resembling English holly. Its
favorite haunt is rocky mountain slopes
and canyon bottoms. From Catalina
Island, where it grows in unmolested
beauty, come very fine specimens. One
tree there is credited with being 40 years
old. It is found in the Coast Ranges,
from Humboldt and Shasta counties in
the north to San Diego County in the
south. A variety producing yellow berries
(var. *cerina*) occurs from San Luis Obispo
to Monterey.

From the Colorado and Mojave
deserts comes the so-called desert holly,
Atriplex hymenelytra, a member of the
salt bush family. This is a shrub up to
three feet high, the holly-shaped leaves
silvery and spine-tipped, the tiny berries
of rosy crimson clustering on short
spikes distributed along the stem.
Neither of the above is a true holly;
the berry or leaf resemblance to true
holly gives it its name.

TOOTHWORT
California Toothwort
Other Common Names — Pepper-root;
ladies' smocks, milkmaids
Scientific Name — *Dentaria integrifolia*
is a variety of *Dentaria californica*
Family — Cruciferae (mustard family)
Range — Southern Oregon to northern
Baja California to central California
Habitat — Sonoran and Transition Zones
Time of Blooming — February to April

In March and April the toothwort
blooms in hill country throughout California. The stems are long and the
leaves are few. The four-petaled flowers
are white or rose color and the plant is
from six inches to two feet high. In wet
meadows the many flowers look like a
large white sheet spread out. The
flowers form little flat seedpods about
1½ inches long. The root has the taste
of pepper — the reason for its sometimes
being called pepper-root.

is gray, with a dull orange throat and a gray or rufous cap. Abert's towhee, *Pipilo aberti,* is similar but more of an orange all over, and with a black throat; it is a desert species residing along the Mexican border.   —G.B.S.

Brown Towhee
Other Common Names—Canyon towhee. California towhee
Scientific Name—*Pipilo fuscus*
Family—Fringillidae (grosbeaks, finches, sparrows, and buntings)
Order—Passeriformes
Size—Length, 7½ to 9½ inches
Range—Southwestern Oregon, central and western Arizona, from northern New Mexico, southeastern Colorado and western Oklahoma and Texas, south through Baja California and the Mexican mainland to Oaxaca and Colima

Brown towhee (bottom); rufous-sided towhee (top)

California toothwart

TOWHEE

The towhees are seedeaters, members of the family Fringillidae, with the sparrows, buntings, grosbeaks, and finches. Most seedeaters hunt their food in grasslands, but towhees prefer woodlands, thickets, or stands of manzanita or sage. They scratch with both feet in the leafy litter, than peck through the trash for hidden seeds.

The rufous-sided towhee, *Pipilo erythrophthalmus,* with contrasting black head and back, white underparts, and reddish sides, nests throughout the United States and southern Canada. The green-tailed towhee, *Chlorura chlorura,* a greenish bird with a rufous cap, white throat, and gray underparts, inhabits dry mountainsides between the Sierra Nevada and the Rocky Mountains, from Oregon to Mexico. The brown towhee, *Pipilo fuscus,* shares its range; it resembles the green-tailed towhee, but

The brown towhee has short, rounded wings and a rusty patch on its rump and throat

Habits of the Brown Towhee

Our Spanish-speaking neighbors in Mexico call the brown towhee *La Viejita* —"the little old woman." The name is an appropriate one, for the demurely dressed, fussily busy bird often reminds one of some little old woman with nothing in particular to do, but always busily doing it. Throughout its range, the brown towhee, *Pipilio fuscus*, spends much time scratching about for food, squabbling with its neighbors, and keeping a sharp eye on all animated objects in its vicinity.

Ranging from southwestern Oregon south through the entire length of California to the southern tip of the peninsula of Baja California, and eastward through northern Arizona and New Mexico to southern Colorado and western Texas, the brown towhee everywhere is a bird of the brushlands, and it never ventures far from such cover except where continuous stretches of dense shrubbery in yards and parks offer a good substitute.

Its dusky, gray-brown color, short, rounded wings, long, rubberlike tail, and strong legs and feet adapt this bird to a life near the ground in the tangled interstices of shrubs and bushes. And on the ground or near it, the brown towhee spends much of its life scratching in the fallen litter for insects and seeds, and hopping along with such speed that it is sometimes mistaken for a running rodent as it vanishes into the bushes. In its chosen habitat the strong legs of the towhee probably carry it farther than do its wings in its daily search for food.

Although much of the food of the brown towhee is insects and weed seeds, yet there are times when it arouses the wrath of the gardener. Like the Chinese, the towhee is very fond of sprouted seeds, and woe to the gardener's crop if a seed bed is left uncovered within the range of these sharp-eyed birds. Since their sharp eyes are just as quick to find weed seeds and insects, seed beds should be protected with fine mesh-wire netting so that the brown towhee can continue to enliven the garden.

Prosaic as the brown towhee is, it adds much interest to the garden. Its sharp chirps may be heard at all hours of the day, even though it does not bring us the glory of a song. There comes a time in early spring when the male tries to sing, but valiant as his efforts are, one is forced to conclude that only the female of his species can possibly be thrilled with the results

achieved. For too long he has been content to chirp. When spring comes, that is all he can do, as his song is just a succession of a wheezy chirps.
—F.G.

Rufous-sided Towhee
Other Common Names—Chewink, ground robin, swamp robin
Scientific Name—*Pipilo erythrophthalmus*
Family—Fringillidae (grosbeaks, finches, sparrows, and buntings)
Order—Passeriformes
Size—Length, 7½ to 8¾ inches
Range—Breeds from Maine, southern Ontario, southern Manitoba, and southern British Columbia, south to California, Texas, Louisiana, Georgia, and Florida. Winters from Massachusetts, the Great Lakes, Nebraska, Utah, and southern British Columbia, southward

Rufous-sided towhees live throughout a large part of the United States and Canada, but in some sections they vary slightly and sing a bit differently! Wherever they are seen, however, the male will be instantly recognized by the black head, vest, and back (the female is brown in these places) and robin-red sides separated by a strip of white.

Ground robin is a good name because the rusty sides do suggest the robin. Both male and female have the reddish flanks and the large white spots toward the tip of the long, ample tail, but the sexes can be readily separated by the color of head, vest, and back. In the dry, brushy tangles and the burned-over scrubby growths that they frequent, rufous-sided towhees can be heard noisily rummaging among the dead leaves, looking for insects. The towhee can turn up leaves by kicking backward with both feet at the same time.

Orginally, the rufous-sided towhee was known as the chewink, undoubtedly from its call, which is a distint, *chewink!* The enunciation is just as clear as the chickadee's *chick-a-dee!* At other times, the male will fly to the top of a small tree from where he will sing a phrase that sounds like *drink-your-tea!* The common name *chewink* was changed to red-eyed towhee, and later to its present name, rufous-sided towhee.

The rufous-sided towhee's nest is not easy to find. It is usually hidden in the tangled undergrowth, often at the foot of a bush or in a clump of grass. Sometimes it is in a low thick bush and, rarely, in a tree.

The four or five white eggs, speckled and blotched with red-brown, take 12 or 13 days to hatch. For 10 or 12 days, the parents feed the young in the nest on moths, hairy caterpillars, flies, grasshoppers, beetles, and even wasps. Most of the rufous-sided towhee's food consists of insects, but at times it eats a few buds and seeds.

The young towhees leave the nest early and scramble about in the underbrush before they can fly. Most ground-nesting birds do this. It is fortunate for the young birds that they are streaked like sparrows, without the bright colors of their parents, which makes it more difficult for predators to see them (*See Predation*).

When severe frosts come in the fall, most of the rufous-sided towhees leave Canada and the northern parts of the United States. They normally winter in the southern tier of states. A few of them stay in the wild grape tangles along the shore of Lake Erie; occasionally, one is found in winter in southern Ontario or New England.

—A.B., Jr.

TREE
A Tree and the Forest

When one enters the woods on a bright sunshiny day in summer and looks about, he usually experiences a feeling of relief and relaxation. This is because under the trees the glare of the sun is shut out, and there is an appreciable lowering of temperature that makes for coolness and refreshment. In all this there is little to suggest the tremendous amount of activity that is actually going on within the leaves and other structures of the trees themselves.

One will find that his enjoyment of the forest will be immeasurably increased if one has an understanding of just how a tree lives and grows, and what its relationships to the other trees and the animals that make up the forest community may be.

Parts of the Tree

First, consider the individual tree. A tree has three main parts. These are its roots, trunk, and leaves. The roots are mainly for anchoring the tree firmly in the ground and for taking up moisture from the soil. The trunk acts as a prop for supporting the branches with their leaves spread toward the sunlight, and for carrying sap to and from the leaves. The leaves are the food factories where a vital manufacturing process goes on.

The tree grows in height and in its spread of branches by lengthening upward and outward from the tips of the twigs. At the same time, it expands in girth around the trunk and branches. Its roots also grow by lengthening from the tips and increasing in girth.

Thus, the ever-increasing weight of the top is supported by a trunk that continually becomes larger and stronger, and by a deeper and more wide-reaching root system.

Inside the tree, if one made a cross section through the trunk or any of its branches, he would note three main parts—the hard center, or heartwood; the outer ring, or sapwood; and the bark.

Looking more closely at the cross section, one would note certain lines in the form of concentric circles, which begin at the center of the section and grow larger and larger until the bark is reached. These are called *annual rings.* Usually one of these rings is laid down every year, representing the growth of new wood for that year. Thus, by count-

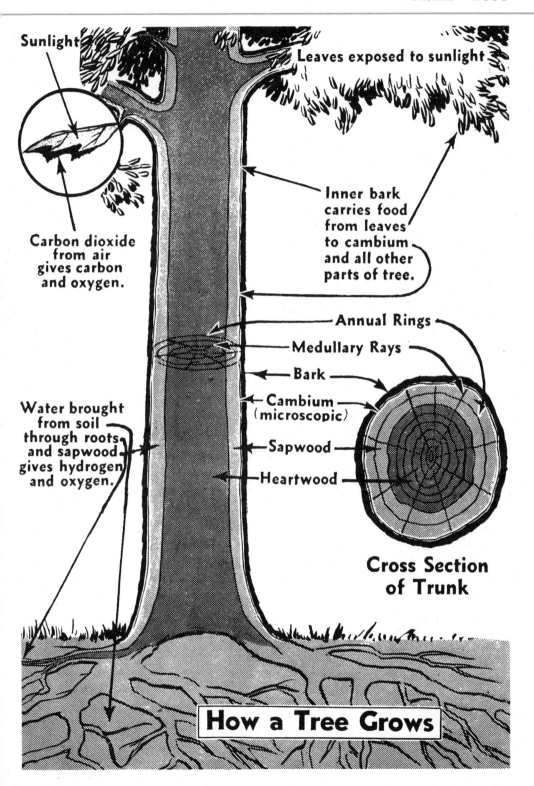

Sunlight

Leaves exposed to sunlight

Carbon dioxide
from air
gives carbon
and oxygen.

Inner bark
carries food
from leaves
to cambium
and all other
parts of tree.

Annual Rings

Medullary Rays

Bark

Cambium
(microscopic)

Water brought
from soil
through roots
and sapwood
gives hydrogen
and oxygen.

Sapwood

Heartwood

Cross Section
of Trunk

How a Tree Grows

ing the annual rings in a cross section of a trunk or branch one may determine the approximate age of that part of the tree. If the cross section comes from near the base of the tree, one may thus estimate closely the age of the entire tree.

Other lines, more or less straight, will be seen radiating from the center like the spokes of a wheel. These are the *medullary rays.*

In the living tree the heartwood is in reality dead wood, and serves no purpose other than to provide strength for the trunk. It is no longer a vital part of the tree. That is the reason why a tree may go on growing, although the heartwood may be completely gone and the trunk quite hollow.

It is through the sapwood that water, with various substances dissolved in it, is carried upward from the roots to the leaves. This takes place through tiny *conducting vessels,* the sap passing from one cell to another through the very thin cell walls.

Between the sapwood and the bark is a layer of cells which can be seen only with the aid of a microscope, but it is one of the most important parts of the entire tree. It is the *cambium* layer.

How a Tree Grows

The cambium cells are very active during the growing season, and it is through them that the growth in circumference of the trunk, branch, and twig takes place. On the inner side of the cylinder of cambium cells, new sapwood is being made and added to the sapwood already there. On the outer side, new inner bark is being made and added to the underside of the bark already there. Thus, the annual rings of growth in the wood are produced. As this process goes on, sapwood toward the center of the tree is gradually turned into heartwood, and bark on the outside of the tree is continually being pushed off. The inner bark, or portion just outside the cambium, contains a system of

conducting vessels of microscopic size, through which foods, manufactured in the leaves, are transferred downward in solution from the leaves to other parts of the tree, including its roots.

The outer bark is largely of cork, which serves as the tree's armor and helps to protect it from injury, from attacks of insects and fungi, and from loss of water by evaporation. There are so many ways of getting rid of the old outer bark as the tree grows that each species of tree has developed bark patterns of its own. These are so characteristic that, with practice, the various species of trees can be recognized by bark alone. One may well ask next how all this activity within the tree is supported, and how the process works.

How a Tree Feeds

Just as with animals, trees must be provided with food, but unlike the animals, trees make their own food. It is mainly in the leaves that the manufacturing of plant food goes forward. One may well think of the leaves of plants as chemical laboratories wherein complex processes are carried on which combine and transform simple substances into highly complex substances, many

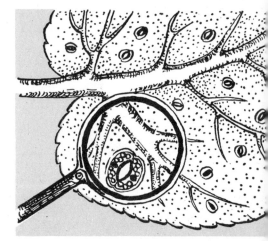

The undersurface of a leaf has many tiny openings, or stomata, through which air enters and moisture leaves the plant

of which can be utilized as food by plants and animals alike.

The most important factor in this chemical process is a green substance called *chlorophyll*, which gives to the leaf its green color. This substance is contained in certain structures within the microscopic cells of the leaf called *chloroplasts*.

The structure of a leaf is such that air may enter and circulate through it, under the control of tiny openings, usually on its underside, called *stomata*. In this way air comes in contact with the interior leaf cells that contain the chloroplasts, and from the air these cells take carbon, which is present in the form of carbon dioxide (CO_2). From the soil about the roots, water is transported from cell to cell until it finally reaches the leaves and the chloroplasts. From this water (H_2O), both hydrogen and oxygen are taken, to be used in the food-manufacturing process.

Now, in the building-up process (as when a load is carried uphill), some energy from outside is needed to make the process work. In the chemical "uphill" process that goes on within the cells in the leaves, this necessary force is supplied by the radiant energy of sunlight. When sunlight falls upon the leaf surface it is absorbed by the chlorophyll, and chemical action takes place. In ways not fully understood, carbon, hydrogen, and oxygen are thus combined under the influence of sunlight to form a sugar. This process is called *photosynthesis*. It is often expressed in written symbols as follows:

$$6CO_2 \ + \ 6H_2O \rightarrow C_6H_{12}O_6 \ + \ 6O_2$$
(carbon dioxide) (water) (glucose) (free oxygen)

As the life processes of all green plants are thus dependent upon the utilization of sunshine, and as man and all other animals are dependent upon the activities of plants for food, it is to the sun (*see under Sun*) that all life looks for its continued existence on the earth, and

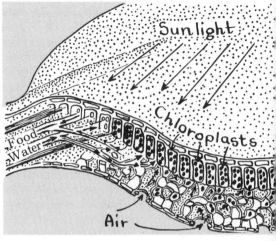

Water, entering the leaf through its stem, or petiole, is utilized in the chloroplast to make plant food from sunlight, air, and other plant substances in a complex life process called photosynthesis

photosynthesis becomes for man the most important chemical process in the universe.

In the course of the chemical reaction that we are considering, it appears that there is an excess of oxygen—more than is needed for the manufacture of sugar and for other purposes. During photosynthesis this excess of oxygen is given off from the leaf surface through the stomata. Thus green plants take from the air carbon dioxide, which is injurious to man, being given off by all animals as a waste product of respiration, and return to the air free oxygen, which is necessary to all animals in respiration. One may thus think of the activities of plants as "purifying" the air that he breathes.

In most plants sugar is changed into starch almost as fast as it is formed, and this is deposited in the leaf cells in microscopic grains. Later, and particularly at night when photosynthesis is not going on, the starch is changed back into sugar and carried in solution in the sap to other parts of the tree. This transfer of food materials from the leaves to other parts of the plant is

In a mature eastern deciduous forest, the forest floor is covered with ferns and other plants that require little sunlight. Where the sun breaks through, other species grow

usually accomplished, as has been indicated, through a system of conducting cells in the inner bark of the tree just outside the cambium layer. In the distribution of food the progress of the sap in inward and outward directions is chiefly through the medullary rays.

Other, and more complex substances, as proteins and fats, are also manufactured by plants, using the sugars as basic materials, as well as other substances which reach the cells dissolved in the soil water. Among these, nitrogen is one of the important elements.

How a Tree "Breathes"

For the utilization of the foods that plants manufacture for their needs, it is necessary, just as in the animal body, that oxidation, or "burning," take place. This process is called respiration.

Through "breathing" pores on leaves, twigs, branches, trunk, and roots, the tree takes in the oxygen necessary for this process from the air. The process of breaking up the foods and releasing the energy stored therein for the needs of growth, reproduction, and other plant activities then takes place. Leaves do several things besides manufacturing food. They occupy space. They create shade. They stop the movement of the

A simple experiment illustrating that leaves transpire water is achieved by placing a potted plant, with the pot and stems covered by a cellophane bag, in a pie pan. If the plant is covered with a wide-mouthed jar and sealed to the pie pan with modeling clay, drops of water will form inside the jar in a day or two

wind. They give off water vapor into the atmosphere.

The Forest Environment

Note how the forest reacts upon its environment and produces certain changes within its boundaries, and how these changes contribute to the welfare and safety of the members of the forest community. By creating shade, the direct rays of the sun are prevented from falling on the forest floor, and the humus moisture—so necessary to the existence of many plants and animals—is thus conserved. By giving off water vapor, the atmosphere is kept moist, and more frequent rainfall is the result (*See Weather*).

This new enveloping mass of foliage in spring seems to emphasize the unity of the forest as a community of living things. It seems to shut the door to the outside world and say, "When you enter here, you are coming to a place apart." This is indeed a household or community of plants and animals that are here, not by accident, but because of

The outer bark of trees is composed largely of cork cells that protect it from injury, such as attacks by insects and fungi, and from the loss of water by evaporation

The barred owl is the last link in one forest food chain and is dependent on a variety of smaller woodland creatures that feed upon plants and each other

the operation of certain well-defined laws governing the distribution of plants and animals throughout the world.

A creature like the wood frog, whose skin must be kept continually moist, could be a woodland animal only under such conditions as certain forests provide. Probably, if one understood the matter thoroughly, he would find that most of the animal dwellers of the woods were so definitely adjusted to a particular kind of environment that they would cease to exist if just the right conditions were not provided.

One may think of the forest further as a great food factory, producing the food that is the basis upon which all of the animal life within the forest must be built up. Not only is food in the form of roots, buds, foliage, and other parts produced for immediate needs, but the very best foods are turned out neatly done up in "packages" that can easily be carried, stored, and used later as needed. These are such things as beech nuts, black walnuts, acorns, hickory nuts, and other seeds. The forest provides food for an enormous insect population that

feeds upon all kinds of plant materials, and many of them feed upon each other. In turn, the insects are devoured by many birds and other animals, which also eat much in the way of seeds and other plant materials, and a few subsist largely on smaller species of their kind. Thus, all woodland creatures that live in association with each other are more or less linked together by food, and in the long run, they are all dependent upon plants for their living. Relationships such as these are referred to as food chains and food cycles. (*See Food Chain*)

A Forest Food Chain

Now one can appreciate that the coming of the leaves means the starting of a vast amount of industry in the forest. And it is the most basic of all industries, for it is at the bottom of all food requirements. Let us trace one of these food chains backward.

Start with the barred owl. Here is a bird that subsists entirely on animal food, such as mice, shrews, a few smaller birds, and some of the larger insects.

Occasionally, snakes or frogs enter its fare (*See under Owl*).

Consider each of these items in turn. Mice, and most insects, are entirely dependent on plant food. Shrews are consumers of insects, which in turn depend on plants for their food. The birds are mostly insect feeders, though some feed on plant material. Suppose a water snake enters into the owl's menu. These snakes feed upon fishes, frogs, tadpoles and the like. Some fishes subsist on other fishes that, in turn, feed on water insects or small crustaceans that feed on plant materials. Thus, without the plant materials, there would be no water snake, no small bird, no shrew, no mouse or insect for the barred owl to live on, and consequently, no barred owl.

One can see now how disastrous is the situation that arises when food supplies normally produced in the forest in abundance happen to be diminished. Not only are those animals affected that subsist directly upon the lost supply, but every animal involved in the food chain also is affected.

As one begins to understand something of the food requirements and food relationships of animals, he finds himself taken behind the scenes in the forest household, and realizes how everything waits upon the silent, secret processes that go on in the leaves of the trees.

—A.B.W.

Sycamore trees are widely planted as ornamental or shade trees along city streets

Some Trees of City Streets

What kinds of trees does one commonly meet along our city streets? How can they be most easily recognized? A little observation and study will lead to an acquaintance with them that will serve as an unfailing source of enjoyment throughout one's lifetime. Trees offer variety to those who get to know them because they are continually changing from month to month in some way— in the unfolding and growth of their leaves, the opening of their flowers, the development and the ripening of their fruits, the tinting of their leaves with autumn colors and, finally, the casting of the leaves and preparation for winter's rest. The color of the bark of the trunk changes from year to year.

Ways to Identify the Maples

All maples have *opposite* leaves, that is, the points of insertion of the leaf stalks (petioles) on the twig or branch are opposite each other. The typical maple leaf is palmately veined, the veins diverging from a central point at the base of the leaf, in general like the skeleton of a hand, or palm. The characteristic fruit is a *key*. The *wings* are outgrowths of the ovary wall and, like parachutes, effectively delay the descent of the fruits (winged seeds) when they fall from the parent tree. This delay, of course, increases the chances for a gust of wind to carry them off to new territory (*See also under Maple*).

Norway Maple. One characteristic is enough to distinguish the Norway maple, *Acer platanoides,* from all other common maples, i.e., its milky sap. One can find the milky juice of a Norway maple by simply cutting or breaking a leaf stalk in two. Then drops of the white milk ooze out. The leaves of the Norway maple are green on both sides; otherwise the leaf strongly resembles that of the sugar maple. The bright yellow flowers are large, for a maple, and are conspicuous in April—especially before the leaves unfold. The bark of a fair-sized Norway maple is *close* and has a multitude of more or less vertical grooves and ridges, something like the bark of the white ash. The Norway maple is one of the best adapted to city life of all trees. It has a pleasing oval shape, gives dense shade, does not grow to an ungainly size, has no disease worth mentioning, does not sucker from the roots, and, with the exception of its keys, does not shed disagreeable litter. Moreover it is strong and stable under stress of wind and storm. As a wild tree it is fairly well distributed throughout Europe but it is said not to occur wild in England or in Holland.

Sycamore maple. Another commonly planted maple is the sycamore maple, *Acer pseudoplatanus,* which grows wild in European countries. Like the Norway maple, it is becoming more and more naturalized in this country. Its leaves are often somewhat hairy on the underside, especially on the veins. The fruit is borne in long, pendent clusters and, in this respect, is unlike that of any other of the common maples. Its bark is flaky and comes off from the trunks of older trees in small roundish or polygonal segments.

Red and silver maples. These are not so much planted in the city because they do not adapt well to the city atmosphere nor do they have such a symmetrical outline. The red maple, *Acer rubrum,* however, is a glorious tree at all times of the year and well deserves its first name. Its flowers, which appear in the North about April first, are red (the staminate flowers have a yellowish cast). The leaves, at least when they first unfold, are red, the leaf stalks are unusually reddish, the fruit has a reddish hue, and the leaves in autumn furnish one of the most brilliant red tints of the landscape. Both red and silver maples, *Acer saccharinum,* have somewhat similar leaves. The principal lobes have sharp angles at their bases—with the silver maple being more deeply cut. Besides this, the leaf of the silver maple has a silvery cast on the underside, hence its common name. The bark of the red maple when it is young is quite pale, almost as pale as that of the American beech. The bark of the silver maple is a little darker. The flowers of the silver maple are borne about two weeks earlier than those of the red, it being our earliest native tree to blossom. The fruits (winged seeds) differ in size and shape.

It is often difficult to distinguish between the red and the silver maples, especially in the winter. Then the silver maple can be recognized by its somewhat darker bark, usually more scaly than that of the red maple—especially in old age—by the habit of the tips of its twigs of turning upward, and by the peculiar rank odor of the freshly broken living twig. The buds are somewhat larger than those of the red maple. In an old tree in winter, the flower buds, more numerous in the upper part of the tree, stand out more prominently in profile against the sky than in the red species. And one must not forget when trying to identify any tree in the winter that the leaves are always on the ground beneath it and in greatest number near the base of the trunk. When the flowers of these two kinds of maples unfold they are seen to be very different, the petals being united in a tube in the silver maple but separate from each other and a pronounced red in the red maple.

In the wild the silver maple is not so generally distributed as the red, being found commonly along the banks of streams or in wet soil; while the red maple is much less particular about its habitat, being found often in swamps and wet soil, but again climbing the mountainside and apparently thriving in dry soil. This tree is also known commonly as the soft, or swamp, maple.

Sugar, or rock, maple. In the cities and towns of the New England states and sometimes in the states to the west and south, the sugar maple, or rock maple, *Acer saccharum,* is a commonly planted street tree. Its leaves are similar to those of the Norway maple but are pale beneath (not shiny green as in the Norway). Both these maples have the angles between the principal leaf lobes, i.e., the sinuses, rounded. *Sinus,* pronounced as in *minus,* is the Latin word for bay or gulf. *Sinus Adriaticus* is the classic name for the Adriatic Sea.

The bark of the sugar maple is irregularly furrowed vertically, at length being divided into large plates, quite unlike the close bark of the Norway. The sugar maple can be readily distinguished in the winter by its buds, especially those at the ends of the branches. Slender and spear-pointed, they contrast with the thicker, blunter, usually dark red buds of the Norway maple. Moreover, the buds when cut into do not show the milky sap characteristic of the buds of the Norway maple. One of the objections to the planting of the sugar maple is that it is sometimes attacked by insect borers which almost, or entirely, girdle the trunk. The sap of this tree when boiled down, yields the commercial maple syrup and maple sugar.

Plane Trees and the American Sycamore

The London plane, *Platanus acerifolia,* is better adapted to city conditions than almost any other tree. A London plane tree stands forth in midsummer, green and fresh, when other trees—even Norway maples—are suffering from the heat, drought, dust, and automobile gases. It can be readily recognized by the shape of the leaf, which somewhat resembles that of the maple, and also by the fact that the heads of the fruit are often in twos. The native sycamore, *Platanus occidentalis (see under Sycamore),* bears only one head of fruit at a time. The bark, as soon as the tree arrives at a diameter of 8 to 10 inches at the base, begins to peel off in plates, showing a greenish-yellow color beneath. In the native sycamore the inner bark thus exposed is whitish. Unfortunately, the London plane is often known as the oriental plane, *Platanus orientalis,* which is quite a different tree and one that is rarely planted in this country.

There is a mystery about the origin of the London plane that remains to be cleared up. It is generally supposed to be a hybrid between the American sycamore, *Platanus occidentalis,* and the oriental plane, *P. orientalis,* because it has some characters of each species and was first found at the Oxford Botanic Garden in England, as a seedling, in the neighborhood of these two species. It would seem easy to settle the matter by making an artificial cross between the two species. The difficulty here is to find an oriental plane to act as one of the parents. At the Brooklyn Botanic Garden there was one tree which seemed to be this species, but it was destroyed by a hurricane in 1944.

The fungous disease called "canker stain," which for a time threatened to kill London plane trees in America, seems now to be under control. If plane trees are pruned there is less danger of infection if the operation is performed between December 1 and February 15. Any dying of plane trees should be reported immediately to the city tree warden or to the United States Forest Service, Washington, D.C.

The Gingko Tree

In an evolutionary sense the ginkgo, *Ginkgo biloba*, is a very old tree. Fossil leaves indistinguishable from those of the existing species have been found in rocks of the Jurassic Age, which according to some geologists, was about 150 million years ago (*See under Geological Time*). In its native home in China no wild individuals are now known; it has been kept alive in Japan and China mainly by priests and monks who have planted it, usually in association with temples, tombs, and palaces (*See also under Gingko*). It has a picturesque type of growth and endures city conditions very well. Handsome specimens are often seen in American cities.

Ginkgo trees are dioecious, that is, the pollen-bearing and seed-bearing flowers are borne on different individual trees. These two forms (*dioecious* comes from *di* + *oikoi* = two houses) of a dioecious tree are popularly known as the male and female tree, although, botanically, no tree has any sex. The individual known as the "male" produces the pollen, while the "female" tree produces ovules containing spores from which the microscopic female plant is developed. The "female" tree can be recognized in the fall by its "fruit," which is really a naked seed with a fleshy outer covering, the size of a sweet cherry, yellow when ripe and of a disgusting rancid odor. When the walks are littered with these seeds the effect is disagreeable in the extreme. However, the kernel can be easily freed from the pulp and, when roasted, is greatly relished by the Chinese and Japanese. The seeds can be planted in the fall and will readily germinate into young seedlings the following spring.

It appears that the ginkgo has lived so long that the weak or disease-susceptible strains have all died out, leaving only a hardy stock immune to any disease, not attacked by insects, and able to endure any amount of punishment in the form of undue heat, drought, smoke, gases, and dust.

American Elm

The American elm, *Ulmus americana*, is distinguished by its alternate, doubly toothed, simple leaves, which are usually very unsymmetrical at the base. In most individuals the trunk divides up into many leaders, producing a vaselike outline. The bark is furrowed more or less vertically. The English elm, *Ulmus procera* or *campestris*, which is sometimes planted, shows bark broken up into more or less polygonal chunks. In habit the two species are very different, the American elm being markedly deliquescent (i.e., literally *melting* or *becoming liquid*), the main trunk losing itself in many leaders; while the English elm is more excurrent (i.e., *running out*), with a single main trunk—although this may, it is true, have very large branches. The leaves of the English elm are smaller, rounder, and rather velvety-hairy, not so rough to the touch as those of the American species. The winter buds are black, or nearly so.

Two serious diseases now threaten the American elm. One of them, called the Dutch elm disease, has been imported in recent years from Europe. At the present time, it is believed not to be as serious as had been feared. Another malady goes by the ungainly name of phloem necrosis, a disease of the bark, induced by a virus, and this has been especially destructive to elms in West Virginia, Ohio, Indiana, and Texas (*See also under Elm*).

In southern cities the winged elm, or wahoo, *Ulmus alata*, is much planted along city streets, as is also its relative, the sugarberry, or southern hackberry, *Celtis laevigata*.

Linden Trees

The kind of linden one is apt to meet on the streets of America is a European species, *Tilia europaea*, with heart-shaped, simple toothed, alternate leaves, with small tufts of hairs in the axils of the veins on the lower surface. The small, spherical fruits, borne in clusters attached to a "sail," are well known. The bud, to be found in the axil of each leaf, is fairly well grown by July and is unique in having a large scale at one side, which gives it a lop-sided appearance (*See also under Basswood*).

Oak Trees

The pin oak, *Quercus palustris*, is well adapted to city life by its form, size, comparatively slow growth, and by its tolerance of city conditions. Its branches are plentifully supplied with small, straight twigs (the "pins") sticking out at wide angles. Both its leaves and acorns are small. The acorns are often striped, lengthwise.

While it is still young the lower branches usually point downward, giving the whole tree a characteristic appearance so that it can be recognized by this feature alone, as far as it can be seen. In old trees, however, these lower branches usually have been pruned or have fallen off, so that this habit is then not so marked. The root system is shallow, with no main taproot as in most other oaks, so that this tree lends itself readily to transplanting (*See under Oak*).

Poplar Trees

The poplar that is often planted along the streets in some of the newer sections of our cities is commonly known as the Carolina poplar, *Populus canadensis*, var. *Eugenei*. It has a broadly conical outline and triangular leaves which unfold early and are reddish while young. Also, the leaves run out into a considerable point, and the leaf margin has rounded teeth with a few fine hairs. But the Carolina poplar, although sometimes called the "Real Estate Man's Tree" because of its remarkably rapid growth, has proved to be a rather undesirable citizen and is not being planted as much now as in earlier years. One

defect is the casting in early spring of its pollen-bearing catkins on the walks, making them untidy, slippery, and dangerous. Most of the trees planted along the streets are of the pollen-bearing form, for the poplar is dioecious (*See under Gingko*). But the seed-bearing form is also disagreeable because of its cottony fruits, the hairs floating in the air and getting into clothes and houses— hence, the other name cottonwood. This species, however, is not the real cottonwood (*See Cottonwood; and under Poplar*).

Requirements for Street Trees

Trees for city planting should possess the following characteristics:

— ability to endure severe winters
— ability to withstand initial transplanting
— tolerance of city dust, smoke, gases
— tolerance of poor soil
— production of abundant shade
— possession of pleasing foliage and habit of growth
— suitability of size (fair size but not enormous)
— suitability of root system (not filling drain pipes or raising sidewalks)
— freedom from "suckering"—production of young shoots
— comparative freedom from litter— objectionable casting of flowers, twigs, messy fruits
— freedom of flowers and fruits from objectionable odor
— resistance to diseases and insect attack
— resistance of trunk and branches to breakage in storms

On the basis of these requirements one might select the following to serve as street trees, in order of preference:

1. Norway maple—*Acer platanoides*
2. Ginkgo—*Ginkgo biloba* (*male trees*)
3. Pin oak—*Quercus palustris*

The London plane, *Platanus acerifolia*, is also most desirable as a street tree, but, if planted, should be watched continually for any signs of the canker stain disease. See Circular 742, United States Department of Agriculture, Washington 25, D.C.

Along the axis of some parkways, in the strip separating the traffic lanes, such trees and shrubs as magnolias, flowering dogwood, red cedar, and mountain laurel can be planted to great advantage, because beauty and not shade is the prime consideration there.

—A.H.G.

Recommended Reading

American Trees: A Book of Discovery—Rutherfored Platt. Dodd, Mead & Company, New York.
A Field Guide to Trees and Shrubs—George A. Petrides. Houghton, Mifflin Company, Boston.
Guide to Trees and Shrubs: Based on Those of Greater New York—Arthur H. Graves and Hester M. Rusk. Published by Hester M. Rusk, 74 Carson Avenue, Metuchen, New Jersey.
The Home Book of Trees and Shrubs—J. J. Levison. Simon & Schuster, New York.
Illustrated Guide to Trees and Shrubs: Native, Naturalized, and Exotic Woody Plants of the Northeastern States—Arthur Harmount Graves. Harper & Brothers, New York.
Knowing Your Trees—G. H. Collingwood. American Forestry Association, Washington, D.C.
1001 Questions Answered About Trees—Rutherford H. Platt. Dodd, Mead & Company, New York.
Trees: A Guide to Familiar American Trees—Zim and Martin. Simon & Schuster, New York.
Trees In Winter—A. F. Blakeslee and Chester D. Jarvis. The Macmillan Company, New York.
Trees of the Northeastern United States, Native and Naturalized—H. P. Brown. Christopher Publishing House, Boston.
Winter Key to Woody Plants—Arthur Harmount Graves. Published by author, 255 South Main Street, Wallingford, Connecticut.

Summer Identification of Trees

A richer and more varied world awaits the person who has learned to recognize the common trees that surround him. Instead of the blur of green that lines the highways, or the mass of unfamiliar foliage that appears as the forest, one looks for familiar tree shapes, well-known flowers, or leaves, or fruits, or for new and interesting trees to add to one's store of knowledge. Every trip afield becomes a richer experience and each new tree a challenging adventure.

Trees may have *simple* or *compound* leaves. The position of the bud (in the axil, or place where stem of leaf is attached to twig) determines whether one is dealing with simple or compound leaves. One should be sure when picking the leaf to collect the entire leaf if it is compound. One should also be careful when picking the leaf to observe if the leaves are borne singly on the stem and are *alternate,* or *opposite* each other, or are in groups of *whorls* of three or more around the stem. The *venation* of the leaf may be pinnate like the barbs of a feather, and the arrangement of the leaflets in a compound leaf, may also be *pinnate* or *palmate* with the veins or leaflets radiating from a central point.

Once one has mastered the trees in this article he will enjoy going on to learn more of the common trees in his locality. There are several hundred kinds of trees in North America and the use of one of the regional manuals or more inclusive books listed in the *Recommended Reading* will help one to recognize these.

—J.W.T.

Recommended Reading

The Tree Identification Book—George W. D. Symonds and Stephen V. Chelminski. M. Barrows & Company, New York.
North American Trees—R. J. Preston, Jr., Iowa State College Press, Ames, Iowa.
Rocky Mountain Trees—R. J. Preston, Jr., Iowa State College Press, Ames, Iowa.
Handbook of Trees of Northern States and Canada, East of the Rocky Mountains—R. B. Hough. The Macmillan Company, New York.
Field Book of American Trees and Shrubs—F. S. Mathews. G. P. Putnam's Sons, New York.
Trees of the Eastern United States and Canada—W. M. Harlow. McGraw-Hill Book Company, New York.
Pacific Coast Trees—H. E. McMinn and Evelyn Maino. University of California Press, Berkeley, California.
Michigan Trees—C. H. Otis, University of Michigan Press, Ann Arbor, Michigan.
Trees of North America—60 post-card size Audubon Cards in color, by Michael Bevans. Short biography on reverse side. Order from National Audubon Society.

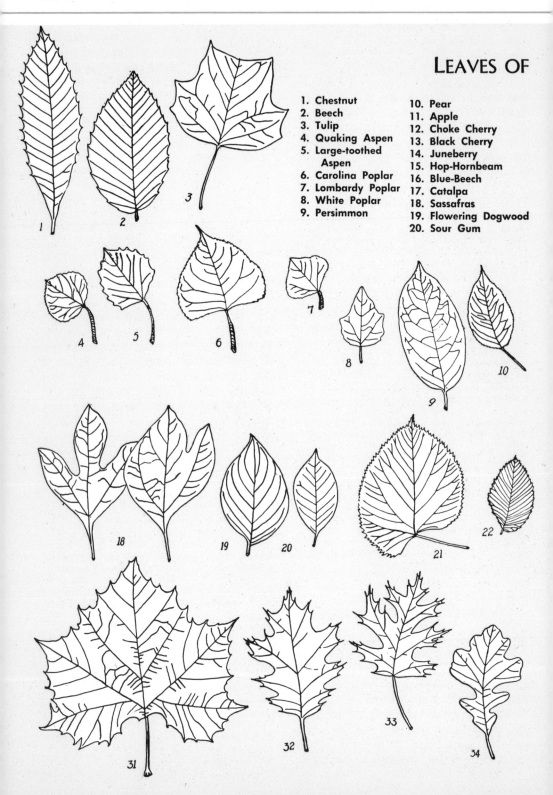

LEAVES OF

1. Chestnut
2. Beech
3. Tulip
4. Quaking Aspen
5. Large-toothed Aspen
6. Carolina Poplar
7. Lombardy Poplar
8. White Poplar
9. Persimmon
10. Pear
11. Apple
12. Choke Cherry
13. Black Cherry
14. Juneberry
15. Hop-Hornbeam
16. Blue-Beech
17. Catalpa
18. Sassafras
19. Flowering Dogwood
20. Sour Gum

COMMON TREES

21. Basswood
22. Rock Elm
23. Slippery Elm
24. American Elm
25. Hackberry
26. Willows
27. Gray Birch
28. White Birch
29. Black Birch
30. Yellow Birch
31. Sycamore

32. Red Oak
33. Black Oaks
34. Burr Oak
35. White Oak
36. Swamp-White Oak
37. Chestnut Oak
38. Red Maple
39. Silver Maple
40. Sugar Maple
41. Norway Maple

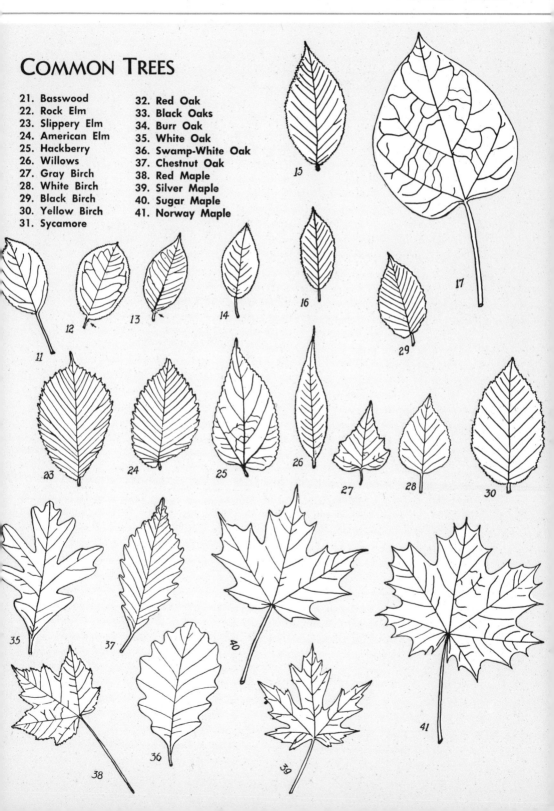

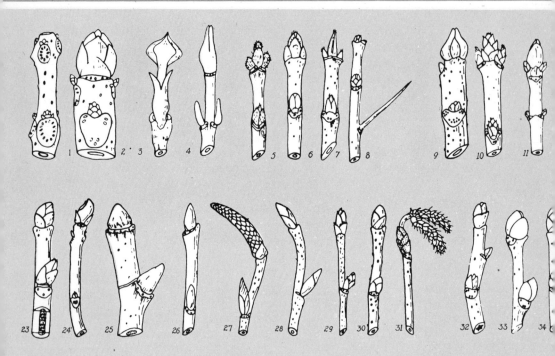

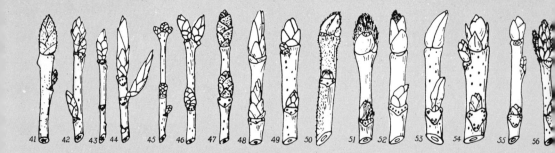

TWIGS OF

1. Catalpa**	12. Black Ash*	23. Sour Gum, Tupelo	33. Basswood
2. Horse Chestnut*	13. White Ash*	24. Sassafras	34. American Hornbeam
3. Flowering Dogwood*	14. Green Ash*	25. Sycamore	or Blue-Beech
4. Black Haw	15. Red Ash*	26. Willows	35. Slippery Elm
5. Box Elder*	16. Honey Locust	27. Black Birch	36. Rock Elm
6. Silver Maple*	17. Black Locust	28. Yellow Birch	37. American Elm
7. Red Maple*	18. Butternut	29. Paper or Canoe Birch	38. Ailanthus
8. Hawthorne	19. Black Walnut	30. Gray Birch	39. Lombardy Poplar
9. Poison Sumac	20. Tulip Tree	31. Hop Hornbeam	40. Cottonwood
10. Sugar Maple*	21. Persimmon	32. Chestnut	41. Silver Poplar
11. Norway Maple*	22. Hackberry		

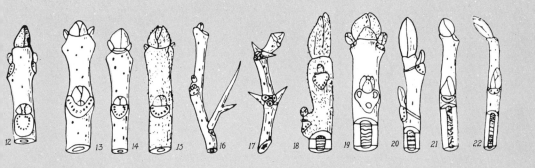

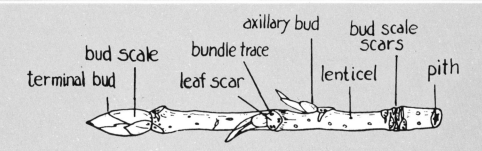

terminal bud — bud scale — bundle trace — leaf scar — axillary bud — bud scale scars — lenticel — pith

COMMON TREES

42. Large-toothed Aspen
43. Quaking Aspen
44. Beech
45. Pin Cherry
46. Wild Black Cherry
47. Choke Cherry
48. Shadbush, Serviceberry
49. Pear
50. Apple
51. Rowan Tree

52. Mountain Ash
53. Bitternut
54. Shagbark Hickory
55. Pignut Hickory
56. Black Oak
57. Scarlet Oak
58. Bur Oak
59. Red Oak
60. White Oak
61. Chestnut Oak
62. Swamp-White Oak

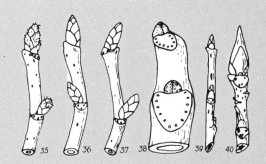

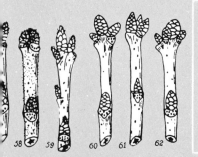

Identify twigs easily by observing:
buds – their shape, size, scales
bark – its color, the pattern
leaf scars – their shape, pattern, if scars are opposite*, in circle of 3**, or alternate
pith – its color, if chambered (e. g. No. 19)

Winter Identification of Trees

If trees have their beauty and fascination in summer what an interesting world awaits those who can enjoy them in frost and winter weather. The trees, so bleak and bare, really become old friends to be recognized by their shapes and by the scars and buds upon their branches. Become an initiate in the art of recognizing trees without their leaves and one adds a new interest and a new pastime to his winter activities. It is not a difficult art, this recognizing of old friends in their cold weather garb.

If one examines a twig of a tree such as a poplar, he will find a *terminal bud* at the tip. Along the side of the twig are the *leaf scars*, marking the place where the stalk of the leaf dropped off in autumn. Above each leaf scar is an *axillary bud*. The buds are protected by *bud scales* and contain the embryonic leaves and flowers which will open up in the spring. In each leaf scar are a number of raised dark marks called the *bundle traces*. These show where the fibrovascular bundles, or strands which bring water and minerals to the leaf and prepared food from it, passed from the stem to the leaf. The traces are usually quite conspicuous and definite in arrangement, if not in number, for a given species of tree. A tiny scar to each side of the top of the leaf scar, the *stipule scar*, shows where the stipules, tiny appendages at the base of the leaf stalk, have dropped off. Clusters of ring-like, narrow scars, the *bud scale scars*, indicate the former positions of the terminal bud and mark off one year's growth from another. These scars persist for several years but eventually growth of the twig in thickness obliterates them. On the twigs, swollen dots called *lenticels* are usually conspicuous. These are spongy pores through which gas exchanges take place. The leaf scars and the buds are the most useful characters in naming the trees in winter. Frequently trees have two types of buds, some larger than others. The larger buds usually open to produce flowers and the smaller buds usually produce leaves and branches. Elms and the blue beech show quite a marked difference in the bud sizes.

In comparing twigs with the illustrations, a hand lens or other magnifying glass will be of great help in observing the bundle traces, stipule scars, and other small characters. The living twigs should be compared with the picture.

—J.W.T.

Recommended Reading

Trees In Winter—A. F. Blakeslee and C. D. Jarvis. The Macmillan Company, New York.
Trees of Eastern United States and Canada—William M. Harlow. McGraw-Hill Book Company, New York.
Illustrated Guide to Trees and Shrubs—Arthur H. Graves. Harper & Brothers, New York.
A Field Guide to Trees and Shrubs—George A. Petrides. Houghton Mifflin, Boston.
The Tree Identification Book—George W. D. Symonds. M. Barrows & Company, New York.
Field Book of American Trees and Shrubs—F. Schuyler Mathews. George P. Putnam's Sons, New York.

Some Familiar Nut-bearing Trees

The American Indians greatly appreciated the food value of nuts and gathered them in large quantities. When the pioneer was making a home for himself and his family in the primeval forest he was quite certain to leave a few promising nut trees near his cabin. Nuts from wild trees had a refining influence on the home life of the child. The pleasure of collecting them during autumn days, the nut-crackings around the open fireplace during the long winter evenings, the roasting of chestnuts in the ashes, were among the happy recreations of the pioneers.

All the trees described bear edible nuts, sweet and pleasant to the taste.

Black walnut, *Juglans nigra*. The black walnut is a stately tree with wide spreading branches and a rounded top. In the cramped condition of the forest it is apt to grow tall with branches more upright. The bark is dark and rough with deep furrows and rounded ridges. The compound leaves are 1 to 2 feet long with

15 to 21 leaflets 3 or more inches long, with saw-toothed edges, sessile on the main leaf stem. The nut, enclosed in a smooth yellowish-green husk, is dark-colored, rough, slightly compressed, about 1 ½ inches across (See Walnut).

Butternut, *Juglans cinerea*. The butternut is a medium-sized tree with spreading or rounded top. The bark is gray and on old trees has broad, flat ridges and shallow furrows. The petioles are slightly hairy and sticky. The oblong nut has a thin husk that is covered with short, clammy hairs. The nut itself is very rough, with thick walls.

Hickories. Hickory is an Indian word given to a milky drink obtained by grinding the nuts in water (See under Hickory: Shagbark Hickory). There are eight or ten species of hickory trees in the eastern United States. No hickories are found on the other continents. The *staminate flowers* of hickories, like those of the walnut and the butternut, hang from the branches in catkins four or five inches long. The *pistillate* blossoms are usually clustered near the ends of the twigs. The hickory weevil, a small white grub, has almost destroyed the hickory trees in some localities. The most common species of hickory are:

Shagbark hickory, *Carya ovata*. The shagbark is our best known hickory. It thrives in deep, rich soil and becomes a tall, straight tree. On old trees the flat ridges of the gray bark break in pieces three or four feet long which are held fast in the middle, giving the trunk a shaggy appearance. The leaves are composed of five, rarely seven, leaflets. The terminal one is short-stalked, the others are *sessile*. The fruit has a heavy husk which splits freely into four pieces. The nut is usually about an inch long and slightly angular.

Mockernut hickory, *Carya alba*. The word *mocker* is believed to have been given to it by the early Dutch settlers. The bark is dark gray and rough; leaflets seven to nine, slightly hairy; the nut is brown with a thick shell.

Pignut hickory, *Carya glabra*. Common in the East, the pignut grows to be a large, stately tree with rough bark. The leaves have five to seven leaflets and the fruit is pear-shaped, slightly flattened, the valves of the husk splitting only halfway to the base. The nut has a smooth, hard shell.

American chestnut, *Castanea dentata*. The American chestnut, before it was killed off by the chestnut blight (*see under Chestnut*), was a large tree with light gray bark with broad, flat ridges and shallow furrows. The oblong, sharp-pointed leaves have coarse teeth. It blooms about the first of July, when the tree is covered with long, yellowish-white catkins. The large prickly burs develop quickly and burst open early in October, showing one to three brown nuts. The seeds are sweet, much sweeter than the big European chestnuts that one sees in the markets.

American beech, *Fagus grandifolia*. This is a large, spreading tree with smooth gray bark. The leaves resemble those of the chestnut. The comparatively small burs have soft prickles. There are two triangular seeds to a bur. The kernel is very sweet but there is so little of it that it scarcely pays to gather the nuts. (*See under Beech: American Beech*).

Hazelnuts. The hazelnuts, or filberts, are shrubs about four to six feet high (*See Hazel*). They grow along roadsides and in thickets. There are two species, the American hazelnut, *Corylus americana*, and the beaked hazelnut, *Corylus rostrata*. The roundish, heart-shaped leaves are nearly alike in the two species. The American hazelnut has brown seeds enclosed in a leaflike husk, while those of the beaked hazelnut are at the bottom of a narrow tube. Chipmunks are very fond of these nuts and generally get their full share. Walnuts, butternuts, and hickory nuts are gathered by red and gray squirrels, and the nuts of hickories and the southern pecans are eaten by wood ducks, wild turkeys, squirrels, and chipmunks. —O.P.M.

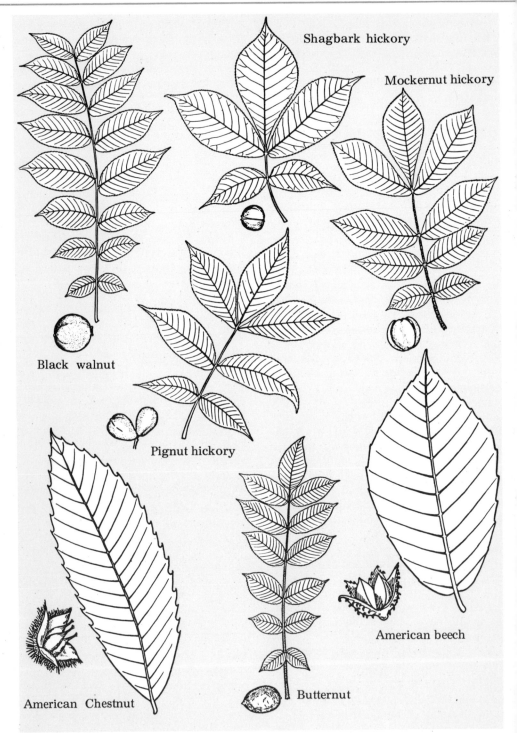

Shagbark hickory

Mockernut hickory

Black walnut

Pignut hickory

American beech

American Chestnut

Butternut

The leaves of some common North American nut bearing trees and their fruits

Trees as History Books

The United States Weather Bureau has been making and publishing official reports only since 1872, yet trees have been keeping continuous weather records for hundreds, even thousands, of years. Through tree rings, pollen grains, and fossil remains, and through evidence in the form of dead trees and their surroundings, man can reconstruct recent, ancient, and geologic history.

It was at William G. Vinal's Nature Lore School that one nature student first discovered how "talkative" trees can be. *Stump Scouting* was what "Capt'n Bill" named his tree-sleuthing operation and ever since that summer this naturalist has found it hard to pass a tree stump without stopping for at least a quick look. He has scouted hundreds of them, along city streets, in parks, along roadsides, or in the wilderness. Children and adults have been equally fascinated as they worked to solve the "mystery of the stump."

When one finds a big, well preserved stump he can go to work. He may be able to answer all of the following questions. The clues will help one off to a fast start. An inquiring person, examining the evidence to be found in a tree stump, can make deductions worthy of a Sherlock Holmes.

Stump-scout Questions and Clues

1. What kind of tree was this? In eastern woodlands, stumps of large size, especially if they are numerous, are likely to be chestnut. In the city, they may be elm or sycamore (or London plane). If the wood shows solid lines radiating from the center (medullary rays) the tree is probably oak, sycamore, or beech. If bark remains it will make identification easier.

2. From what did it grow? A single tree usually has grown from a seed (acorn, beechnut, chestnut, etc.); a circle, or multiple growth, probably represents sprout or coppice growth from a stump.

3. What tools were used in felling this tree? In what order? An axe and a saw both leave recognizable marks. So does a wedge. Gasoline "chain" saws have largely replaced the smoother cutting cross-cut saw. Each type leaves its "trade-mark."

4. How many workmen were there? Where did he (they) stand? A cross-cut saw is a two-man saw. Small chain saws can be operated by one person but usually a helper is on hand. On a freshly cut stump the saw leaves slight ridges that point to where the man (men) stood.

5. In what direction did the tree fall? Did it do any damage? Find where the lower cut was made (either with axe or saw). This controls the direction of fall. Look for broken limbs or crookedness in nearby trees, and clear space—possibly part of the fallen tree itself remains. Compass direction can be determined by the sun, quite accurately if you have a watch. "Moss" on the tree trunk is not a reliable guide.

6. Was it cut during a strong wind or a calm? By amateur(s) or experienced woodsman (men)? Presence of a "chairback," or of much splintered wood, indicates wind or that the tree leaned a good deal. The extent of the lumbering operation, the cleanness of the cuts, and the height of the stumps reveal the ability of the woodcutters. Commercial loggers leave short stumps.

7. How long ago was it cut? The approximate year when it was cut may be revealed by the age of the sprouts from the stump, or by the time a particular species of tree, like a chestnut, was affected by blight. The landowner might supply the answer, and much additional information of interest.

8. How old was the tree? Annual growth rings add up to a tree's exact age. In slow-growing species like hemlock, they are narrow. In ones that grow rapidly, like white ash, sycamore, and white

Instructed by a naturalist, a group of students learn to interpret tree rings

oak, the rings are much wider. In a single tree they may vary in size from year to year, due to differences in moisture and other factors affecting growth. The rings will be conspicuous in trees like oaks, where the spring wood is markedly different in appearance from the summer wood. The best trees for showing such difference are oak, chestnut, elm, ash, hickory, locust, and mulberry. On the other hand, no conspicuous rings will be found in birch, maple, beech, tulip, gum, hornbeam, and basswood. Their even, diffuse pores make the rings much more difficult to count.

9. At what time of the year did it grow most rapidly? Sugar stored in the roots and outer trunk, and water from spring rains and melting snows combine to produce a good flow of sap and result in rapid growth. In trees that show marked rings, the dark colored spring wood is made up of large cells. They form the inner part of each annual ring.

10. At what part of the year did it produce the most wood? A band of smaller, thicker walled cells is formed outside the spring wood. This is the summer wood. It looks lighter, and generally is broader. Growth is then halted till the following spring.

11. What was its greatest increase in diameter in one year? Its least? Remember that the same annual ring must be measured at opposite sides of the trunk to determine the full annual growth.

12. Did it grow most in its youth, middle age, or maturity? Various trees in the same forest may show different patterns of growth rate, unrelated to rainfall. A sudden spurt in growth usually indicates that the tree was "released" from competition when a nearby, taller tree fell victim to axe, wind, or lightning.

13. Account for any scars, knots, etc., and differences in wood thickness in various directions from the center.

14. Why was it cut? In the case of chestnut blight, whole forests were cut

to salvage the wood. Infected elms are cut and burned to destroy the insect carrier of Dutch elm disease. Dead shade trees are cut to remove a hazard to pedestrians or traffic. In the woods, isolated dead trees are valuable nesting places for wildlife and should be left standing.

15. Was it cut before or after it died? If cut while living, bark is more likely to cling to a stump for some years; otherwise bark may drop off.

16. If killed by disease, how may it be combatted? Spread of insect-borne plagues like Dutch elm disease may be checked by the cutting of infected trees and brances. There is no protection against wind-blown spores such as chestnut blight. White pines, however, may be saved from blister rust by removing wild currants and gooseberries because these plants are alternate hosts to the fungus and are necessary for its existence.

17. What evidence can be found of animals that have visited or used the stump? Remember that the term "animal" includes man, and also insects. Tunnels of carpenter ants, boring beetle grubs, webs of spiders, gnawing by rodents, bird droppings, and mammal scats, partly eaten acorns, etc., may be found. Look also for marks of knife or axe.

18. What plants are growing in the stump dust? The older the stump the more algae, mosses, lichens, and seedlings of shrubs and trees may be found, since decaying wood provides a fine growing medium.

Tree-ring "Calendars" and Climate

Men have known for centuries that tree rings tell the age of trees. Leonardo da Vinci noted the difference in size between the various rings in the same tree and attributed the variation to wet and dry years. This climatic effect on trees is widely recognized today but foresters have discovered that variations

The rings in a cross section of a bur oak trunk revealed its age to be 334 years

in growth also may be due to other causes.

Trees which are over-topped by others and cut off from direct sunlight may grow slowly but when "released" by the removal of such competition, their new growth rings clearly show the effect of improved conditions. On the other hand, a very poor year's growth may be the result of defoliation by insects such as the spruce budworm or elm leaf beetle.

The experienced observer can distinguish between these three types of growth variation and even can determine from tree rings the nature of climate hundreds of years ago. It was an astronomer, A. E. Douglass of the University of Arizona, who wrested from tree rings their full secrets of prehistoric climate. His search for a relationship between sunspot cycles and tree-ring growth led to the establishment of the science of *dendrochronology,* or the study of tree-ring timing.

The findings of this science are based partly on the annual variations in the growth of a single tree and partly on the fact that similar growth patterns may be recognized in different trees. Obviously, a series of "good" growing years will produce a series of noticeably large annual rings. A very dry growing season will result in a narrow ring, perhaps only one-tenth the amount of the best year's increase.

The swing from wet to dry years and back again traces a pattern that may be recognized in widely scattered trees. The clearest patterns will be found in "sensitive" trees. Often such trees are found on hillsides where their water supply comes exclusively from rain or melting snow. Trees in the lowlands, near a never-failing water supply, do not qualify as natural rain gauges.

If a sensitive tree is cut, each ring clear to the center can be dated, and each ring by its width will give some measure of that year's rainfall. In Philadelphia, some years ago, an amateur tree-ring student examined and recorded the annual rings in the huge wooden log that formed the fireplace mantle of an early colonial house. When matched with the rings of a nearby stump of known age, similar patterns were found in each.

The identical rainfall record was found near the outer edge of the fireplace log, and near the center of the recently cut stump. The overlapping, or cross-dating, carried the tree-ring calendar back to 1580, more than 100 years before William Penn settled Pennsylvania. It is quite possible that even earlier dates could be determined from timbers in some of the oldest buildings along the Atlantic seaboard.

Where there are older trees, naturally there are more extensive tree-ring calendars. In the arid Southwest where moisture for trees comes chiefly from melting snow in the mountains, ponderosa pine and Douglas-fir are excellent calendar trees.

Tree-ring Calendars and Ancient Indian Tribes

It was in that region, particularly in the pueblo villages of the Four Corners, where Utah, Colorado, New Mexico, and Arizona meet, that the search for tree-ring records was first undertaken. There the searchers, led by Douglass, found beams that had been cut and used by the Indians before any tree living today had begun to grow.

Thousands of wood fragments from 40 ruins and occupied villages were collected. Painstakingly they were studied and step by step they pushed the calendar back until the earliest annual ring was dated 1260!

The search went on. Even charred wood, delicately handled and soaked in paraffin and gasoline, gave up a clear tree-ring record. Many of these oldest records overlapped each other. A continuous chronology of 551 years was worked out but nowhere did it appear to overlap with the "modern" calendar that went back to 1260. This undated calendar they called a "floating" chronology.

Finally in 1929, in an ancient pueblo at Showlow, Arizona, Douglass found a charred log that proved to be the missing link. Comparison with the modern chronology proved that it had been cut in 1380, and had started growing in 1237. And then the researchers discovered that its early rings cross-dated with the top of the floating chronology. It was like a bridge which rested upon abutments in both the old and new series.

This was a discovery comparable to the finding of the famous Rosetta stone which solved the mystery of Egyptian hieroglyphics. It could now be shown that the Mummy Cave dwellings, in Canyon del Muerto were under construction from 1253 to 1284; the Chaco Canyon cliff dwellings between 919 and 1130.

Likewise it dated the mysterious departure of the inhabitants of the cliff dwellings and supplied a plausible explanation for their leaving. The new continuous tree-ring chronology revealed that a calamitous drought occurred, beginning in 1276 and extending to 1299. The pine forests that once grew to the edge of Chaco Canyon probably died as a result of this drought, the worst in the whole tree-ring record. Springs failed and crops withered with the drying out of the Chaco region. Without food and water the Indians were forced to abandon their otherwise impregnable fortress dwellings, migrating to new territory less affected by the drought.

According to the tree rings two other major droughts occurred, at 300-year intervals. One lasted from 1573 to 1593; the other, starting in 1870, became especially severe from 1894 to 1904. Each drought was followed by periods of abundant rainfall but the trees did not return to the edge of the Chaco. The nearest pine forests today are 60 miles away.

Tree-ring Autobiographies

The tree-ring chronology of the Southwest has now been carried back to nearly 200 years B.C., but in California, sequoias living more than 30 centuries supply a continuous record dating back to 1305 B.C. However, because of more uniform climatic conditions these trees cannot be used for dendrochronology. In several of the world's largest museums are exhibited sections of sequoias. The big-tree section displayed at the American Museum of Natural History in New York City measures 16½ feet in diameter, inside the bark, and was 1,341 years old when felled, in 1891. The tree had probably not even reached "middle-age". It is believed that sequoias may reach an age of 5,000 years; some naturalists think they may live for 10,000 years.

The history of this tree includes four forest fires which severely burned the tree. Healing, following fires in 245, 1441, and 1580, was so successful that smooth, complete annual rings eventually grew over the scar though it took 105 years to heal one of the burns. In 1797 a fire caused a burn 18 feet wide. This was only partly healed by 1891 when the tree was cut.

Many museums cannot house such a tremendous cross-section. Instead, some of them exhibit a section of some tree cut in the local community. At West-town School, near West Chester, Pennsylvania, a 220-year old tulip tree, cut on the campus, supplied a section now used to chart the school's history.

Two extremely fine pieces of nature writing have been spun around the felling of a tree. "Good Oak," in *A Sand County Almanac*, is Aldo Leopold's sensitive story of the 80-year history of a Wisconsin oak. Woven into the description of the cutting is the year by year record of climate, and of events in the use or misuse of natural resources.

The Story of a Thousand Year Pine by Enos Mills, is a fascinating account of the painstaking examination of a fallen, shattered yellow, or ponderosa, pine. The story is based entirely on evidence found in the tree itself.

Tree-ring Rubbings—How to Record Tree Rings

For the person who finds interesting tree stumps but who cannot bring back sections of them, a way of recording the tree-rings will be described.

Equip yourself with a roll of adding-machine paper, a few thumb tacks, and a soft lead pencil or a colored marking pencil. Then go to the stump and,

(1) locate the smoothest diameter of the stump, preferably the longest, and roll out enough paper to cross it, with a few inches to spare.

(2) Double over the end of the paper twice and tack it into the bark. Do the same at the far side. Now it won't tear so easily.

(3) Holding your pencil almost parallel with the surface of the stump, rub nearly at right angles to the annual rings as you would in getting a rubbing of a penny. Work from outer edge to center.

(4) Although you will now have a complete record of the tree's lateral growth, the accuracy of your record will be improved if you will do this while the tape is still in place: slip a postcard under the tape, and with a sharp pencil mark the outer edge of each tenth ring from the year the tree was cut till you come to the center. Some rings may be so thin that your rubbing might be inconclusive without these additional notes. The opposite half of your rubbing will not always be an exact duplicate but will provide a useful check on your count. Along the unmarked edge of your strip write the location of the tree stump, and of other large neighboring trees, the

Tree-ring rubbings are a convenient way of recording a tree's age and history

species, slope, and altitude.

Rubbing of exposed beams and timbers in old houses can be made in the same way. It may even be possible to cross-date them with some of the oldest tree stumps or to correlate the records from "nature's rain gauges" with local weather notes preserved in a library, museum, or historical society.

More than fifty persons took part in such a project in the Delaware River valley, around Philadelphia. Close correlation between tree-ring growth and diary notes on wet and dry years was obtained. Equally interesting were comparisons of growth rings of hemlocks in northern New England with diaries for the period from 1727 to 1780. Very narrow tree rings were found for 14 out of 16 years described in the diaries as being very dry.

What Live Trees Can Tell

Foresters can extract a record of growth from living trees by the use of a special instrument, an *increment borer*, but they can also read history in a stand of trees. They have learned that in northern Wisconsin, for instance, a stand of aspen means that the former forest burned. Likewise, white, or "cabbage,"

pines in New England tell a story. They are the aftermath of abandoned farms. Most forest types are the result of an orderly, predictable evolution or succession (*See Wildlife: The Wildlife Community*).

The wealth of detailed information that trees will reveal presents a stimulating challenge. Any persistent, alert observer, using the methods here outlined, can truly use the trees around him as history books. They provide fascinating reading. —C.E.M.

Recommended Reading

Bristlecone Pine, Oldest Known Living Thing—Edmund Schulman, in *National Geographic Magazine*, March, 1958. Washington, D.C.

The Secret of the Southwest Solved by Talkative Tree Rings—Andrew E. Douglas, in *National Geographic Magazine*, December 1929. Washington, D. C.

The Story of a Thousand Year Pine—*Audubon Nature Bulletin*, National Audubon Society, New York.

Stump Scouting—William Gould Vinal, in *Nature Recreation*. American Humane Education Society, Boston.

Good Oak—Aldo Leopold in *A Sand County Almanac*. Oxford University Press, New York.

Precision of Ring Dating in Tree-Ring Chronologies—A. E. Douglass. University of Arizona Publications in *Dendrochronology*, Vol. 17, No. 3, 1946.

TREE FROG

Tree frogs, sometimes called tree "toads," are classified in the genus *Hyla,* and belong to the family Hylidae, a group in which their associated members, or relatives, are the diminutive cricket frogs (genus *Acris*), and the chorus frogs (genus *Pseudacris*). Because of well-developed adhesive disks on their toes, tree frogs are expert climbers. (The toe disks are smaller in the nonclimbing cricket frogs, and the slightly arboreal chorus frogs).

Not all tree frogs are tree-dwellers as their name would indicate, and many species seek other types of habitat in which to live. Tree frogs of the United States and Canada of the genus *Hyla* include the spring peeper, *H. crucifer;* green tree frog, *H. cinerea;* pine barrens tree frog, *H. andersoni;* pine woods tree frog, *H. femoralis;* squirrel tree frog, *H. squirella;* gray tree frog, *H. versicolor;* bird-voiced tree frog, *H. avivoca;* barking tree frog, *H. gratiosa;* Cuban tree frog, *H. septentrionalis;* little grass frog, *H. ocularis;* and the Mexican tree frog, *H. baudini.*

Tree frogs range in size from the diminutive little grass frog, the tiniest North American frog, only about a half an inch long, to the Cuban tree frog, largest of our tree frogs and an immigrant from the West Indies. The Cuban tree frog may grow to 5½ inches long. Even larger tree frogs live outside of the United States.

Tree frogs vary greatly in color, and one individual may change its color radically depending on conditions of light, moisture, temperature, or the tree frog's general activity. Male tree frogs have a single throat pouch under the chin that when inflated, as they call, resembles a small balloon. The only exception is the Mexican tree frog, that has a pair of throat pouches, one at each side of the chin, and the Cuban tree frog, whose single throat pouch inflates more on each side than in the middle. This suggests a double throat

patch. The true tree frogs, *Hyla,* live throughout the range of virtually the entire family Hylidae.   —G.P.

Cuban Tree Frog
Other Common Name—Giant tree frog
Scientific Name—*Hyla septentrionalis*
Family—Hylidae
Order—Salienta
Size—Length, 1½ to 5 inches
Range—Extreme southeast Florida and Florida Keys

The Cuban tree frog is an immigrant from Cuba and the West Indies. It is the largest tree frog in the United States, which accounts for its common name, Giant tree frog. Its color ranges from a drab, dark green to dark brown. The best way to identify it is by its size, and by the unusually large adhesive disks on its toes. Smaller specimens however, may be difficult to identify. During the day it is commonly found hiding in crevices, cellars, and eaves of buildings, wherever it is moist. It has a rasping or snoring call.

The Cuban tree frog has been known to eat smaller frogs and toads.

Gray Tree Frog
Other Common Names—Common tree frog, tree toad, changeable tree toad, chameleon tree frog
Scientific Name—*Hyla versicolor*
Family—Hylidae (cricket frogs, tree frogs, and chorus frogs)
Order—Salienta
Size—Length, 1¼ to 2 inches
Range—New Brunswick, Canada, to northern Florida, west to North Dakota and Texas

Usually a denizen of trees and the lower shrubbery, the gray tree frog may also be found clinging to fences, rocks, or stone walls. As its scientific name, *Hyla versicolor,* implies, the gray tree frog is able to change its color rapidly and effectively, ranging from near-white through gray, brown, and even green. It blends so perfectly with its background

Cuban tree frog

Gray tree frog

that, despite its relatively larger size, it is extremely difficult to see. However, no matter what the overall color may be, the inner sides of its hind legs remain a bright orange. Its skin is dry and somewhat warty, which has earned it the common name of tree toad, although it otherwise bears no resemblance to toads (*See Toad*). Its call is a short, resonant trill.

Pine Barrens Tree Frog
Other Common Name—Anderson's tree frog, Anderson's hyla, green and yellow tree toad
Scientific Name—*Hyla andersoni*
Family—Hylidae (cricket frogs, tree frogs, and chorus frogs)
Order—Salienta
Size—Length, 1¼ to 1¾ inches
Range—Pine Barrens of New Jersey, occasionally found in North Carolina and Georgia

This is a strikingly beautiful frog, green on the upper parts of the body, set off by a white stripe bordered with black, against a lavender band. The inner side of its hind legs are orange. Its call is a ducklike *quack*, which may be heard in the breeding season during the later part of spring.

In view of its limited range, particularly so uncomfortably close to the great Metropolitan and industrial centers of New York and New Jersey, the Pine Barrens tree frog should be considered an endangered species, although within its range it is still quite abundant. It would be a pity if, through unwise urban and industrial expansion, the habitat of this beautiful creature should be destroyed.   —G.P.

Spring Peeper
Other Common Names—Peeper, Pickering's hyla, peeping frog, Bartramian peeper, Florida peeper, coastal peeper
Scientific Name—*Hyla crucifer*
Family—Hylidae (cricket frogs, tree frogs, and chorus frogs)
Order—Salienta
Size—Length, ¾ to 1½ inches
Range—Maritime Provinces to northern Florida, west from Manitoba to Texas

The spring peeper derives its scientific name, *Hyla crucifer,* from the X mark which it carries on its back. In color it is usually a light copper-brown, but

Pine barrens tree frog

Spring peeper

during the breeding season it changes to a dark brown that blends with the dead leaves and foliage found in and near the bodies of water in which it breeds. This tiny frog is truly the herald of the northern spring: its call is one of the first that can be heard after the passing of winter. Considering the small size of the creature, the intensity of sound it can produce is astonishing. During the breeding season, when spring peepers congregate in large numbers in shallow waters, their ear piercing, high-pitched, short calls can be heard at great distances. It is a frustrating experience to attempt to sight a calling spring peeper as it blends against the tussocks or stalks of dead foliage from which it calls. However, with sufficient patience, and good eyesight, one may be fortunate enough to get a glimpse of the caller, a gnomelike little creature with an enormously inflated vocal sac.

After the breeding season the spring peepers leave the water and return to the woodland which is their regular habitat. In late summer and early fall they often call, singly, from wooded hillsides.   —G.P.

TREEHOPPER (*See Froghopper and Treehopper*)

TREE OF HEAVEN (*See Ailanthus*)

TREE TOAD (*See Tree Frog*)

TREMBLING ASPEN (*See under Aspen*)

TRILLIUM
Painted Trillium
Other Common Names—Wake-robin, birthroot, painted lady
Scientific Name—*Trillium undulatum*
Family—Liliaceae (lily family)
Range—Gaspe Peninsula, Quebec, to eastern Manitoba, south to Nova Scotia, New England, northern New Jersey, Pennsylvania, West Virginia, upland to Georgia and Tennessee, Michigan and Wisconsin

Painted trillium

Habitat—Acid or subacid woods and swamps
Time of Blooming—April into June

The crimson V near the base of the white petals accounts for its common name, painted trillium. It is a member of a small group of plants known also as wake-robins, whose flowers have three sepals, three petals, and six stamens and produce only one flower to a plant. The scientific name, *Trillium*, refers to the three-parted flower and to the three leaves. These grow in in a whorl near the top of a single stem that may be 10 to 15 inches tall. The flower stalk tops the stem. Its fruit is a bright red ovate berry that develops late in the summer, ripens in September, and falls at a touch.

The plant survives the winter by means of a thickened underground stem, as is true of so many of the early blooming spring flowers. This food, which has been stored in the stem during the previous summer, is used to make a quick growth while sunlight is available to aid in the manufacture of food. Later, leaves of the deciduous trees expand and cut off much of the light from the plants living in the forest floor.

There are 12 species of wake-robin in the eastern United States and others in western North America. The largest and showiest in the eastern states is the large-flowered wake-robin whose white, or pinkish, petals are more than two inches long.

Purple Trillium
Other Common Names—Stinking Benjamin, squawroot, wake-robin, red trillium, birthroot
Scientific Name—*Trillium erectum*
Family—Liliaceae (lily family)
Range—Western Gaspe Peninsula, Quebec, to Ontario, and Michigan,

Purple trillium

south to Nova Scotia, New England, northern Delaware, Pennsylvania, West Virginia and upland to Georgia and Tennessee
Habitat—Rich woods
Time of Blooming—April into early June

This flower is common in rich woodlands of the East. The dark blossom varies from red to purple and maroon, or may even be brownish. The plant grows erect to its whorl of three leaves but the flower stalk which rises from the center of the whorl is reclining.

Although good to look at, the flower is ill-scented and has an odor like spoiled meat. The carrion-eating flesh fly, *Lucilia carnicina,* is attracted by both the odor and the color of the purple trillium and feasts on its pollen grains to fertilize the next purple trillium it visits.

The three leaves of the purple trillium are broadly oval—almost four-sided. Young plants are topped by only a single leaf. The plants vary in height from 7 to 15 inches. Like other trilliums they are perennial and grow from a thick underground stem. The fruit is an oval red berry.

There is another trillium with dark magenta flowers common in much the same area. This is the stemless, or sessile, trillium, *Trillium sessile.* Its stemless flower rises directly from the whorl of leaves. The petals are more narrow than those of the purple trillium and it has a pleasing fragrance.

All species of the genus *Trillium* are protected by being on the wildflower conservation lists of many states.

Western Wake-robin
Other Common Names—Coast trillium
Scientific Name—*Trillium ovatum*
Family—Liliacea (Lily family)
ley family)
Range—British Columbia and Montana southward through Oregon and the Coast Ranges of California to the Santa Cruz Mountains

Western wake-robin

Habitat — Wooded slopes, Transition and Canadian Zones
Time of Blooming — February through April

The naked stem of this plant is from 8 to 18 inches high. At the very top there are three pointed leaves that are from 2½ to 5½ inches long. They are close up under the single white flower that has three petals. As the flower grows older the petals turn to a deep rose color. Sometimes the flower is greenish-yellow. The common trillium has deep red or lilac petals. Very often the leaves have strange markings on them, made by the veins. These plants are found on northern hillslopes and in canyons.

TROGON
Coppery-tailed Trogon
Other Common Names — None
Scientific Name — *Trogon elegans*

Family — Trogonidae (trogons)
Order — Trogoniformes
Size — Length, 11½ inches
Range — A Central American species occurring in the United States only in southern Arizona, rarely in Texas

A large, lethargic bird of the middle branches of deep woodlands, where it sits quietly giving its cooing call, the coppery-tailed trogon is usually difficult to find. The bright red underparts and the glossy green head and back of the male become lost in the shadows. The female has less red and is brown where the male is green.

Trogons feed on insects and on fruit, taking both while on the wing and finishing the meal from a nearby perch. They nest in natural cavities or in rotten stumps and are not migratory.

Other trogons occur in Central and South America, a few in Arica, and others in Southeast Asia. Most probably the family was widespread in past ages, when most of the earth had a warmer climate. The best known trogon is the quetzal, once worshipped by Mayas and Aztecs and now the national bird of Guatemala. — G.B.S.

Coppery-tailed trogon

TROPIC-BIRD
White-tailed Tropic-bird
Other Common Names—bosun bird, yellow-billed tropic-bird
Scientific Name—*Phaethon lepturus*
Family—Phaethontidae (tropic-birds)
Order—Pelicaniformes
Size—Length, 32 inches
Range—Breeds in the West Indies and Bermuda and islands off tropical South America, Africa, and Asia, and in Oceania

Seldom seen from land except near its breeding islands, tropic-birds range widely over warm seas. They dive into the water for shrimps, small fishes, and other marine animals. The long central tail plumes take about a year to develop. Young birds are spotted black on white, but adults are all white with black on the wing tips, and wing coverts. They also have a black eyeline.

The red-billed tropic-bird, which breeds in the Gulf of California, sometimes ranges well off the coast of southern California.   —G.B.S.

TROUT
There are a number of fishes commonly called trout (*See under Fish*).

Characteristics common to all trout include the presence of an adipose fin (a small fatty structure on the fish's back, near the tail), small scales, soft-rayed (spineless) fins, sharp teeth on the jaws and on the tongue, and a very large mouth which extends back further than the rear margin of the eyes. Trout are among the better known of fishes, for they are one of the most highly regarded by sport fishermen. Four particularly well-known trout are brook trout, brown trout, lake trout, and rainbow trout.

Brook Trout
Other Common Names—Speckled trout, native trout, brookie, char
Scientific Name—*Salvelinus fontinalis*
Family—Salmonidae (trouts, whitefishes, and graylings)
Order—Clupeiformes
Size—Length, up to 24 inches
Range—Particularly abundant in northeastern United States and eastern Canada. Highly successful artificial introduction has been achieved in many scattered parts of the United States

Adult brook trout are very attractively colored. The back and upper sides are

The brook trout lives in cold clear, fresh water but sometimes enters salt water

Inhabiting warm lakes and sluggish rivers, brown trout may weigh up to 15 pounds

dark olive-green, marked heavily with light marbled patterns. The top of the head and the dorsal fin are also marked this way. The lower three-quarters of the sides are lighter in color and are marked with many blue, red, and yellow spots. Near the belly, the sides turn yellowish and have an orange or red band. The belly is white or yellowish-white, except in breeding males, whose entire ventral area is red. The fronts of the pectoral, pelvic, and anal fins are white.

Brook trout eat mostly insects, along with some mollusks, small fishes, and crayfishes. They seem to prefer cool water and thrive well in unpolluted spring-water streams and brooks in which the temperature rarely goes above 50° F. Brook trout are tasty food fishes.

Brown Trout
Other Common Names—German brown, spotted trout, loch leven, Von Behr trout, brownie
Scientific Name—*Salmo trutta*
Family—Salmonidae (trouts, whitefishes, and graylings)
Order—Clupeiformes

Size—Length, up to about 30 inches
Range—Native to Europe but introduced with great success throughout the United States and parts of Canada

Adult brown trout have greenish to yellowish-brown backs which are sometimes spotted. The top of the head and the dorsal fins have few or no spots. The sides are lighter than the back and are marked with many blue-ringed, orange, and red spots. The belly is yellowish or silvery white. The fins are yellowish or the same color as the rest of the body.

The brown trout eats mostly insects and some insect larvae, worms, mollusks, small crayfishes, and small fishes. They are prized by fishermen more for their size than for their flavor. Although they are fairly tasty, they are inferior in flavor to other trout.

Lake Trout
Other Common Names—Mackinaw trout, Great Lakes trout, forktail trout
Scientific Name—*Salvelinus namaycush*
Family—Salmonidae (trouts, whitefishes, and graylings)

Order—Clupeiformes
Size—Length, up to 4 feet
Range—Throughout northern North America as far south as the Great Lakes. Introduced with some success to more southerly parts of the western portion of the United States

This species has a fairly long and slender body (its length is about 4 times its depth). Very large specimens reach weights in excess of 50 pounds but the usual adult size is 15 to 36 inches long and 1 to 20 pounds in weight. Both the dorsal and anal fins have 11 rays. The tail fin is deeply forked.

The lake trout's back and head are olive-gray to brownish-gray in color with a vermiculated pattern of light grays. The sides are lighter and more silvery with a lighter vermiculated pattern. The sides are also sparsely marked with light spots ringed with red. The belly is very light to silvery. Both the dorsal fin and the tail fin have vermiculated markings like those on the fish's back and head.

Lake trout make very good eating.

Rainbow Trout
Other Common Names—Coaster, Pacific trout, steelhead, red-sided trout
Scientific Name—*Salmo gairdneri*
Family—Salmonidae (trouts, white-fishes, and graylings)
Order—Clupeiformes
Size—Length, up to 30 inches or more
Range—The Pacific Coast of North America. Introduced artificially to more inland areas of western United States and Canada and in northeastern United States

The adult fish's back is bluish-olive to silvery olive in color. The sides are lighter and more silvery and have a pink or reddish band running horizontally through their center. The belly is white to silvery. Many small, distinct black spots mark the back, sides, and the top of the head. The dorsal fin, tail fin, and adipose fin are also marked with these spots.

Rainbow trout eat a wide variety of foods. They seem to prefer insects and their larvae but also consume many small mollusks and fishes.   —M.R.

The rainbow trout, or steelhead, is a popular western gamefish

TULIP—TREE

Other Common Names—Tulip-poplar, whitewood, yellow-poplar
Scientific Name—*Liriodendron tulipifera*
Family—Magnoliacea (magnolia family)
Range—Southern Vermont and central Massachusetts west to eastern and central Illinois and southeastern Missouri. South into Louisiana and northern Florida
Habitat—Eastern deciduous forests in rich soils
Leaves—Broad, roughly tulip-shaped with four lobes forming blunt points. On trees—four to six inches wide with shallow indentations and a smooth, leathery texture; on sprouts—considerably larger and very deeply notched
Bark—On young trees reddish gray-brown, developing pale, ash-gray splits. With age these cracks deepen and the corky ridges thicken, producing a heavily furrowed bark
Flower—Tuliplike, pale yellow-green with an orange band across each of the six petals. Blooms in early summer
Fruit—An upright, cone-shaped unit two to three inches long which persists after ripening and shedding its curved, winged seeds

Tulip-tree

Few American trees equal this one in average size—it is generally the tallest species in the eastern deciduous forests. The name, which may refer either to the shape of the leaves or the blossom, does not adequately describe the general character of this forest giant. The tree is actually related to the magnolias and the pawpaw (*Asimina*), both of which are associated with temperate or semitropical climates. Likewise the tulip-tree is not tolerant of the severe Canadian weather and crosses that border only in the region of southern Ontario.

The rather soft, light wood of the tulip-tree known in the lumber trade as whitewood is easily worked with tools and is used for various purposes that do not require great strength or hardness and also for pulp in making paper. Nearly 800 million board feet of this lumber were cut during one year in the 1940's—this representing about eight percent of the estimated stand of growing trees of this species. From this statistic it may be seen that the tulip tree is quite abundant, particularly in the Appalachian areas and parts of the Mid-west. With red oak it forms a large proportion of the forest on the slopes around the New York City area.

The tulip-tree is a fairly fast-growing tree and although not much used as a street tree in most areas it is well suited for this purpose. It does not, however, attain the tall columnar trunk of native trees when grown in the open and tends to grow more in breadth than in height unless the lower branches are quite severely trimmed. Because of the size the tree attains and because its roots have an appetite for water it is best to plant it away from other trees.

Some very young tulip-trees that have been handled roughly fall prey to

gall or fungus diseases but carefully
planted trees will usually take hold very
well in all but the poorest soils and
when supplied with adequate moisture
grow with vigor, rapidity, and a mini-
mum of mess and debris. Many birds—
cardinals, red-winged blackbirds, purple
finches, and others—eat the seeds of the
tulip tree.   —M.H.B.

TUNA: *Bluefin Tuna (See Albacore)*

TUPELO
Other Common Names—Sour gum, black
gum, pepperidge
Scientific Name—*Nyssa sylvatica*
Family—Nyssaceae (sour gum family)
Range—Central Maine south to southern New England, Long Island, New
York, Florida. West to Illinois
Habitat—Acidic soils in low woods,
swamps, and shores
Leaves—Two to four inches long, bluntly
pointed, broadly or narrowly oval with
a short stem, rarely toothed. Upper surface waxy, paler beneath, turning many
shades of scarlet, peach, and wine in
the fall, often when the surrounding
forest is still quite green
Bark—Tan-gray, rather flaky when
young, split with shallow lengthwise
grooves. More deeply cracked and much
thicker with age
Flower—Inconspicuous greenish sprays
of five-pointed blossoms appearing with
the new leaves in midspring
Fruit—Groups of one to four oval, blue-
berry-colored fruits about one-half of an
inch long, borne on a slender stem,
ripening in autumn

The tupelo is a large flat-crowned tree
that attains heights of 40 to 50 feet and
sometimes rises to 100 feet. It grows
best along stream margins and in moist
lowland forests.

The three outstanding characteristics
of the tupelo are its light-twigged, overall form, its lustrous, blunt-pointed
leaves that turn scarlet early in the fall,

and its rather distincitve bark. This is
usually light in color, has a tendency
to build up in deeply cracked blocks
like that of sassafras or persimmon, but
has fewer and narrower cracks at the
bottom. The berries are a favored item
for many birds and may be, because of
their color, the reason for the tree's
name. The moderate-weight wood has a
rather close, crooked grain and considerable toughness, which suit it to special
purposes rather than to general use (*See
also under Gum*).   —M.H.B.

TURACIN (*See under Animal: Colors of
Animals*)

The formerly abundant native American turkey is now a rare woodland bird

TURKEY

Other Common Names—American turkey, wood turkey
Scientific Name—*Meleagris gallopavo*
Family—Meleagrididae (turkeys)
Order—Galliformes
Size—Length: males, 48 inches; females, 36 inches
Range—Formerly eastern and southwestern United States; now rare and local, Pennsylvania to Florida west to Texas, New Mexico, Colorado, and California

The wild turkey is a large, grounddwelling bird, a strong runner, and a rather poor flier. The subspecies common in the East has chestnut tips to the long tail feathers, while the western subspecies has white, as does the barnyard turkey—the descendant of wild birds shipped to Spain from Yucatan.

Open woodlands are preferred by turkeys, where they find the insects, grains, and fruits on which they feed. The males are solitary except in the breeding season, when they fight each other to establish harems. They do not help with the incubation nor the feeding of the young.

Although they feed on the ground and prefer to escape danger by running, turkeys roost in trees.   —G.B.S.

TURNSTONE
Ruddy Turnstone
Other Common Names—Sea dotterel, sea quail, calico bird
Scientific Name—*Arenaria interpres*
Family—Charadriidae (plovers, turnstones, and surf birds)
Order—Charadriiformes
Size—Length, 8 to 9½ inches
Range—Arctic in summer; migrates along coast and center of continent, wintering from North Carolina and central California south to Argentina

The black-and-white harlequin pattern identifies the ruddy turnstone when the bird is flying. Spring adults are gaudy, with white-and-black face markings, a black chest band, and reddish backs. In winter plumage the wing pattern remains and the chest band becomes brown. The legs are reddish to orange.

Turnstones are squat and compact, with short bills that look slightly upturned. They feed on all manner of small marine creatures and their eggs that are found as they root in seaweeds and under stones. They migrate in loose flocks, running over sand and rocks, and flying in tight formation.

The black turnstone, *Arenaria melanocephala*, of Alaska winters along the Pacific Coast. The dull gray surfbird has the same range as the black turnstone, preferring rocky areas.   —G.B.S.

Ruddy turnstones

TURTLE
Turtles are reptiles along with snakes, lizards, crocodilians (crocodiles and alligators), and the almost extinct lizard-like *Sphenodon* of the New Zealand region. Reptiles are vertebrates, or backboned, animals that stand in the scale of evolution between the higher birds and mammals and the lower fishes and amphibians. They are, in fact, the highest of the cold-blooded vertebrates, animals that do not have a "central heating system" but must get along with a temperature approximating that of the air, earth, or water surrounding them (*See Reptile*). The lack of control of body temperature forces cold-blooded animals to hibernate in winter and to avoid long exposure to direct rays of a hot sun (*See Hibernation*). The turtle with its bizarre shell has remained almost unchanged for about 200 million years. In comparison, man is a mere upstart who must learn about the great dinosaurs from records of the rocks, whereas the turtle actually lived while these creatures arose, reigned, and then vanished (*See Geological Time*). At present about 250 kinds of turtles inhabit the earth. The numerous fossils that are found on all the continents indicate that at least this many kinds have existed at any one time for more than 100 million years.

Just what is a turtle's shell? Man, in common with other higher animals, has an abundance of bone, but instead of the hard bone protecting his soft flesh, the flesh is forced to protect the bone. The upper part of the turtle's shell is composed of the backbone and ribs which have grown together with plates of bone that start in the skin. Before this could happen the ribs had to get on the outside of the bones that support the arms and legs, the so-called "limb girdles," a feat accomplished by the turtle before hatching.

There often seems to be a handicap or some imperfection in the finally evolved body of any animal. Since the turtle uses its ribs as part of its armor the ribs are no longer able to help in expanding its chest for breathing. If man's ribs could not move he would have difficulty getting enough air in and out of his chest. However, the turtle takes care of this matter with three muscles that control the lungs during breathing. Inspiration is accomplished by two flank muscles that enlarge the body cavity and thus suck air into the turtle's lungs, acting somewhat like the human diaphragm. Air is forced out by a complex third muscle that presses the turtle's viscera against its lungs. Many books state erroneously that breathing is accomplished by movements of the throat or even of the legs; such actions at best only supplement the work of the three muscles and are by no means necessary for a turtle's normal respiration.

In the evolution of the turtle, vertebrae between its neck and its tail were relieved of their original task of supporting the body because the shell as a whole is more than able to do this. In fact, the shell of a box turtle only five inches long can readily support the weight of a man. The upper, arched part of the shell is known as the *carapace,* the flat, lower one as the *plastron.* Carapace and plastron are joined on either side by a part called the *bridge.* The box turtles of the United States can retreat within the shell and close the hinged plastron so tightly against the carapace that a thin knife blade cannot be forced between the two. These turtles sometimes get so fat that when they close the forward half of the plastron their hind legs and tails protrude, and when they protect these tender parts, the head and front legs stick out. In contrast to these and other well-encased kinds are many species of turtles, among them the common snapping turtle, with a plastron that does not begin to cover its soft body parts. The snapper's vicious nature and formidable jaws compensate for this deficiency in its shell development.

Food and Feeding

Although a turtle has no true teeth, the sharp edges of its horny jaws are a good substitute and these often have projections much like the teeth of a saw and about as sharp. However, food is chewed by a turtle only enough to

Turtles have remained unchanged in general appearance for 200 million years

WOOD TURTLE

COMMON SNAPPING TURTLE

EASTERN BOX TURTLE

MAP TURTLE

BLANDING'S

EASTERN SPINEY SOFT-SHELL

SPOTTED TURTLE

BOG TURTLE

ATLANTI

STINK POT

EASTERN MUD TURTLE

EASTERN PAINTED TURTLE

RED-BELLIED TURTLE

NORTHERN DIAMONDBACKED TERRAPIN

MIDLAND PAINTED TURTLE

ATLANTIC GREEN TURTLE

ATLANTIC RIDLEY

RHEAD

ATLANTIC LEATHERBACK

reduce it to fragments that it can readily swallow. The claws of the forelimbs often assist the jaws in tearing food to pieces. Most species of turtles eat a variety of foods, not confining themselves either to plants or to animals. Only the tender parts of plants are consumed by them because of the mechanical difficulty of tearing fibrous parts to bits. Small invertebrate animals such as earthworms, snails, slugs, thin-shelled bivalves, crayfishes and other crustaceans, and insects and their larvae make up the great bulk of a turtle's animal food. The larger species, especially the snapping turtles, devour a limited number of birds and small mammals. Box turtles and wood turtles feed on wild berries, in season, as well as on insects and earthworms.

The fact that a turtle readily survives a year's fast does not keep it from eating almost as regularly as a mammal, the surplus nourishment being stored in its body as fat. Its digestion is relatively slow and the rate varies greatly with the temperature of the turtle. One species has been shown to double its rate of digestion when its stomach temperature is raised from 64° to 84° F. Turtles drink regularly when water is available and some kinds have a remarkable capacity to store water in receptacles in the body known as cloacal bladders and thus survive long periods of drought.

Reproduction

The preliminary to mating by turtles is sometimes a highly characteristic courtship. The giant tortoise of the Galapagos Islands, for example approaches his mate, uttering resounding roars and, once at her side, violently lunges against her and bites her elephant-like legs. In some aquatic species the male gracefully swims backward in front of the female, gently stroking her lores (cheeks) with his excessively long fingernails.

The height of the mating season in the United States comes in the spring; autumn unions are not uncommon, and a limited number may nest during the summer. A remarkable thing about turtle reproduction is that a single mating suffices to fertilize eggs for several seasons. This fact was discovered through experiments on the artificial propogation of diamondback terrapins.

After laying her eggs, the female turtle has fulfilled her obligation to the species and wanders off without being the least interested in her nest or in the tiny turtles that emerge after several weeks of incubation. The crisis of turtle existence is this period of incubation plus the first few months of the hatchling's life. During this time countless enemies dig up and eat the eggs or feast upon the soft, defenseless hatchlings. Skunks, raccoons, and other mammals, and snakes and birds devour countless millions of eggs and young every year. Thus the vulnerability of the developing eggs and the baby turtles are in strong contrast to the marvelously protected adult.

Most turtle nests are flask-shaped holes about as deep as the turtles's leg is long. The eggs are laid on top of each other or side by side in the bottom of the hole and buried under a few inches of earth or decaying vegetable matter. The laying female is usually oblivious of her surroundings and behaves like a machine that was set off by the push of a button. The approach of a human being or even a blow on her shell may go unheeded while she is laying her eggs. Inhabitants of tropical islands often sit behind a giant sea turtle and catch the eggs as they are extruded. The victimized female fills the empty hole quite as carefully as though it contained a hundred of her eggs. On one occasion a box turtle just finishing the filling of earth over her nesting hole and eggs was carefully moved to a new place. There she continued to tamp the ground mechanically with the same care that she had exhibited before the interference.

The method of construction of a nest

by a turtle is far more interesting than the nest itself. The turtle although bound forever to the land by laying habits, has, nevertheless, become adapted to life in every type of warm environment. In becoming adapted to movement over land and in water, the limbs of turtles have assumed various forms: webbed toes for the fresh waters, flippers for the seas, elephantlike limbs for the hard ground. No matter what shape of limb it has, the female turtle must use it in digging a nest at least once a year. Every kind instinctively

The male eastern box turtle usually has red eyes. A female's eyes are brown

knows how to use its particular digging tool, for there is no parent standing by to give lessons, nor has the recently matured female ever watched another turtle dig a nest. The desert tortoise chooses a spot in sandy waste and digs a hole with its stump-shaped limb; the sea turtle, weighing 300 pounds, accomplishes the same end with deft movements of its paddle-shaped flipper; the river turtle uses its webbed toes something like a human hand.

When hatching time arrives, the shell of the turtle eggs becomes a prison instead of an incubator; the mature embryo must turn into a jail breaker. Advanced unhatched turtle embryos have on the end of the snout a hard

The nest and eggs of the painted turtle

protuberance or "egg-tooth" that has always been assumed to be necessary for their escape from the eggs. Recent studies indicate that another factor is involved in freeing the hatchling and that the egg-tooth may even be useless in some species. This factor is rapid absorption of water to such a degree that the shell is ruptured from internal pressure.

Age, Growth, and Size

The greatest age that any individual turtle has positively been shown to attain is one hundred and fifty-two years. It is probable that this one saw even two centuries roll by, but the belief that turtles survive for many hundreds of years is entirely unfounded. The common box turtle has been known to live for a little more than a century; however, three score years may be considered much nearer to its normal span of life. Some of the best information on the age of turtles is based on records of captivity, chiefly those made in zoological parks. Careful compilations of such records show that individuals of 13 kinds of turtles have survived 41 or more years of confinement. The chances are good that a great many more of the 250 known species live at least that long. The length of life of the turtle exceeds that of any other backboned animal, including man, with the greatest life-span of any mammal.

The best way to determine the length of life and rate of growth of any animal is to mark and recapture individuals living in a state of nature. Students of reptiles are now using this method, although a long time will pass before they can increase man's knowledge of turtle longevity; however, they have already made valuable contributions to what is known about growth rate. The seasonal increase in size of the horny plates of the shell of some species helps considerably in studies of growth, but unfortunately the shell tends to wear smooth with maturity and the growth rings on the plates become obscure long before old age is reached. In the common box turtle, for example, the age can be accurately determined through only the first five or six years of life, and with a fair degree of certainty through the age of fifteen.

Although so little is known about the growth rate of most turtles, the indications are that no species requires more than 12 years to attain sexual maturity and a good size. In fact, it seems that species of moderate size in the United States reach maturity in about half this time. Even the giant tortoises which when adult weigh from 300 to 400 pounds, increase their weight each year by 12 or more pounds—and this under captive conditions. One of these giants actually had an average annual increase of 45 pounds for a 7 year period. Apparently these Goliaths grow more rapidly than man.

The habit of carving dates on the shells of turtles is an old one but results based on such shells must be taken with a grain of salt. The story is told of how a credulous nature lover found a specimen with a date indicating great age and later in the day showed it to a farmer. The farmer went into the woods and returned in a few minutes with another turtle on whose shell was carved "10 B.C."

In spite of not having produced the largest of reptiles, turtles have long held their own in size attained by individuals. A hundred million years ago, marine *Archelon* swam in seas covering South Dakota and grew to be 12 feet long and weighed perhaps a ton. In comparatively recent times, only a million or so years ago, gigantic *Colossochelys*, probably the largest turtle that ever lived, wandered over the hills of northern India, no doubt to the amazement of man's earliest ancestors. This creature stood four or five feet high in its stockingless feet and had a shell seven feet long. Even today the leatherback may tip the scales at three-fourths

The box turtle has a hinged plastron

of a ton. whereas the hard-shelled marine turtles, also found in all tropical seas, sometimes weigh three hundred pounds. The land tortoises of the Galapagos, now nearing extinction, rival the hard-shelled marine species in size.

Senses and Intelligence

The senses of sight, smell, and taste are developed in turtles. It is interesting that colors at the red end of the spectrum are more readily recognized by turtles and it is just these colors that most frequently adorn the turtles themselves (*See under Animal: Color Vision in Animals*). The good development of the middle ear would lead one to believe that turtles can also hear well but such does not seem to be the case. No one has proved beyond doubt that turtles ever respond to sound waves carried by the air. Slight vibrations transmitted through solids to the skin and shell are, however, quickly noticed. Scientists who have taught turtles to run mazes proclaim them to be about as good at doing this as are various mammals. Painted turtles have been taught to discriminate between patterns of vertical and horizontal black and white lines.

The northern diamondback terrapin has several concentric rings in each large scute

Conservation

Diamondback terrapins are chief among the few turtles that have received much attention from conservationists. The delicious flavor of the diamondbacks created such a devastating demand that the Bureau of Fisheries found it expedient to work out a good method of propogation, and laws have been passed protecting them from undue persecution. The wood turtle is also protected in New York, New Jersey, and other states. The snapping turtle, when its natural predators are lacking, may become too numerous and, therefore, destructive to fishes and waterbirds. However, this species, under natural conditions, occupies its niche in the balance of nature without affecting the normal population of fishes and birds (*See under* Wildlife: *The Wildlife Community*).

Captivity

Turtles are the most popular reptile pets in this country. Unfortunately, the vast majority of those kept as pets are delicate infants slowly dying of malnutrition. A very young turtle is at least as hard to care for as a dog of fancy breed; the difference is that a sick dog is a pitiful sight, whereas a sick turtle may appear relatively normal for months before its death. It is not fair to expect a boy or girl not yet in high school to care for a young turtle properly.

In spite of all this, the infant turtle can be reared if certain basic requirements are provided. The difficulty centers about nourishment; calcium and growth-promoting vitamins must be given turtles daily. Cod-liver oil and its concentrates are good sources of the necessary vitamins. Calcium can be supplied to captive turtles in the form of bone sawdust (from the butcher), bonemeal (from hardware stores), or crushed backbone of fish from the market. The turtles appetites will suffer if the temperature is not kept at least as high as ordinary room temperature. Since turtles have individuality, persuading them to consume vitamins and calcium is not always easy. The matter usually boils down to human ingenuity against turtle perversity. The wise person will only get turtlets with an appetite; a test can be made at the pet store with a few bits of raw fish or beef held by tweezers and presented either in or out of water, as the case requires.

The first signs of malnutrition in captive turtles are loss of appetite and sore eyes. In turtles more than a few weeks old a soft shell is also a warning. Needless to say, the little turtle with a painted back already is badly handicapped. Some kinds of paint can be removed by chipping with a thin, sharp knife, but extreme care must be exercised to avoid damaging the horny plates of the shell. Nail polish remover, also used with great care, may be helpful as a last resort.

It is far wiser to let nature take care of early growth. Adult turtles thrive on two or three feedings a week, although they will eat daily and get fat against a time when it might be convenient to neglect them for as much as a month. Nor do adult turtles need extra vitamins and calcium; enough of these will be supplied by the ordinary food. The strong turtle shell protects the adult against rough treatment by children. Most children are fascinated by turtles of all kinds. The United States, especially the central and eastern parts, has so many species of turtles with such varied habits that directions for their care should be sought in one of the recommended references. Terrestrial species are in general easier to keep and can often be allowed to wander at will through the home.

In some states permission to keep wood and box turtles and the desert tortoise as pets must be obtained from the state's Department of Convervation.
—C.P.

Recommended Reading

The Book of Wild Pets—Clifford B. Moore. Charles Branford Company, Boston.
The Book of Reptiles and Amphibians—Michael H. Bevans. Garden City Books, Garden City, New York.
Field Guide to Reptiles and Amphibians—Roger Conant. Houghton Mifflin Company, Boston.
Handbook of Turtles: The Turtles of the United States, Canada, and Baja California—Archie Carr. Comstock Publishing Associates, Ithaca, New York.
The Natural History of North American Amphibians and Reptiles—James A. Oliver. D. Van Nostrand Company, Princeton, New Jersey
Pet Turtles—Julien L. Bronson and Hobart M. Smith. All-Pets Books, Fond du lac, Wisconsin.
Reptiles and Amphibians of the Northeastern States—Roger Conant. Zoological Society of Philadelphia, Philadelphia.
The Reptile World—Clifford H. Pope. Alfred A. Knopf, New York.
Turtles of the United States and Canada—Clifford H. Pope. Alfred A. Knopf, New York.

A young box turtle

U

UNGULATE (*See under Deer*)

UNITED STATES NATIONAL FORESTS

[Editor's Note: The following article courtesy of United States Department of Agriculture—Forest Service.]

National Forests and National Parks

Many people do not understand the difference between national forests and national parks and monuments. The national forests are managed by the Forest Service of the United States Department of Agriculture on a multiple-use basis—to produce water, timber, livestock, wildlife, minerals and recreation. The national parks and monuments are administered by the National Park Service of the United States Department of the Interior. The parks were established by Congress exclusively to preserve outstanding recreational, inspirational, and historic values on the American scene and make them available for public use and enjoyment. No logging, grazing, hunting, or mining are permitted. Both types of management bring very great rewards and are the express will of the people of the United States on specific parts of the publicly owned lands.

The national forests cover 181 million acres, or about an acre per person in the United States. These national forests are owned by you, the American people. They are administered for you by the forest rangers of the Forest Service, United States Department of Agriculture. Since the establishment of the Forest Service under President Theodore Roosevelt, the guiding policy has been "the greatest good of the greatest number in the long run."

These farflung public lands provide many things—timber for industry, water for city and farm, forage for livestock and wildlife—as well as many kinds of outdoor recreation. These important lands are managed for the perpetual yield of their renewable forest resources under a system of coordinated multiple use. As long as the national forests continue to be protected and developed, used but not abused, they will continue to yield rich harvests, both tangible and intangible, forever.

National Forest Wilderness

The Forest Service has set aside nearly eight percent of the national forests as wilderness, wild, and primitive areas. Here lies a big country uncrowded by man and his works.

In 84 areas totaling over 14 million acres, anyone able and willing to ride a horse, hike, or paddle a canoe may penetrate the roadless wilderness to rediscover nature as the pioneers saw it. Roads, motorized travel, logging, resorts, or other commercial use except grazing are not allowed here. This is the National Forest Wilderness, the first units of which were set up in 1930 under Forest Service leadership.

Varying from the spectacular Three Sisters in northern Oregon to the blistering desert of the Superstition Mountains in Arizona, from the newly created Great Gulf Wild Area in New Hampshire to the Devil Canyon just above Los Angeles, National Forest Wilderness Areas contain examples of all types of wilderness country. These beautiful places, protecting wilderness trails for you and your grandchildren, are immeasurably valuable as reservoirs for the physical and spiritual renewal of the American people. Dedicating a reasonable amount of the national forests to such use is entirely compatible with the concept of miltiple use for the greatest public good.

A unique part of the National Forest Wilderness is the Boundary Waters Canoe Area in Superior National Forest in Minnesota. Here is a lake-and-stream wonderland left over from the ice age. hundreds of miles of wilderness paddle-and-portage routes accessible only by canoe.

Many visitors to the national forests penetrate the wilderness entirely on their own, either afoot or on horses rented from nearby ranches. In some areas a popular method is to lead a single burro carrying the camp outfit while the hiker enjoys the trail unburdened by a load. Several organizations also sponsor group pack trips into the National Forest Wilderness, for hunting, or sightseeing, or just to get people away from city streets for a while. Guides who double as cooks, packers, and horse wranglers accompany these trips. Any ablebodied person is eligible to join a group. Among these organizations are:

American Forestry Association, 919 17th Street NW., Washington, D.C. 20006.

Dude Ranchers' Association, Billings, Montana.

Wilderness Society, 2144 P. Street, NW., Washington, D. C.,20007; or P.O. Box 1229, Santa Fe, New Mexico.

Trails in National Forests

There are approximately 112,000 miles of hiking and riding trails in your national forests. As the nation's recreation development increases, this mileage will undoubtedly go up, particularly in the wilderness areas.

In the East is the 2,000-mile Appalachian Trail, exending from Mount Katahdin in Maine to Springer Mountain in Georgia. Almost one-third of this great trail winds through eight national forests. It is beautiful country to hike through, especially in spring or fall; and opened faced shelters and lean-tos are spaced along this trail at regular intervals. Open shelters are free for anyone to use, while closed shelters, usually owned by local Appalachian Trail Clubs, rent for a moderate fee. For maps, information, and guide service if desired, write the Appalachian Trail Conference, 1916 Sunderland Place NW., Washington, D.C. 20006.

In the West is the Pacific Crest Trail System, which will eventually stretch more than 2,000 miles from Canada to Mexico, traversing 19 national forests. Almost 900 miles of this trail through Washington and Oregon are finished, and many national-forest sections of the 1,000-or-so-mile stretch in California are also. These run along the summits of the Southern Cascade, Sierra Nevada, and Sierra Madre Mountain Ranges. Some parts of this trail have been equipped with shelters, and about 1,500 miles of it are in the National Forest Wilderness.

Less well known but equally inviting are thousands of other trails in the scenic back country of the national forests throughout the United States. For example, in the Southwest, in the Pecos Wilderness Area of Santa Fe National Forest, you can ride a horse or hike up a switch-back trail to high Lake Katherine or the top of Pecos Baldy Peak (1,000 feet) for a great view of the New Mexico high country. If you do, chances are you will come away feeling glad to be part owner of this and 150 more national forests.

Recreation—One of the Multiple Uses of National Forests

The national forests are not single-use properties. They are publicly owned lands managed for the sustained production of a variety of products and values, both tangible and intangible. The national forests provide not only an important part of the nation's recreation, but produce vital quantities of water, one-fifth of the nation's timber, substantial forage crops sustaining more than three million head of livestock, and a large part of the wildlife in America. These multiple forest resources are managed by the Forest Service under a coordinated system of multiple use. Multiple use means that most of the national-forest areas yield not one but several different crops and services at the same time. Thus on one large forest unit timber harvesting, live-stock grazing, various uses of water, recreation, hunting and fishing, berry-picking and similar activities may take place at the same time by so adjusting each that it does not measurably interfere with the others. Here and there, of course, some one use may be so important as to give it the right-of-way to the exclusion of the others, and the multiple-use plan provides for this. The controlling ob-jective is to maintain a coordinated pattern of use which will produce the largest net total of public benefits.

The sale of national-forest timber for lumber and pulp, plus fees for various uses of national-forest land, brings in more than 120 million dollars a year to the United States Treasury. One-fourth of this income is returned to the States from which it came for use on schools and roads in the counties having national-forest land. An additional 10 percent is used for roads and trails within the national forests. Thus the benefits of multiple-use management are not just in having beautiful forests and mountain-sides, or enough water to drink, but in jobs and industry and dollars and cents too.

As America grows—in population, liv-ing standard, leisure, and mobility—her use and appreciation of the vast rec-reational resources of the national forests increase year by year. In 1959 over 81 million recreation visits were made to the 151 national forests scattered across 39 states. This is the equivalent to almost half of our people making one visit each And it is a 19-percent increase in rec-reation use of national forests over the previous year—a sharp rise on a graph

that has been climbing vigorously the past 15 years.

The most popular reason for visiting the national forests is to get out and see pretty country—the trees and lakes, the mountains and valleys, the cliffs and canyons, the meadows and snowclad peaks. The next most popular attractions are picnicking, fishing, hunting, and camping, in that order. There is still plenty of "elbow room" in the national forests, particularly in the West where most of the acreage lies. However, the development of camp and picnic sites, sanitary facilities, fireplace grates to reduce forest fire hazard, and other needed improvements cannot keep pace with the mushrooming demand. Even under Operation Outdoors, the short-term (five year) recreation development program of the Forest Service, many people in the new surge of Americans discovering and enjoying their national forests find campgrounds full and hunt out undeveloped camp or picnic sites on their own in less convenient places. This disturbs your forest rangers, since part of their job is to see that you have pleasant places to ride or hike, swim or canoe, without damage to your beautiful national forests.

Camping and Picnicking in National Forests

Some 5,100 developed camp and picnic sites, that can handle 285,000 people at one time, are available for public use and enjoyment in the national forests. This is a good start, but a glance at 1959 national-forest recreation use figures (25 million visits to the camp and picnic sites plus 16 million overflow—or roughly a million and a half campers in the average weekend) shows that the demand far exceeds the supply. Facilities usually include tables and benches, fireplaces, toilets, garbage receptacles, and wherever possible, approved drinking water. In some places, beaches, diving boards, bathhouses, parking areas, and community shelters have been built. The more popular sites have as many as 100,000 visitors each year; others have only a few hundred. A few of the campgrounds have water connections or electricity for trailers (with a fee charged). Most do not. Trailers are permitted at some campgrounds on condition they be used as shelters. In these campgrounds sewage and waste water may not run on the ground. Trailers must be parked so that they do not obstruct normal access along the roads.

A few national-forest campgrounds are so popular that it is necessary to limit the length of stay for each party. At such camps notices of time limits are posted prominently.

Forest Service camp and picnic sites are developed in the most attractive surroundings available in each national forest. You may find your campsite in dense timber on the shore of a lake in the Great Lakes region, or beside an irrigation reservoir in the Arizona desert with a giant 40-foot cactus standing guard on the dry hills. Or you may picnic on a national-forest beach with the surf pounding at your feet. Or camp in an alpine meadow where flowers bloom near eternal snow. Almost anywhere you go among the developed recreation sites on your national forests you will find scenic beauty, shade, forest environment, and outdoor recreational opportunity.

In some cases the passing traveler would never know except for modest roadside signs, that a well-screened national forest campground is just a little way off that arterial highway. On the other hand, many national forest camps may be reached only by traveling the quiet forest roads or wilderness trails. Some of the camps are open the year round; others are usable only during the summer.

Campers bring their own tents, bedding, cooking utensils, and food. Near many of the campgrounds are smalltown stores where most of the needed staples are available. However, other campgrounds are miles from a source of supply. To avoid disappointment it is always best to plan carefully, get proper equipment, and take enough food and drinking water along, especially if you are going into out-of-the-way places.

Roads in the National Forests

Most of the secondary roads in the national forests have been built for forest protection and development. Often they are narrower and steeper than the surfaced highways familiar to the motorist. Nevertheless, if traveled at reasonable speeds and with caution, they are usually quite safe. Of the 150,000 miles of roads in the national forest transportation system, hardly a mile is without some scenic appeal. The beauty of the forest environment is considered in the locating of roads through the national forests. During road construction (as well as timber sales) special efforts are made to retain all the trees and scenic values along the roadsides. Unnecessary scarring of the landscape is avoided, slash is cleaned up, and disturbed soil reseeded.

In the remote sections of the West, roads put in for timber access or fire control often open up vast, virtually unused areas for widespread public hunting, fishing, and forest recreation.

Water Sports in National Forests

With more than 70,000 miles of streams and rivers, plus thousands of lakes and ponds, the national forests form an important part of the nation's water recreation resources. Swimming, skindiving, sailing, speedboating, lake fishing, and waterskiing are some of the more popular sports enjoyed on national-forest waters. For those who would explore by canoe, the Boundary Waters Canoe Area is waiting. For the dwellers of Phoenix and Tucson, the spectacular national-forest lakes nearby have made boating and swimming big business in the desert.

Sailboats, speedboats, and excursion craft ply many other national-forest lakes, while some smaller ones are reserved for motorless fishing boats only.

For swimming the visitor can choose anything from the warm waters of Florida to mountain lakes, or streams. The Lake States, the Northwest, and the Rockies are known for plentiful waters; and the best swimming in the West occurs where clear mountain rivers have run far enough into the valleys to lose their high-country chill. In many places the Forest Service has developed beaches, removed sharp rocks, installed diving boards, rafts, and dressing rooms, dammed streams to raise water levels, and built public boat ramps.

Winter Sports in National Forests

The best way to make winter a cheerful time of year is to become an enthusiast for downhill skiing, ski touring, skating, tobogganing, snowshoeing, ice fishing, or—for the more daring—ski jumping. The most popular of these is downhill skiing. Developed areas with up-ski facilities have boomed the sport of skiing. The deep mountain snows in many of the national forests provide excellent settings for this popular pastime. Most major ski areas in the western states are in whole or in part on national-forest land; and the 1960 Winter Olympics were held in Tahoe National Forest at Squaw Valley, California. The national forests of the Lake States and of New England also contain fine slopes for ski enthusiasts. In the Southwest several of the ski runs are 1 or 2 hours' drive from a balmy winter climate.

There are some 130 developed ski areas on the national forests with varying combinations of facilities such as shelters, ski shops, and ski lifts or tows. Many areas have restaurants, lodges, ski schools, and other services operated by concessioners under permits from the Forest Service. There are cleared slopes and ski trails for the beginning and inter-mediate skier, as well as the country's most famous ski trails for the experts.

Forest Service snow rangers and engineers carefully inspect all ski lifts and tows and provide avalanche control where needed for public safety.

The National Ski Patrol, that searches for lost skiers and renders competent first aid to injured persons, works closely with snow rangers who are in charge of t areas. Instructors certified by a-tional Ski Association are available at all but the smallest areas. Whatever your skiing skill, you will have more fun and be better able to avoid accidents if you take lessons from a good instructor.

There are extensive stretches of ideal ski touring country. Ski touring, or cross-country skiing, is no sport for the novice. It requires competence, stamina and careful preparation. Cross-country skiing, like mountain climbing and wilderness hiking, should never be undertaken alone.

Other Pastimes in National Forests

A variety of other forms of recreation are pursued on the national forest. One of them is mountain climbing, a most vigorous, fascinating, and at times dangerous outdoor sports. If you plan to climb high or precipitous mountains, don't go alone. Join a mountain club and learn safe techniques and get plenty of practice.

The grand scenery, colorful outdoor sports, and wildlife of the national forests offer great opportunity and challenge to photographers, be they amateur or professional. In fact, "shutterbugs" go slightly mad shooting pictures in certain national-forest areas such as north Idaho's lake country, the Mackinac Island country of Michigan, the Colorado Rockies, the colorful cliffs of Oak Creek Caynon in Arizona, or the beautiful Cherokee National Forest in Tennessee.

Geologists and amateur prospectors find much of interest in the spectacular rock outcrops, fossil deposits, and caves in the national forests. Botany scholars prowl from the weird Cranberry Glades of West Virginia to the exotic plants of the Oregon coast, from the Calaveras

Mountain climbers scale the cliffs at White Mountain National Forest, New Hampshire

giant sequoias to the jungle growth in Caribbean National Forest, Puerto Rico. Archeological remains and cliff dwellings may still be found in the Southwest, some of them in the national forests. Your interest may be bird study, or wild flowers, or collecting rocks and minerals, or picking wild huckleberries in season. For many people the magnet is autumn color, the golden aspens of the Rockies, the red-and-gold-maples of the Lake States, or the scrambled multihued pink of New England's forests.

Wild flowers are a national-forest recreation and scenic resource. Let them stay in place for others to enjoy. Digging or pulling up plants and shrubs is not allowed except when it is authorized by a written permit.

A Guide to the National Forests

[Note—The first city or town named after each national fore is the forest supervisor's headquarters. Write to him for detail information.]

ALABAMA

William B. Bankhead National Forest (178,895 acres)

Montgomery, Alabama. Highways: US 31, 78, 278; Alabama 5, 74, 195. **Attractions:** Limestone gorges, Lewis Smith Reservoir, two natural bridges, wildlife refuge and management area. Deer, turkey, and squirrels. Bass and bream fishing in Brushy Lake. **Facilities:** 1 camp and picnic site, 3 picnic only, 1 swimming site. **Nearby towns:** Cullman, Decatur, Haleyville, Jasper, and Russellville

Conecuh National Forest (83,790 acres)

Montgomery, Alabama. Highways: US 29; Alabama 137. **Attractions:** Large, clear ponds. Bass and bream fishing. Deer, turkeys, and small-game. **Facilities:** 1 picnicking, 1 camping, and 1 swimming site. **Nearby town:** Andalusia

Talladega National Forest (357,847 acres)

Montgomery, Alabama. Highways: US 78, 231; Alabama 5, 6. **Attractions:** Payne Lake Wildlife Management Area; Skyway scenic drive; Mount Cheaha, 2,407 feet, highest point in Alabama; Lake Chinnabee. Deer, turkeys, ducks, and squirrels; bass, bream, and perch fishing; swimming at Cheaha State Park. **Facilities:** 4 camp and picnic sites, 7 picnic only, 1 swimming site. Resort, hotel, and cabins at Cheaha State Park. **Nearby towns:** Anniston, Centerville, Heflin, Marion, Selma, Sylacauga, Talladega, and Tuscaloosa

Tuskegee National Forest (10,777 acres)

Montgomery, Alabama. Highways: US 29, 80; Alabama 81. **Attractions:** Pine plantation of advanced size. Bream fishing in streams. **Facilities:** 2 picnicking sites. **Nearby towns:** Auburn and Tuskegee

ALASKA

Chugach National Forest (4,726,145 acres)

Anchorage, Alaska. Highway to Anchorage and Seward. Most travel by sea or air. Rail service from Anchorage to Seward. **Attractions:** Tidewater, Hanging, and Piedmont Glaciers. Remote Aleut villages. Picturesque old Russian churches; native bidarkis (boats). Shrimp, crab, clam, and salmon canneries. Kenai Mountains with road down Kenai Peninsula; fiords of Port Wells. Unexcelled scenery. Trout and salt-water fishing. Moose, sheep, mountain goats, and Alaska brown bear; also ducks, grouse, and ptarmigan. Scenic trails and roads. **Facilities:** 5 camp and picnic sites, 16 picnic only. 1 swimming site; 3 winter sports areas. Plane service to many of these places. **Nearby towns:** Anchorage,

Cordova, Kodiak, Seward, Valdez, and Whittier

Tongass National Forest (16,016,140 acres)—South Division

Ketchikan. Alaska. Direct plane service to Ketchikan. **Attractions:** Fiords of Walker Cove and Rudyerd Bay of the Behm Canal, and Portland, Canal. Trout fishing; salt-water fishing for salmon and halibut. Alaska brown, black, and girzzly bears, goats, and deer. Totems. Indian villages. Salmon canneries; pulpmill. Boating on inland waterways. **Facilities:** 2 camp and picnic, 1 picnic only, 1 swimming site; 1 winter sports area. Hotel accomodations in all southeastern Alaska towns, such as Ketchikan and Wrangell; all these served by plane

ARIZONA

Coconino National Forest (1,801,091 acres)

Flagstaff Arizona. Highways: US 66, 89, 89A. **Attractions:** Graceful San Francisco Peaks, 12,611 feet, highest in Arizona; Oak Creek Canyon and the Red Rock country near Sedona offer exceptional scenic and photographic opportunities; Sycamore Canyon Wild Area and Mogollon Rim. Scenic drives: Lake Mary-Long Valley Road; Mogollon Rim Road; Baker Butte Fire Lookout offering vast view of Arizona timber. Numerous national monuments nearby plus Lowell Astronomical Observatory, Museum of Northern Arizona, Flagstaff; Meteor Crater near Painted Desert. Deer, antelopes, turkeys, elk, mountain lions; lake and stream fishing: horseback riding; boating on Lake Mary. **Facilities:** 18 camp and picnic sites, 5 picnic only; Arizona Snow Bowl Winter Sports Area. Resort hotels, dude ranches. **Nearby towns:** Camp Verde, Clarkdale, Cottonwood, Flagstaff, Sedona, and Winslow

Coronado National Forest (1,796,534 acres—partly in New Mexico)

Tucson, Arizon. Highways: US 80, 84, 89, 666; Arizona 82, 86. **Attractions:** Rugged mountains rising abruptly from surrounding deserts; cactus to fir trees, swimming to skiing in an hour's time— 40 miles apart. Santa Catalina Mountains Recreation Area with Rose Canyon Lake, Sabino Canyon, and Mount Lemmon Snow Bowl, southernmost winter sports area in the Continental U.S. Chiricahua Mountains with Chiricahua Wild Area and several small trout lakes. Pinaleno Mountains Recreation Area with Mount Graham, 10,713 feet, Riggs Flat Lake. Pena Blanca Lake, 52 acres of bass fishing 4 miles from the international boundary with Mexico. Galiuro Wild Area. Nearby are Arizona-Sonora

Desert Museum, Colossal Cave Sta Park, Tucson Mountain Park. Dee javelina, mountain lions, quail, ar doves. Scenic drives. Pack-trip and hi ing trails in the rugged ranges of sout ern Arizona (caution: carry adequa water). Dude ranch and winter reso country. **Facilities:** 32 camp and picn sites, 17 picnic only. **Nearby town** Benson, Bisbee, Mexican border tow of Douglas and Nogales, Fort Huachuc Patagonia, Safford, San Simon, Tom stone, Tucson, and Wilcox

Kaibab National Forest (1,715,190 acre

Williams, Arizona. Highways: US 89, 64, 67. **Attractions:** Grand Canye National Game Preserve with the famo North Kaibab deer herd, a wild buffa herd and the only habitat of the Kaib squirrel. Access to both north and sou rims of the Grand Canyon and Sup Indian village in Havasu Canyon. Oth points of interest are beautiful No Kaibab high country; pine, spruce, a aspen forests with open meadows; Ea Rim, North Canyon, Bill Willia Mountain, Whitehorse Lake, Catara Lake, and Sycamore Canyon Wild Are Deer, elk, antelopes, bears, mounta lions, turkeys, and buffalo. Scenic drive fishing, riding pack trips. Photograph opportunities; wildlife and vivid geolog formations. **Facilities:** 6 camp and picn sites. Motels, resorts, guest ranche **Nearby towns:** Ashfork, Cottonwoo Flagstaff, Fredonia, Grand Canyon, a Williams, Arizona; Kanab, Utah

Prescott National Forest (1,248,210 acre

Prescott, Arizona. Highways: US 8 **Attractions:** Ideal year-round clima Rugged back country, many roads, prir itive. Granite Basin Lake near Gran Mountain, Hassayampa Lake. Limit trout fishing. Sycamore Canyon a Pine Mountain Wild Areas. Jermo Nation's largest ghost town. Deer, an lopes, doves, and quail. Many ho trails; scenic drives. **Facilities:** 8 car and picnic sites, 8 picnic only. Resor motels, and dude ranches. Nearby town Clarkdale, Cottonwood, Jerome, May and Prescott

Sitgreaves National Forest (744,8 acres)

Holbrook, Arizona. Highways: US Arizona 77; 173. **Attractions:** Scer Mogollon Rim Drive; pueblo ruins, la elk herd. Woods Canyon Lake. De turkeys, antelopes, and bears. Sade and pack trips. **Facilities:** Public g and swimming at White Mounta Country Club. 4 camp and picnic sit numerous resorts, hotels, summer hom guest ranches. **Nearby towns:** Holbro Lakeside, Pinetop, Showlow, Sno flake, and Winslow onto National Forest (2,902,072 acres) Phoenix, Arizona. Highways: US 60, 0, 80, 89. Attractions: Semidesert to ine-fir forests, elevations 1,500 to 7,300 eet. The lakes in the low country form n all-year haven in the desert; the cool ine forests along the Mogollon Rim are ery popular in summer. Famous Super- tition Mountains, Tonto Basin, Bloody asin, Mazatzal and Superstition Wil- erness Areas, Pine Mountain Wild Area; ierra Ancha Wild Area. Thirty thou- and acres of manmade lakes including oosevelt, Apache, Canyon, and Saguaro akes on the Salt River; Bartlett and lorseshoe Lakes on the Verde River. opular for boating, swimming, skin- living, water skiing, bass fishing. Public oat ramps at most lakes. Boats and ackle also for rent. Limited trout fish- ng in high country. Deer, elk, bears, avelina, turkeys, and mountain lions. addle and pack trips. Scenic drives: pache Trail, Beeline Highway, Payson- Iogollon Rim drive. Facilities: 16 camp nd picnic sites, 12 picnic only. No feguards. Swim with care. Resorts, dude anches. Nearby towns: Globe, Mesa, Aiami, Payson, Phoenix, Pine, Superior

ARKANSAS

Ouachita National Forest (1,542,412 cres—partly in Oklahoma) Hot Springs, Arkansas. Highways: US 9, 70, 71, 270, 271; Arkansas 7, 10, 1, 27. Attractions: Ouachita, Kiamichi, nd Winding Stair Mountains; 8 major nd numerous smaller artifical lakes in r near the national forest. Caddo Gasp, vhere DeSoto fought Indians; lands ex- lored by La Salle and DeTonti, ac- ounting for the many French names. Crystal Cave, Little Missouri Falls, four ame refuges, medicinal springs. Bass shing; deer, quail, and squirrels; scenic rives, hiking, and swimming. Facilities: camp and picnic sites, 17 picnic only, 1 swimming sites. Hotels, resorts, and abin camps. Nearby towns: Booneville, Iot Springs, and Mena, Arkansas; Ieavener and Poteau, Oklahoma

Ozark National Forest (1,046,309 acres) Russellville, Arkansas. Highways: US 4, 71; Arkansas 7, 22, 23. Attractions: nviting summer climate, oak forest rock liffs and pools, scenic drives, 5 game efuge. Three recreational lakes; Mount Magazine. Stream and lake fishing, deer nd small-game, 2 large reservoirs near he national forest. Facilities: 10 camp nd picnic sites, 7 swimming sites. Iount Magazine Lodge and cabins. White Rock Mountain cabins, others earby. Nearby towns: Clarksville, ayetteville, Ft. Smith, Harrison, Ozark, aris, and Russellville

CALIFORNIA

ngeles National Forest (648-754 acres) Pasadena, California. Highways: US 6, 66, 99; California 2, 39. Attractions: Steep, rugged mountains adjoining Los Angeles metropolitan area; Old Baldy, 10,000 feet. Chiefly a chaparral forest that serves as a watershed for the Los Angeles area and as an easily reached mountain playground for the area's inhabitants. Devil Canyon-Bear Canyon Wild Area. Scenic drives with wonderful views, especially of the city lights at night. Riding and hiking trails, skiing in season, fishing, and some swimming and boating. Facilities: 82 camp and picnic sites, 11 picnic only. (Because of extreme fire danger in southern Cali- fornia, no open campfires are permitted in this national forest.) 2 swimming sites; 6 winter sports areas with ski lifts and other facilities. Resorts, cabins, pack and riding stables. Hotels and motels in Los Angeles and foothill towns

Cleveland National Forest (391,682 acres) San Diego, Calfiornia. Highways: US 101, 395, 80; California 78, 79, 71, 74. Attractions: Primarily a watershed forest with an unusually mild climate, between the desert and the sea. Agua Tibia Wild Area. The world's largest telescope at Polomar Observatory on Mount Palomar. Camping; warm water fishing on the impounded lakes of the water systems. Deer, ducks, pigeons, and quail. The Mexico-to-Oregon Trail starts here. Facilities: 22 camp and picnic sites, 4 picnic only. (Because of extreme fire danger in southern California, no open campfires are permitted in this national forest.) Dude ranches, resorts, motels. Nearby towns: El Centro, Los Angeles, Oceanside, and San Diego

Eldorado National Forest (640,619 acres) Placerville, California. Highways: US 50; California 88. Attractions: Rugged mountains in the Sierra Nevada. Hundreds of mountain lakes; including south shore of spectacular Lake Tahoe, 23 miles long, 13 miles wide, elevation 6,225 feet. California Gold Rush coun- try, famous Mother Lode mining com- munities including site of Sutter's Mill. Desolation Valley Wild Area. Lake and stream fishing, deer and bears. Scenic drives: Highway 50 to Lake Tahoe, Carson Pass Highway 88 (route of Fremont expedition of 1844); Georgetown to Wentworth Springs. Riding trails, wil- derness trips. Facilities: 28 camp and picnic sites, 3 picnic only 2 swimming sites; 7 developed winter sports areas. Resorts, motels, and dude ranches. Near- by towns: Placerville and Sacramento, California; Carson City and Reno, Nevada

Inyo National Forest (1,774,176 acres— partly in Nevada) Bishop, California. Highways: US 395, 6; California 168. Attractions: High Sierra Wilderness Area; Mt. Dana-

Minarets Wild Area; Hoover Wild Area. Palisade Glacier, southernmost glacier in the United States. Ancient Bristlecone Pine Forest Botanical Area with many 4,000-year-old trees—the oldest living things on earth. Many wild granite peaks 12,000 to more than 14,000 feet in elevation. Mount Whitney, 14,495 feet, highest point in continental United States, and its closest approach road. Lake and stream fishing, deer, and wilderness trips. Dozen of natural lakes, some accessible by paved road up to 9,700 feet in elevation. Mammoth and Reversed Creek Recreation Areas. Facilities: 61 camp and picnic sites, 4 picnic only 2 swimming sites; 6 winter sports areas. Resorts, motels. Nearby towns: Bigpine, Bishop, Independence, Leevining, and Lone Pine

Klamath National Forest (1,697,600 acres —partly in Oregon) Yreka, California. Highways: US 99; California 96, 97. Attractions: Big timber forest. Klamath River and tributaries, famous for salmon and steelhead. Marble Mountain and Salmon-Trinity Alps Wilderness Areas. High mountain lakes and streams. Great scenic beauty in a wild setting. Steelhead and salmon fish- ing; deer. Hiking, riding, pack trips. Facilities: 28 camp and picnic sites, 2 picnic only, 1 swimming site; 2 winter sports areas. Motels, resorts, dude ranches. Nearby towns: Eureka, Mount Shasta, and Yreka, California, Medford, Oregon

Lassen National Forest (1,047,372 acres) Susanville, California. Highways: US 395; California 36, 89. Attractions: Caribou Peak and Thousand Lakes Wild Areas. Many lakes; southern end of Cascade Wonderland; volcanic lava flow tubes, hot springs, mud pots. Indian pictographs and hieroglyphics, old emigrant trails. Lake and stream fish- ing for rainbow, Lochleven, and steel- head trout; deer and bear; riding and hiking trails. Facilities: 59 camp and picnic sites, 5 picnic only, 1 swimming site; 4 winter sports areas. Privately owned resorts, hotels, cabins. Nearby towns: Chester, Chico, Mill Creek, Red Bluff, and Redding

Los Padres National Forest (1,749,245 acres) Santa Barbara, California. Highways: US 101, 99, 399; California 1, 166, 150, 178. Attractions: Undeveloped, rugged country, varying from lonely coast to semidesert, from brush to oak country to pine timber; elevations from near sea level to almost 9,000 feet; home of the rare California condor. Ventana and San Rafael Wild Areas; snowcapped peaks in winter. Quail, pigeons, deer, and wild bear; trout fishing, scenic drives, ocean- side camping, wilderness trips. Facil- ities: 286 camp and picnic sites, 7 picnic only. (Because of extreme fire danger in southern Calfironia, **no open campfires** are permitted in this national forest.) 3 swimming sites; 2 winter sports areas including Kern County Ski Lodge. Hotels, cabins, and a few dude ranches. **Nearby towns:** Atascadero, Carmel, King City, Monterey, Ojai, Paso Robles, Taft, San Luis Obispo, Santa Barbara, Santa Maria, and Ventura

Mendocino National Forest (867,425 acres)

Willows, California. Highways: US 99W, 101; California 20. **Attractions:** Coast Range of Calfironia about 100 miles north of San Francisco. Peaks up to 8,600 feet. Beautiful lake country. Yolla Bolly-Middle Eel Wilderness Area. Columbian black-tailed deer. Fishing, saddle and pack trips. **Facilities:** 49 camp and picnic sites. Dude ranches, motels. **Nearby towns:** Corning, Laytonville, Sacramento, Ukiah, Willits, and Willow

Modoc National Forest (1,688,789 acres)

Alturas, California. Highways: US 299, 395; California 139. **Attractions:** Remote northeast corner of California. Scenic rides, wilderness trips on trails such as summit trail through South Warner Wild Area. Glass Mountain lava flows, scene of Modoc Indian wars. Winter range of interstate deer herd, Clear Lake Reservoir migratory bird refuge. Stream and lake fishing; mule deer and waterfowl. **Facilities:** 25 camp and picnic sites, 2 picnic only, 1 swimming site; 2 winter sports areas. Hotels, cabins. **Nearby towns:** Adin, Alturas, Canby, Cedarville, and Tulelake

Plumas National Forest (1,147,611 acres)

Quincy, California. Highways: US 40A, 395; California 89, 24. **Attractions:** Beautiful Feather River country; Feather Falls, one of the highest and most picturesque waterfalls in the United States. Historic gold mining areas of La Porte, Johnsville, and Rich Bar; extensive hydroelectric developments. Limestone caves; large, beautiful mountain valleys, such as Indian, American, Mohawk, and Sierra Valleys. Lake and stream fishing; mule and black-tailed deer, bears, ducks, geese, quail, and doves. Scenic drives include Feather River Canyon, Bucks Lake, Bald Rock Canyon, Quincy-La Porte and Lake Basin Recreational Areas, and Little Last Chance Creek. Pacific Crest Trail. **Facilities:** 27 camp and picnic sites, 2 picnic only. Resorts, hotels, and cabins. **Nearby towns:** Chico, Greenville, Marysville, Oroville, Quincy, Sacramento, and Sierraville

San Bernardino National Forest (613,912 acres)

San Bernardino, California. Highways: US 60, 70, 99, 66, 395; California 2, 18, 74. **Attractions:** Highest mountains

in southern California: San Gorgonio, 11,485 feet; 6 others more than 10,000 feet. San Jacinto, San Gorgonio, and Cucamonga Wild Areas. Historic landmarks: Big Bear and Arrowhead Lakes; Mt. San Jacinto. Lake and stream fishing, deer. Life zones from desert to alpine within a few miles. Camping and pack trips, winter sports. **Facilities:** 41 camp and picnic sites, 10 picnic only. (Because of extreme fire danger in southern California, **no open campfires** are permitted in this national forest.) 2 swimming sites; 9 winter sports sites. Resorts, hotels, motels, cabins at Arrowhead, Big Bear Lakes, Idyllwild. **Nearby towns:** Banning, Indio, Palm Springs, Riverside, and San Bernardino

Sequoia National Forest (1,118,551 acres)

Portervill, California. Highways: US 395; California 190. **Attractions:** Giant sequoia big-trees, Hume Lake, Boydens Cave, High Sierra Wilderness Area, Mineral King Game Refuge. High mountain lakes and stream fishing, home of the golden trout. Mule deer and bear. Scenic drives: Kern River Canyon, Kings River Canyon. Wilderness hiking and riding trails; swimming and boating. **Facilities:** 45 camp and picnic sites, 8 picnic only, 8 swimming sites; 3 winter sports areas. Motels, resorts, lodges. **Nearby towns:** Bakersfield, Fresno, Porterville, and Visalia

Shasta-Trinity National Forests (2,036,836 acres; two forests)

Redding, California. Highways: US 99, 299; California 44, 96, 89. **Attractions:** Beautiful Mount Shasta, 14,162 feet with eternal snow, 5 living glaciers. Shasta and Trinity Lakes with outstanding boating. Lava beds, Glass Mountain, and Castle Crags. Salmon-Trinity Alps Wilderness Area and Yolla Bolly-Middle Eel Wilderness Area. Lake and stream fishing, home of Dolly Varden trout. Waterfowl, upland birds, deer and bears. Limestone caves, lava caves and chimneys. Riding trails in the wilderness. Skiing. Scenic drives. **Facilities:** 64 camp and picnic sites, 5 picnic only, 8 swimming sites; 2 winter sports areas. Resorts, hotels, motels, guest ranches. **Nearby towns:** Callahan, Dunsmuir, McCloud, Mount Shasta, Redding, Weaverville, and Weed

Sierra National Forest (1,295,832 acres)

Fresno, California. Highways: US 99; California 168, 180, 41. **Attractions:** Huntington Lake, Florence Lake, Shaver Lake, Dinkey Creek, and Bass Lake Recreation Areas, Nelder and McKinley Groves of big-trees (giant sequoia), Central Sierra section of the John Muir Trail. High Sierra Wilderness Area; Mount Dana-Minarets Wild Area. Rainbow Falls in the Reds Meadow area. Lake and stream fishing; deer, bears, quail. Boating, mountain climbing, pack

and saddle trips, winter sports. **Facilities:** 79 camp and picnic sites, 19 picnic only, 12 swimming sites; 1 winter sports area. Hotels, resorts, dude ranches. **Nearby towns:** Fresno and North Fork

Six Rivers National Forest (935,268 acres)

Eureka, California. Highways: US 101, 299; California 36, 96. **Attractions:** Giant Coast redwood and fir forests stretching 135 miles south from the Oregon line. Klamath, Smith, Eel, and Mad Rivers. Mild, cool climate yearlong in redwoods; rugged back country. Trout fishing, spring and summer; steehead and salmon fishing fall and winter in rivers; deer and bears; riding trails, scenic drives. **Facilities:** 33 camp and picnic sites, 1 picnic only, 2 swimming sites; 1 winter sports area. Resorts, hotels, cabins. **Nearby towns:** Arcata, Crescent City, Eureka, Fortuna

Stanislaus National Forest (896,1__ acres)

Sonora, California. Highways: US 99, 395; California 4, 108, 120. **Attractions:** Nearest high mountain country to San Francisco Bay region and portion of San Joaquin Valley; elevations 1,1__ to 11,575 feet. Deep canyons cut by Merced, Tuolmne, Stanislaus, and Mokelumne Rivers; fine timber stands. Emigrant Basin Wild Area. Gold Rush country with many a tall tale. Route of pioneers, Sonora and Ebbets Passes. Calaveras Bigtree National Forest. Fishing in lakes and 715 miles of stream; deer and bears. Scenic drives, saddle and pack trips, winter sports. **Facilities:** 55 camp and picnic sites, 2 swimming sites; 3 winter sports areas. Resorts, cabins, stores, boating, packer stations. **Nearby towns:** Angels Camp, Columbia, Groveland, Jamestown

Tahoe National Forest (694,112 acres)

Nevada City, California. Highways: US 40; California 20, 49, 89. **Attractions:** Squaw Valley, site of 1960 Winter Olympics. Outstanding conditions and facilities for winter sports; adjacent valleys being developed. Lakes and streams, including northwest shore of beautiful Lake Tahoe. Historic Donner Pass Emigrant Trail; Gold Rush country. Lake and stream fishing, deer and bears. Riding and hiking trails, scenic drives through historic gold mining towns. **Facilities:** 54 camp and picnic sites, 2 picnic only, 3 swimming sites, 6 winter sports areas. Summer resort cabins, hotels. **Nearby towns:** Downieville, Grass Valley, Nevada City, Sierra City, Sierraville, and Truckee California; Carson City and Reno, Nevada

COLORADO

Arapaho National Forest (990,371 acres)

Golden, Colorado. Highways: US

0. **Attractions:** highest auto road in U.S.
o the crest of Mount Evans, 14260 ft.
old, silver mining; ghost towns. Gore
ange-Eagle Nest Wild Area. Moffat
unnel, 6.2 miles long under Continental
ivide. Lake and stream fishing. Elk,
eer, and bears, small-game. Scenic high
ountain routes; Loveland and Berthoud
asses, Peak to Peak Highway. Riding
ails, wilderness trips. **Facilities:** 33
amp and picnic sites, 20 picnic only;
winter sports areas. Resorts, hotels,
abin camps, dude ranches. **Nearby**
wns: Denver, Dillon, Golden, Granby,
rand Lake, Hot Sulphur Springs, Idaho
prings, and Kremmling

**rand Mesa-Uncompahgre National
orests** (1,317,865 acres; two forests)
Delta, Colorado. Highways: US 50,
50, 6. **Attractions:** Grand Mesa Plateau,
0,500 feet; 250 lakes and reservoirs;
iffs, canyons, waterfalls, wild flowers.
ncompahgre Plateau. Uncompahgre
nd Wilson Mountains Wild Areas;
uray and Telluride Scenic Areas. Lake
nd stream fishing. Deer, elk, bears,
nd ducks. Scenic drives, saddle trips.
acilities: 31 camp and picnic sites, 6
icnic only; 1 winter sports area. Mo-
els, resorts in and near the national
rest. **Nearby towns:** Delta, Grand
unction, Montrose, Norwood, Ouray,
nd Telluride

unnison National Forest (1,660,147
res)
Gunnison, Colorado. Highway: US 50;
olorado 135, 149. **Attractions:** Trout
shing streams, many high lakes.
wenty-seven mountain peaks more than
2,000 feet; Ruby Range. Taylor Park
eservoir and valley; ghost town. West
lk Wild Area. Trout fishing. Elk, deer,
ountain sheep, and bears. Saddle trips,
ilderness trips. **Facilities:** 34 camp and
cnic sites, 1 winter sports area. Com-
ercial hotels, resorts, motels in and
ear the national forest. **Nearby towns:**
unnison, Lake City, Montrose

ike National Forest (1,084,947 acres)
Colorado Springs, Colorado. High-
ays: US 24, 85, 87, 285. **Attractions:**
ikes Peak with highway to summit,
istoric Cripple Creek and Alma gold
amps, scenic Rampart Range Road.
evil's Head Forest Fire Lookout,
onument Forest Nursery, Platte and
rkansas River watersheds. Abyss Lake
cenic Area. Fishing; scenic drives.
ountain sheep and other wildlife.
acilities: 37 camp and picnic sites, 40
icnic only; 1 winter sports area. Com-
ercial hotels, resorts, motels in and
ear the national forest. **Nearby towns:**
olorado Springs, Cripple Creek, and
enver

io Grande National Forest (1,800,322
res)
Monte Vista, Colorado. Highways: US

160, 285. **Attractions:** Mountain lakes
and trout streams, Wolf Creek Pass,
rugged high country. Upper Rio Grande
and La Garita-Sheep Mountain Wild
Areas. Fishing; deer, elk, and ducks.
Saddle and pack trips, scenic drives.
Facilities: 31 camp and picnic sites, 5
picnic only; 1 winter sports area. Motels
in and near the national forest. **Nearby
towns:** Alamosa, Antonito, Creede,
Monte Vista, and Saguache

Roosevelt National Forest (784,051 acres)
Fort Collins, Colorado. Highways: US
34, 287; Colorado 14, 160. **Attractions:**
Arapaho, Isabelle and South St. Vrain
Glaciers; rugged Continental Divide
with many alpine lakes; Poudre, Big
Thompson, St. Vrain, and Boulder Canyons. Rawah Wild Area. Boating; fishing; deer, elk, mountain sheep, bears,
mountain lions, grouse and ducks.
Saddle and pack trips, scenic drives.
Facilities: 21 camp and picnic sites, 18
picnic only. Motels and dude ranches
in and near the national forest. **Nearby
towns:** Boulder, Denver, Estes Park,
Fort Collins, Longmont, and Loveland

Routt National Forest (1,145,111 acres)
Steamboat Springs, Colorado. Highway: US 40; Colorado 84, 131. **Attractions:** Continental Divide with perpetual
ice and snow, trout streams and alpine
lakes. Mount Zirkel-Dome Peak Wild
Area, Big Creek Lakes Recreation Area.
Fishing; deer, elk, grouse, and ducks.
Saddle and pack trips; scenic drives.
Facilities: 48 camp and picnic sites, 5
picnic only. Commercial cabins, motels
in and near the national forest. **Nearby
towns:** Craig, Kremmling, Steamboat
Springs, Walden, and Yampa

San Isabel National Forest (1,104042
acres)
Pueblo, Colorado. Highways: US 24,
50, 85, 87; Colorado 69, 165. **Attractions:** Highest average elevation of any
national forest; Sangre de Cristo Range;
12 peaks more than 14,000 feet; Mount
Elbert, second highest in the United
States. More than 40 timberline lakes.
Snow Angel on Mount Shavano; molyb-
denum mines; Lake Isabel Recreation
Area. Fishing; deer, elk, bears, mountain
goats, grouse, and ducks. Scenic drives,
saddle and pack trips. **Facilities:** 26
camp and picnic sites; 3 winter sports
areas. Motels and dude ranches in and
near the national forest. **Nearby towns:**
Canon City, Leadville, Pueblo, Salida,
and Walsenburg

San Juan National Forest (1,850,053
acres)
Durango, Colorado. Highways: US
160, 550; Colorado 145. **Attractions:**
Alpine lakes; Mount Wilson, 14250 feet;
canyons, waterfalls, cataracts, peculiar
gologic formations. Archeological ruins,
historic mines. San Juan Wilderness

Area; Wilson Mountains Wild Area. Fishing; deer, elk, bears, mountain lions,
grouse, and ducks. Scenic drives; saddle
and pack trips. **Facilities:** 34 camp and
picnic sites, 7 picnic only; 1 winter
sports area. Motels and dude ranches
in and near the national forest. **Nearby
towns:** Cortez, Durango, Pagosa Springs,
and Silverton, Colorado; Farmington,
New Mexico

White River National Forest (1,961,798
acres)
Glenwood Springs, Colorado. Highways: US 24, 6; Colorado 82, 132. **Attractions:** Spectacular Glenwood Canyon, Hanging Lake, Bridal Veil Falls,
mineral hot springs, caves, alpine lakes.
Source of marble for Lincoln Memorial
and Tomb of the Unknown Soldier. Flat
Tops Wilderness Area; Gore Range-
Eagle Nest Wild Area; Maroon Bells-
Snowmass Wild Area. Fishing; elk, deer
and bears. Saddle and pack trails; scenic
drives. **Facilities:** 58 camp and picnic
sites, 1 picnic only, 1 swimming site,
3 winter sports areas. Motels and dude
ranches in and near the national forest.
Nearby towns: Aspen, Craig, Eagle,
Glenwood Springs, Gypsum, Leadville

FLORIDA
Apalachicola National Forest (556,480
acres)
Tallahassee, Florida. Highways: US
98, 319; Florida 20, 65, 369. **Attractions:**
Pine-hardwood forests, Coastal Plain
type. Natural sinks, bottom-land hardwood swamps along large rivers with
trees typically found far to the north.
Old Fort Gadsen, old river landings.
Three rivers and their tributaries with
many miles of fishing waters—bass,
bream, perch. Quail, deer, and bears.
Numerous lakes, sinks and ponds provide boating and swimming. **Facilities:**
4 camp and picnic sites, 10 picnic only,
4 swimming sites. Hotels not far away.
Nearby towns: Apalachicola, Blounts-
town, Bristol, and Tallahassee

Ocala National Forest (361,029 acres)
Tallahassee, Florida. Highways: US
17, 301; Florida 19, 40, 42, 314. **Attractions:** Juniper Springs and Alexander
Springs; large, clear-flowing streams
through subtropical wilderness; botanical lore, palms, hardwoods, and pine.
Hundreds of clear lakes. The Big Scrub,
characterized by vast stands of sand
pine, is unique. Wildlife management
area deer and bears. Silver Springs is
nearby. Numerous lakes, streams, and
ponds with fishing and camping sites.
Facilities: 12 camp and picnic sites,
10 picnic only, 4 swimming sites. Com-
merical accommodations near the forest.
Nearby towns: DeLand, Eustis, Lees-
burg, Mount Dora, Ocala, and Palatka

Osceola National Forest (157,233 acres)
Tallahassee, Florida. Highways: US

41, 90, 441; Florida 100. **Attractions:** Flat country, dotted with numerous ponds, sinks, and cypress swamps. State game breeding ground. Bass, perch and bream fishing; deer, turkeys, quail, and dove. Swimming and boating at Ocean Pond. **Facilities:** 1 camp and picnic site, 3 picnic only, 2 swimming sites; opportunities for aquatic sports. **Nearby towns:** Jacksonville and Lake City

GEORGIA
Chattahoochee National Forest (680,333 acres)
Gainesville, Georgia. Highways: US 19, 23, 27, 41, 76, 123, 129, 441; Georgia 5, 60, 75. **Attractions:** Brasstown Bald, 7,784 feet, highest point in Georgia; Blue Ridge Mountains; lakes; Tallulah Gorge; waterfalls; southern end of Appalachian Trail. Deer and small-game; trout and bass fishing. Swimming, boating, hiking. **Facilities:** 10 camp and picnic sites, 23 picnic only, 6 swimming sites. **Nearby towns:** Atlanta, Blue Ridge, Clarkesville, Clayton, Dahlonega, Dalton, and Toccoa, Georgia; Chattanooga, Tennessee

Oconee National Forest (96,066 acres)
Gainesville, Georgia. Highways: US 278, 129; Georgia 12, 44, 77. **Attractions:** Heavily forested Piedmont hills, archeological remains, Rock Eagle Lake, Effigy of Eagle, Mammoth 4-H Center, Piedmont Wildlife Refuge; deer and small-game, bass and bream fishing. **Facilities:** 2 picnicking sites. **Nearby towns:** Eatonton, Greensboro, and Madison

IDAHO
Boise National Forest (2,629,465 acres)
Boise, Idaho. Highways: US 20, 30, 95; Idaho 15, 16, 17, 21, 52, 68. **Attractions:** Rugged back country including portions of Sawtooth Wilderness Area. Abandoned mines and ghost towns. Scenes of early Indian camps and massacres. Virgin stands of ponderosa pine. Arrowrock, Anderson Ranch, Cascade, Deadwood, and Lucky Peak Reservoirs; other lakes. Includes headwaters of Boise, Payette, and Salmon Rivers. Lake and stream fishing for trout and salmon. Bears, elk, and deer. Spectacular scenic drives in Payette and Boise River Canyons, along Boise Ridge and edge of Sawtooth Wilderness Area. **Facilities:** 121 camp and picnic sites, 22 picnic only, 1 swimming site; Bogus Basin Winter Sports Area. Resorts, motels, dude ranches with horses, boats, and other facilities. **Nearby towns:** Boise, Cascade, Emmett, Horseshoe Bend, Idaho City, and Mountain Home

Caribou National Forest (976,041 acres —partly in Utah and Wyoming)
Pocatello, Idaho. Highways: US 91, 191, 30N. **Attractions:** High country:

towering mountain ranges divided by beautiful valleys. Historic markers and trails,. natural soda springs, rushing streams and waterfalls. Stream fishing; game birds, deer, and bears. Scenic drives: Mink Creek to Scout Mountain, Skyline Road, Snake River-McCoy Road along south bank of South Fork of Snake River, Georgetown Canyon-Diamond Creek and Snowslide-Crow Creek Roads. Numerous riding trails into wilderness country. **Facilities:** 16 camp and picnic sites, 6 picnic only, 2 winter sports areas. Resorts and motels. **Nearby towns:** Idaho Falls, Malad City, Montpelier, Pocatello, Soda Springs, and Swan Valley, Idaho; Afton, Wyoming

Challis National Forest (2,447,696 acres)
Challis, Idaho. Highways: US 20, 93, 93A. **Attractions:** Lost River Range with Mount Borah, 12,655 feet, highest peak Idaho. Lemhi, Lost River, and White Cloud Peaks; Salmon River and White Knob Mountain Ranges, headwaters of the Salmon River. Majestic Sawtooth Wilderness Area and Stanley Basin; Middle Fork of the Salmon River in the Idaho Wilderness Area. Stream and lake trout, salmon fishing. Deer, elk, mountain goats, mountain sheep, antelopes, and bears. Stanley Basin scenic drive, riding and hiking trails, wilderness boating and pack trips. **Facilities:** 19 camp and picnic sites. Resorts, hotels, cabins, and dude ranches; commercial packers and guides. **Nearby towns:** Challis, Mackay, Salmon, and Stanley

Clearwater National Forest (1,248,455 acres)
Orofino, Idaho. Highways: Idaho 9, 11. **Attractions:** Famous Lolo Trail, Selway-Bitterroot Wilderness Area. Spring log drive on the Middle Fork and North Fork, Clearwater River; large stands of virgin white pine. Large timber operations. Trout and salmon fishing in back country. Elk, deers, bears. Scenic drives; North Fork and Lewis & Clark Highway. **Facilities:** 8 camp and picnic sites. Motels, cabins, pack trip outfitters available. **Nearby towns:** Kooskia, Lewiston, Orofino, and Pierce, Idaho; Lolo Hot Springs and Missoula, Montana

Coeur d'Alene National Forest (723,217 acres)
Coeur d'Alene, Idaho. Highways: US 10, 10A, 95A. **Attractions:** Lovely Coeur d'Alene Lake, 30 miles long and with 104 miles of shoreline. Cataldo Mission, built in 1846. Coeur d'Alene River; fishing; elk, deer. Rich Coeur d'Alene mining district (zinc, lead, silver), several large sawmills. **Facilities:** 7 camp and picnic sites, 2 picnic only, lookout Pass Winter Sports Area. Resort hotels and cabins. **Nearby towns:** Coeur d'Alene, Kellogg, Spirit Lake, and Wallace, Idaho; Spokane, Washington

Kaniksu National Forest (1,625,383 ac —partly in Montana and Washingt Sandpoint, Idaho. Highways: US 195, 10A, 2; Washington 6. **Attractic** Rugged back country, Selkirk Mount Range. Massive Pend Oreille Lake (L Drive, 107 miles); Priest Lake. Kullysp House, Clark Fork River; Roosev Ancient Grove of Cedars; Chimney Ro Cabinet Mountains Wild Area. L and stream fishing; big game. Sce drives, boating. **Facilities:** 12 camp a picnic sites, 3 swimming sites, 1 wir sports area. Resorts, hotels, lodg cabins. **Nearby towns:** Bonners Fe Clark Fork, Priest River, and Sandpc

Nezperce National Forest (2,195, acres)
Grangeville, Idaho. Highways: US Idaho 9, 13, 14. **Attractions:** Selw Bitterroot Wilderness Area. Seven De Range between Salmon and Sn Rivers, Hells Canyon on the Snake Ri Red River Hot Springs. Historic Elk C Elk, deer, and bears; lake and stre fishing. Hiking and horse trails; wilc ness pack trips. Scenic drives: Loc River, Salmon River, Selway Riv **Facilities:** 6 camp and picnic sites picnic only. Resorts, hotels, cabins, p trip outfitters. **Nearby towns:** Grar ville, Kamiah, Kooskia, and Rigg

Payette National Forest (2,307,205 ac McCall, Idaho. Highways: US Idaho 15. **Attractions:** Idaho Wildern Area. Hells Canyon of Snake Riv 5,500 to 7,900 feet deep, deepest go in the U.S., Payette Lakes Recreatic Area, Seven Devils Mountains. Fish for trout and salmon, 154 fishing lal 1,530 miles of fishing streams. D elk, mountain goats, bighorn sheep, bears. Scenic drives; wilderness tr **Facilities:** 31 camp and picnic si Payette Lake Winter Sports Area. D ranches. **Nearby towns:** Cascade, Cc cil, McCall, New Meadows, and We

Salmon National Forest (1,768,718 ac Salmon, Idaho. Highways: US Idaho 28 **Attractions:** Idaho Wildre Area, Big Horn Crags, historic Le and Clark Trail, Salmon River Cany Fishing; deer, elk, bighorn sheep, mc tain goats, bears, cougars, and antelo Salmon River and Panther Creek fo roads; boat trips on "River of No turn" and Middlefork. **Facilities:** 5 ca and picnic sites, 2 picnic only. D ranches. **Nearby towns:** Leadore Salmon

St. Joe National Forest (866,269 ac St. Maries, Idaho. Highway: US S Idaho 7, 8, 43. **Attractions:** Rug Bitterroot Range of Idaho-Mont divide; St Joe River drainage; Maries River Valley; canyon areas Little North Fork of Clearwater Ri Clearwater-St. Joe divide, Palouse R area; virgin stands of white pine. La

Campers enjoy the stillness of a mountain pond in an Oregon national forest

ber operations. Elk, deer, bears, and untain goats; lake and stream fishing. enic drives along St. Joe River from urce to mouth in Coeur d'Alene Lake. cilities: 8 camp and picnic sites, 1 imming site and North-South Winter orts Area. Dude ranch nearby. bins on St. Joe River. **Nearby towns:** ery, Clarkia, Moscow, Potlatch, and Maries

wtooth National Forest (1,802,680 es—partly in Utah) 'win Falls, Idaho. Highways: US 30N, 5, 93. **Attractions:** Panoramic views Snake River Valley. Sawtooth Wilness Area. Colorful mountains, lakes, veloped hot springs. Sun Valley with four-season opportunities for outdoor orts. "Silent City of Rocks," fantastic mations worn by wind and water. shing; swimming; big-game and use; saddle and pack trips, scenic ves. **Facilities:** 57 camping and pic- sites, 15 picnic only, 1 swimming e, 5 winter sports areas including agic Mountain, Mount Harrison, dier Creek, and Sun Valley. Numer- s dude ranches, camps, and motels. arby towns: Burley, Gooding, Sun ley, and Twin Falls

rghee National Forest (1,666,370 acres artly in Wyoming) it. Anthony, Idaho. Highways: US 26, 89, 91, 191; Idaho 22, 28, 31, 47. **Attractions:** Island Park Reser- r; Grand Canyon of the Snake River; on and Snake Ranges, Big Falls; rth Fork of Snake River; Cave Falls; lls River; Palisades Dam. Lake and eam fishing; bears, deer, elk, and ose. Many riding and hiking trails

into remote mountain country. Scenic drives. **Facilities:** 16 camp and picnic sites, 7 picnic only; Bear Gulch, Moose Creek, and Pine Basin Winter Sports Areas. Resorts, motels, dude ranches, boating facilities, fishing camp. **Nearby towns:** Ashton, Driggs, Dubois, Idaho Falls, Rexburg, Rigby, St. Anthony and Victor, Idaho; Afton and Jackson, Wyoming

ILLINOIS

Shawnee National Forest (211,013 acres)

Harrisburg, Illinois. Highways: US 45, 51; Illinois 1, 3, 34, 127, 144, 145, 146, 151. **Attractions:** Prehistoric stone forts and Indian mounds; interesting rock formations. Much of the Illinois shore of the Ohio River and some of the Mississippi; their confluence nearby at Cairo, Illinois. Stream and river fishing; quail, migratory waterfowl, squirrels, rabbits, foxes, and raccons. Artificial lakes in and adjacent to the national forest provide fishing, boating, and swimming. **Facilities:** 1 camp and picnic site; 24 picnic only 1 swimming sites. Hotels and cabins. **Nearby towns:** Anna, Cairo, Carbondale, Harrisburg, Marion, Metropolis, and Murphysboro, Illinois; Paducah, Kentucky; St. Louis, Missouri

INDIANA

Hoosier National Forest (117,906 acres)

Bedford, Indiana. Highways: US 50, 150; Indiana 37, 46, 62, 64. **Attractions:** Pioneer Mothers Memorial Forest containing Nation's outstanding specimen of black walnut. Final outlet of Lost River; Ten O'Clock Indian Boundary Line crosses the forest. Old trail of migrating buf-

falo between Western Plains and French Lick. Squirrels, foxes, and quail; fishing in the East Fork of the White River, Salt Creek, and the Ohio. Lost and Patoka Rivers for catfish, bass, and bluegill. Scenic drives among spring flowers (dogwood and redbud) and fall coloring. **Facilities:** 1 camp and picnic site, 2 picnic only, 1 swimming site. Hotels and motels. **Nearby towns:** Bedford, Bloomington, Evansville, Jasper, Paoli

KENTUCKY

Cumberland National Forest (458,352 acres)

Winchester, Kentucky. Highways: US 25, 27, 60, 421 and 460. **Attractions:** Western rim of Cumberland Plateau, sandstone cliffs 100 feet high, Red River Gorge, natural rock arches, numerous limestone caves and mineral springs. Cumberland Falls and Natural Bridge State Parks within the national forest. Bass and pike fishing in larger streams. Lake Cumberland created by Wolf Creek Dam provides 250 miles of national-forest shoreline. About 500 miles of fishing streams. Squirrels, deer, cottontails, and upland game birds. **Facilities:** 4 camp and picnic sites, 8 picnic only. Swimming sites at Cumberland Falls and Natural Bridge State Parks; also hotels and cabins. Motels and cottages at the boat docks on Lake Cumberland at confluence of Laurel and Rockcastle Rivers. **Nearby towns:** Boonesboro, Corbin, Lexington

LOUISIANA

Kisatchie National Forest (591,726 acres)

Alexandria, Louisiana. Highways: US

71, 165, 167, 84; Louisiana 19, 21, 28. **Attractions:** Colonial homes; Natchitoches, oldest town in Louisana on Old San Antonio Trail; Stuart Forest Service Nursery, one of the largest pine nurseries in the world. Extensive plantations of longleaf, loblolly, and splash pines. Many bayous and lakes screened with Spanish moss. Fishing in lakes and bayous; deer, quail, and migratory birds; boating, camping, and scenic drives. **Facilities:** 2 camp and picnic sites, 6 picnic only; 4 swimming sites. Hotels. **Nearby towns:** Alexandria, Leesville, Minden, and Winnfield

MICHIGAN

Huron National Forest (414,819 acres)
Cadillac, Michigan. Highways: US 23, 27; Michigan 33, 65, 72, 144, 171. **Attractions:** Lumberman's Monument. A national forest easily reached from heavily populated southern Michigan, northern Ohio, Indiana, and Illinois. Trout fishing in the Au Sable River and smaller streams; deer, small-game, and birds. At eastern edge, Lake Huron with excellent beaches. **Facilities:** 9 camp and picnic sites, 8 picnic only, 2 swimming sites; Au Sable and Silver Valley Winter Sports Areas. Many resorts, hotels, and cabins. **Nearby towns:** Grayling, Harrisville, Mio, Oscoda, and Tawas City

Manistee National Forest (445,775 acres)
Cadillac, Michigan. Highways: US 10, 31, 131; Michigan 20, 37, 46, 55, 63, 82. **Attractions:** Another national forest less than a day's drive from Chicago, South Bend, Detroit, Toledo, and Cleveland. Lake and stream fishing; deer and small game. Good skiing on northern part of the national forest. Many of the lakes, including Lake Michigan, have fine beaches for swimming. Canoeing. **Facilities:** 12 camp and picnic sites, 17 picnic only; 1 swimming site; Caberfae and Manistee Winter Sports Areas. Many resorts, hotels, and cabins. **Nearby towns:** Big Rapids, Cadillac, Ludington, Manistee, Muskegon, and Reed City

Ottawa National Forest (858,352 acres)
Ironwood, Michigan. Highways: US 2, 45; Michigan 28, 35, 64, 73. **Attractions:** Numerous accessible lakes and streams; Bond, Agate, Sturgeon, Conglomerate, George, Sandstone, and Rainbow Falls. Victoria Dam, James Toumey forest Service Nursery, State Fish Hatchery, forest plantations, Porcupine Mt. State Park. Lake and stream fishing, deep-water trolling in Lake Superior, deer and bears. Several winter sports areas nearby. Many scenic drives. **Facilities:** 13 camp and picnic sites, 10 picnic only. 7 swimming sites. Numerous hotels and cabins. **Nearby towns:** Bessemer, Iron River, Ironwood, Ontonagon, Trout Creek, Wakefield, and Waersmeet, Michigan; Duluth, Minnesota

Hiawatha-Marquette National Forests 830,179 acres—two national forests)
Escanaba, Michigan. US 2, 41; Michigan 28, 94, 48, 123. **Attractions:** Lakes Huron, Michigan, and Superior; some shoreline in the national forest. Many smaller lakes among mixed evergreen and hardwood forests. Pictured Rocks on Lake Superior; Mackinac Island country; scenic drives; waterfalls. Lake and stream fishing for trout, bass, northern, and walleyed pike perch; smelt dipping; deer, black bear, ruffed and sharptailed grouse. Canoeing. **Facilities:** 18 camp and picnic sites, 16 picnic only; 3 swimming sites; Gladstone Winter Sports Area. Resorts, hotels, many cabins. Nearby well-equipped State parks. **Adjacent towns:** Escanaba, Gladstone, Manistique, Munising, Rapid River, Saint Ignace, Sault Sainte Marie, and Trout Lake

MINNESOTA

Chippewa National Forest (639,452 acres)
Cass Lake, Minnesota. Highways: US 2, 71, 371; Minnesota 6, 34, 38, 46. **Attractions:** Headwaters of the Mississippi River; Leech Lake, Lake Winnibigoshish, Cass Lake, and hundreds of smaller lakes; stands of virgin red pine. Home and present headquarters of the Chippewa Indians. Lake fishing for walleyes, northern pike, and pan fish; waterfowl and upland game bird; deer and black bear. Hundreds of miles of good roads and scenic drives; swimming, boating, and water sports. Winter sports include skiing, tobogganing, snowshoeing, and ice fishing. **Facilities:** 21 camp and picnic sites, 33 picnic only; 4 swimming sites; Shingobee Winter Sports Area. 300 resorts in and adjacent to the national forest. Hotels, cabins. **Nearby towns:** Bemidji, Blackduck, Cass Lake, Deer River, Grand Rapids, Remer, and Walker

Superior National Forest (1,957,981 acres)
Duluth, Minnesota. Highways: US 53, 61; Minnesota 1, 35, 73, 169. **Attractions:** 5,000 lakes, rugged shorelines, picturesque islands, sand beaches, more than a million acres of virgin forest. Boundary Waters Canoe Area, part of the National Forest Wilderness System. Finest canoe country in the United States here in the land of the French *voyageurs,* along their historic water route to the Northwest. 16 unusual canoe routes in wilderness country. Adjacent Quetico Provincial Park in Canada also maintains a canoe-wilderness character over a large area. Lake and stream fishing, deer. 2 ski areas nearby. Scenic drives: Honeymoon and Ely Buyck Roads, Gunflint and Sawbill Trails. **Facilities:** 185 canoe camp sites, 29 camp and picnic sites, 12 picnic only

Resorts, hotels, cabins outside th wilderness area. **Nearby towns:** Dulut Ely, Grand Marais, International Fal Two Harbors, and Virginia, Minneso Port Arthur and Winnipeg, Canada

MISSISSIPPI

Bienville National Forest (175,657 acre
Jackson, Mississippi. Highways: U 80; Mississippi 35. **Attractions:** Coast Plain second-growth pine and hardwoo forest; numerous forest management d monstration areas. Eighty acres of virg loblolly pine surrounding Bienvi Ranger Station. Quail; fishing. **Fac ities:** 2 camp and picnic sites, 3 p nic only; 1 swimming site. **Near towns:** Jackson and Meridian

DeSoto National Forest (500,335 acr
Jackson, Mississippi. Highways: U 11, 49, 90; Mississippi 26. **Attractio** Site of South Mississippi Gun and D Club field trails. Quails, fishing, boa ing. Ashe Forest Service Nursery. **Fac ities:** 3 camp and picnic sites, 8 pic only; 3 swimming sites. Gulf coa resorts. **Nearby towns:** Biloxi, Gulfpo Hattiesburg, Laurel, and Wiggins

Holly Springs National Forest (143,3 acres)
Jackson, Mississippi. Highways: U 72, 78; Mississippi 7, 15. **Attractio** Intensive erosion control projects. A nual bird-dog field trials at Hol Springs. Quail and small-game. No i proved recreation sites. **Nearby tow** Holly Springs, New Albany, and Oxfc

Homochitto National Forest (189,0 acres)
Jackson, Mississippi. Highways: U 61, 84; Mississippi 33. **Attractions:** O of the finest natural timber growi sites in the United States; numero forest management demonstration are Picturesque eroded loess country ne Natchez. Fishing, swimming. Trai spaces at Clear Springs Recreation Are **Facilities:** 3 picnicking, 1 camping, a 1 swimming site. **Nearby towns:** Broc haven, Gloster, Meadville, and Natche

Tombigbee National Forest (65,232 acre
Jackson, Mississippi. Highways: ▪ 82; Mississippi 8, 15, Natchez Tra Parkway. **Attractions:** Upper Coas Plain pine and hardwood forests, Indi mounds, Davis and Choctaw Lak Natchez Trace Parkway. Deer and qua fishing, boating. **Facilities:** 2 picnickir 1 camping, and 2 swimming sites. Rese lodge and cabins at Choctaw La Nearby towns: Ackerman, Housto Kosciusko, and Tupelo

MISSOURI

Clark National Forest (766, 193 acr
Rolla, Missouri. Highways: US 60, 67; Missouri 8, 17, 21, 32, 49, 72. At tractions: Clear fast-flowing strean Ozark Mountains covered with oak a

pine forests, spring bloom of redbud and dogwood and brilliant fall coloring. Smallmouth bass and other fishing; squirrels, raccoons, and foxes. Black and St. Francis Rivers and others provide hundreds of miles of streams for float trips. Riverbank campsites in places. Several lakes. **Facilities:** 5 camp and picnic sites, 4 picnic only. **Nearby towns:** Fredericktown, Ironton, Piedmont, Poplar Bluff, Potosi, St. Louis, and Salem

Mark Twain National Forest (595,870 acres)

Springfield, Missouri. Highways: US 60, 63, 66, 160; Missouri 5, 14, 19, 39, 76, 87, 95, 125, 148, 173. **Attractions:** Ozark Mountains, numerous caves, rock cairns, and Big Springs. Current and Eleven Point Rivers; hundreds of miles of streams for "John-boat" float trips. Fishing for pan fish, bass, and walleye; deer, quail, and samll-game. Fall Color tours. Several State Parks. **Facilities:** 14 picnic and 6 campsites, 6 swimming sites. Resorts and hotesl. **Nearby towns:** Branson, Doniphan, Springfield, Van Buren, West Plains, and Willow Springs

MONTANA

Beaverhead National Forest (2,131,136 acres)

Dillon, Montana. Highways: US 91; Montana 41, 34, 43, 287. **Attractions:** Anaconda-Pintlar Wilderness Area, Big Hole Battlefield Monument, Sacajawea Memorial Area, Bannack, the first capital of Montana. Tobacco Root, Madison, Gravelly, Snowcrest, and Continental Divide Ranges; Madison, Ruby, Beaverhead, and Big Hole Rivers; alpine lakes. Fishing; deer, elk, moose, antelopes, and bears. Hot springs, scenic drives, wilderness trips. **Facilities:** 28 camp and picnic sites; Rainy Mountain Winter Sports Area. Resorts, hotels, cabins and dude ranches in and near the national forest. **Nearby towns:** Dillon, Ennis, Jackson, Lima, Sheridan, Virginia City, and Wisdom

Bitterroot National Forest (1, 574, 563 acres—partly in Idaho)

Hamilton, Montana. Highways: US 93; Montana 43, 38. **Attractions:** Bitterroot Valley and spectacular Bitterroot Mountains, scores of mountain lakes and hot springs. Ancient Indian hieroglyphics, Saint Mary's Mission and Fort Owen. Selway-Bitterroot Wilderness Area; Anaconda-Pintlar Wilderness Area. Lake and stream fishing; elk, deer, and mountain goats. Bitterroot Valley scenic drives, riding trails, wilderness trips. **Facilities:** 11 camp and picnic sites; Lost Trail Winter Sports Area. Resorts, hotels, cabins, and dude ranches. **Nearby towns:** Corvallis, Hamilton, Missoula, and Stevensville

Custer National Forest (1,171,476 acres —partly in South Dakota)

Billings, Montana. Highways: US 10, 12, 85; Montana 8, 7; South Dakota 8. **Attractions:** Spectacular Red Lodge-Cooke City Highway; snow-clad peaks and alpine plateaus; Granite Peak (12,962 feet), highest point in Montana; hundreds of lakes; Woodbine Falls, 900 feet high; glaciers and ice caverns. Rich fossil beds, Indian hieroglyphics and burial grounds. Beartooth Wilderness Area. Trout fishing, big-game, saddle and pack trips. **Facilities:** 13 camp and picnic sites, 2 picnic only; Willow Creek Winter Sports Area. Resorts, hotels, cabins, and dude ranches. **Nearby towns:** Absarokee, Ashland, Billings, Columbus, Hardin, Laurel, and Red Lodge

Deerlodge National Forest (1,134,639 acres)

Butte, Montana. Highways: US 10, 10A, 91; Montana 38, 41. **Attractions:** Anaconda-Pintlar Wilderness Area, Tobacco Root Mountains, Mount Powell and Flint Creek Range, numerous alpine lakes. Lake and stream fishing; bears, deer, elk, and moose. Riding trails wilderness trips. **Facilities:** 21 camp and picnic sites, 5 picnic only; Cable Mountain and Pipestone Pass Winter Sports Areas. Resorts, hotels, cabins, and dude ranches. **Nearby towns:** Anaconda, Boulder, Butte, Deer Lodge, Phillipsburg, and Whitehall

Flathead National Forest (2,336,378 acres)

Kalispell, Montana. Highways: US 2, 93; Montana 35, 40. **Attractions:** Spectacular geological formations, including massive Chinese Wall and jagged Mission Mountains; hanging valleys; glaciers and scores of glacial lakes. Hungry Horse Dam and Lake. Mission Mountains Wild Area; Bob Marshall Wilderness Area. Fishing; elk, deer, moose, bears, mountain sheep, and goats. Boating; canoeing; riding; scenic drives around Flathead Lake; wilderness trips. **Facilities:** 12 camp and picnic sites, 1 picnic only, 2 swimming sites; Big Mountain Winter Sports Area. Resorts, hotels, cabins, and dude ranches. **Nearby towns:** Belton, Bigfork, Columbia Falls, Coram, Kalispell, and Whitefish

Gallatin National Forest (1,700,139 acres)

Bozeman, Montana. Highways: US 191, 20, 10, 89; Montana 19, 287. **Attractions:** Fertile Gallatin Valley; Crazy Mountains; snow-clad peaks; 11 outstanding waterfalls; more than 200 lakes and thousands of miles of trout streams. Madison River Canyon earthquake area. Spanish Peaks and Absaroka Wild Areas. Lake and stream fishing; bears, moose, elk, and deer. Scenic drives: Gallatin Canyon, Boulder Canyon, and Yankee

Jim Canyon; trail riding and wilderness trips. **Facilities:** 33 camp and picnic sites; Bridger Bowl and Lionhead Winter Sports Areas. Resorts, hotels, cabins, and dude ranches. **Nearby towns:** Big Timber, Bozeman, Gardiner, Livingston, and West Yellowstone

Helena National Forest (966,613 acres)

Helena, Montana. Highways: US 12, 91; Montana 20. **Attractions:** Continental Divide; Big Belt and Elkhorn Mountain Ranges. Boat trip up through Gates of the Mountains Wild Area on Missouri River; old Fort Logan original blockhouse; ghost towns: Diamond City, Marysville, Crow Creek Falls. Lake and stream fishing; deer and elk. Scenic drives. Trout and Beaver Creek Canyons. Hiking and horse trails, wilderness trips. **Facilities:** 6 camp and picnic sites, 2 picnic only; Grass Mountain Winter Sports Area. Resorts, hotels, cabins, and dude ranches. **Nearby towns:** Helena, Lincoln, Townsend, and White Sulphur Srpings

Kootnai National Forest (1,817,975 acres—partly in Idaho)

Libby Montana. Highways: US 2, 93; Montana 37. **Attractions:** Cabinet Mountains Wild Area; Yaak River, Kootenai Canyon, and Fisher River. Lake and stream fishing; black bear and deer. Scenic drives: Yaak River, Kootenai Canyon, Fisher River; riding trails. **Facilities:** 5 camp and picnic sites; Libby and Troy

Lewis and Clark National Forest (1,862,011 acres)

Great Falls, Montana. Highways: US 12, 87, 89, 91; Montana 21, 287. **Attractions:** Bob Marshall Wilderness Area. Chinese Wall and Continental Divide, scenic limestone canyons and rolling mountains with many open parks. Stream and lake fishing; deer, elk, antelopes, grizzly, and black bears. Wilderness trips; riding trails; numerous scenic drives: Kings Hill, Judith River, Crystal Lake, Sun River, and Teton River. **Facilities:** 12 camp and picnic sites; Kings Hill Winter Sports Area. Many resorts, cabins, and dude ranches. **Nearby towns:** Augusta, Choteau, Great Falls, Harlowton, Lewistown, and White Sulphur Springs

Lolo National Forest (2,502,698 acres—partly in Idaho)

Missoula, Montana. Highways: US 10, 10A, 93; Montana 20; Idaho 9. **Attractions:** Selway-Bitterroot Wilderness Area; Rattlesnake, Bitterroot, and Swan Ranges. Clark Fork and Blackfoot Rivers. Stream and lake fishing; grouse, elk, deer, and bears. Wilderness pack trips; scenic drives; Lochsa River, Seeley Lake, Buffalo Park, Rock Creek. Mountain saddle trails, foot trails to a hundred lakes and peaks. **Facilities:** 18 camp and picnic sites, 1 picnic only; 1 swimming site; Snow Park Winter Sports Area. Resorts, dude ranches. **Nearby towns:** Alberton, Drummond, Ovando, Plains, St. Regis, Superior, Thompson Falls, and Missoula (Forest Service Regional Office—also Aerial Fire Depot and Smoke jumper Headquarters)

NEBRASKA
Nebraska National Forest (206,082 acres)
Lincoln, Nebraska. Highways: US 20 83; Nebraska 2. **Attractions:** Bessey Nursery; extensive forest plantations on sand hills; entire forest in game refuge; mule deer; nesting ground of great blue heron, grouse, and prairie chicken. Fishing. **Facilities:** 3 camp and picnic sites, 2 picnic only; 1 swimming site. Hotel accommodations at Broken Bow, Valentine, and Halsey

NEVADA
Humboldt National Forest (2,507,869 acres)
Elko, Nevada. Highways: US 40, 93, 95; Nevada 43, 46. **Attractions:** Wildhorse Reservoir; Owyhee River Canyon; Humboldt, Independence, Ruby, and Santa Rosa Mountains. Spectacular canyons, colorful cliffs, old historic mining camps. Fishing in streams and Wildhorse Reservoir; deer; saddle and pack trips. **Facilities:** 24 camp and picnic sites, 3 picnic only, Ward Mountain Winter Sports Area. Resort and dude ranch at Wildhorse Reservoir; hotels. **Nearby towns:** Ely, Elko, Mountain City, Wells and Winnemucca

Toiyabe National Forest (3,118,966 acres —partly in California)
Reno, Nevada. Highways: US 395, 6, 50, 95; California 4, 108; Nevada 8A, 52, 39, 31, 28, 27, 22. **Attractions:** Lake Tahoe; Nevada Beach Forest Camp historic ghost towns; rugged High Sierra country. Many beautiful lakes and streams. Notable trout fishing. Hoover Wild Area. Big-game; saddle and pack trips. Scenic drives: Mt. Rose, Lake Tahoe, Ebbetts and Sonora Passes; wilderness trips. **Facilities:** 33 camp and picnic sites, 1 swimming site; Kyle Canyon, Lee Canyon, and Reno Ski Bowl Winter Sports Areas. Motels, resorts, dude ranches. **Nearby towns:** Austin, Carson City, Minden, Reno, and Tonopah

NEW HAMPSHIRE
White Mountain National Forest 723,394 acres—partly in Maine)
Laconia, New Hampshire. Highways: US 2, 3, and 302: N.H. 16. **Attractions:** Very popular mountains and forest including a major part of the White Mountains. Mount Washington, 6,288 feet, highest point in New England; Presidential Range; Great Gulf Wild Area; Glen Ellis Falls; Tuckerman Ravine; the

Dolly Copp Recreation Area. Some 650 miles of streams, 39 lakes and ponds, provide brook trout fishing. Deer, bear, and small-games. Scenic drives through famous notches and over mountain highways. Outstanding skiing with spring skiing often lasting into June. Rock climbing; 1,000 miles of foot trails; swimming. **Facilities:** 14 camp and picnic sites, 6 picnic only, 26 shelters and high-country cabins for hikers; 1 swimming area; Wildcat, Tuckermans Ravine, Waterville Valley Winter Sports Areas. Cabins, motels, hotels. **Nearby towns:** Berlin, Conway, Gorham, Lancaster, Littleton, Pinkham Notch

NEW MEXICO
Carson National Forest (1,225,408 acres)
Taos, New Mexico. Highways: US 64; New Mexico 3, 75, 38,. **Attractions:** Massive timbered Sangre de Cristo Mountains and other ranges flanking the upper Rio Grande Valley. Wheeler Peak, 13,151 feet, highest in New Mexico. Pecos Wilderness Area; Wheeler Peak Wild Area; alpine lakes and timberline country. Trout streams, 12,000–13,000-foot peaks. High green valleys with Spanish-speaking villages. Scenic drives, Taos-Questa-Red River-Eagle Nest Loop. Tres Piedras-Langunitas lake country. Santa Barbara Canyon near Penasco. Taos: Home and burial place of Kit Carson; well-known art colony; Taos Indian Pueblo. Near Abiquiu, Thost Ranch, Wildlife Museum. **Facilities:** 34 camp and picnic sites, 1 picnic only. Fine skiing at Red River, Taos Ski Valley (Hondo Canyon), and Sipapu. **Nearby towns:** Chama, Cimarron, Espanola, Farmington, Taos and Tierra Amarilla, New Mexico; Alamosa and Pagosa Springs Colorado

Cibola National Forest (1,696,703 acres)
Albuquerque New Mexico. Highways: US 85, 66, 60. **Attractions:** Magdalena, Manzano, Sandia, San Mateo, and Zuni Mountain Ranges. Mount Taylor, 11,389 feet, and Sandia Crest, 10,700 feet, accessible by car. Deer and antelopes; bighorn sheep often visible at Sandia Crest in summer. Nearby are Pueblo Indian villages, prehistoric ruins, ancient "sky city" of Acoma. Limited fishing at Bluewater and McGaffey Lakes. Scenic drives. **Facilities:** 15 camp and picnic sites; 12 picnic only; La Madera Winter Sports Area in Sandia Mountains. Motels, hotels, dude ranches. **Nearby towns:** Albuquerque, Belen, Bernalillo, Gallup, Grants, Magdalena

Gila National Forest (2,715,520 acres)
Silver City, New Mexico. Highways: US 60, 70, 80, 85, 260; New Mexico 61, 25, 78. **Attractions:** Semidesert to alpine country, most of it very remote and undeveloped. Elevation 4,500 to 10,700 feet. Pack trips into the large

Gila and Black Range Wilderness Areas Mogollon Rim; many prehistoric ruins Lake fishing in Wall Lake and Bea Canyon Reservoir. Stream fishing in the three forks of the Gila, other streams most of it "packing in" to little-use streams. Abundant game; uncrowde big-game; black bears, mule deer, white tailed deer, antelopes, mountain lions turkeys. Scenic drives: Outer Loop Inner Loop; ghost town of Mogollon Riding and hiking trails. **Facilities:** 1! camp and picnic sites, 3 picnic only Some motels, resorts, dude ranches **Nearby towns:** Deming, Las Cruces Lordsburg, Reserve, Silver City, and Truth or Consequences, New Mexico Clifton and Springerville, Arizona

Lincoln National Forest (1,087,855 acres
Alamogordo, New Mexico. Highways US 54, 70, 380; New Mexico 83, 24 37, 48. **Attractions:** White Mountain 12,000 feet (summit is in Mescaler Apache Indian Reservation) with beauti ful scenery, hiking trails. White Moun tain Wild Area. Sacramento, Capitan and Guadalupe Mountain Ranges wit extensive ponderosa pine and fir stands Resort cities of Cloudcroft, Ruidosc Fishing, big-game. Limited winte sports; scenic drives; saddle and pacl trips. Golfing at Ruidoso (7,000 ft.) ani at Cloudcroft (9,000 ft.). **Facilities:** 1 camp and picnic sites, 2 picnic only 1 winter sports area. Resorts, hotels dude ranches organization camp. Near by towns: Alamogordo, Artesia, Capita ("Birthplace of Smokey Bear"), Carls bad, and Roswell, New Mexico; El Pasc Texas

Santa Fe National Forest (1,233,55 acres)
Santa Fe, New Mexico. Highways: U! 285, 85, 64, 84, New Mexico 4, 126 96, 63. **Attractions:** Southern Sangre d Cristo Range including 13,000-foo Truchas Peaks; across Rio Grande t the west, Jemez and San Pedro Ranges 10,000–12,000 feet. Headwaters Pecos Jemez, and Gallinas Rivers; mountai streams and lakes; Pecos Wilderness Area; San Pedro Parks Wild Area. Wilder ness pack trips, saddle trails. A doze living Indian Pueblos nearby, grea vistas, ancient ruins, Spanish missions cliff dwellings. Turkeys, elk, deer ani bears. **Facilities:** 29 camp and picni sites, 9 picnic only. Winters sports a Santa Fe Basin; scenic double chai lift to 11,600 feet, operates summer b oppointment (inquire Santa Fe). Resort: hotels, guest ranches on Pecos River u as far as Cowles, and Jemez River nea Jemez Springs. **Nearby towns:** Albuquer que, Bernalillo, Cuba, Espanola, La Vegas, Pecos, and Santa Fe

NORTH CAROLINA
Croatan National Forest (152,351 acres
Asheville, North Carolina. Highways

S 17, 70; NC. 24, 58. **Attractions:** istoric New Bern, founded 1710; Civil ′ar breastworks. Five large lakes; pine nd swamp hardwoods, 3 miles from ltantic Ocean, Neuse River Estuary. ·eer, bears, turkeys, quail, and migra- ·ry birds; fishing, boating, swimming. acilities: 2 picnic and 2 swimming tes. Resorts and motels. **Nearby towns:** oldsboro, Morehead City, New Bern, nd Wilmington

Iantahala National Forest (448,278 ·res)

Asheville, North Carolina. Highways: ·S 19, 23, 64, 129; N.C. 28, 107. **At- ·ractions:** Fontana, Hiwassee, Sante- ·tlah, Nantahala, Cheoha, Glenville, nd Apalachia Lakes; Fontana Dam, 8 ·sorts, Cullasaja, White Water River, ·ridal Veil, Toxaway, and Dry Falls. ·yce Kilmer Memorial Forest; 60 miles f Appalachian Trail. European wild ·oar, deer; also turkeys and birds. ·outh Appalachian Mountains, famous ·r azaleas and rhododendrons. Lake nd stream fishing for bass and trout. ·liking, swimming, and boating. Scenic ·rives. **Facilities:** 10 cam and picnic ·ites, 15 picnic only; 3 swimming sites. ·ourist and cabin accommodations avail- ble. **Nearby towns:** Bryson City, ·ranklin, Hayesville, Highlands, ·lurphy, and Ribbinsville

·isgah National Forest (479,697 acres)

Asheville, North Carolina. Highways: ·S 19, 23, 25, 64, 70, 221, 276, 321, nd Blue Ridge Parkway. **Attractions:** ·lount Mitchell. 6,674 feet, highest ·oint east of the Mississippi; Linville ·alls and Gorge. Pisgah National Game ·reserve and 5 other cooperative wild- ·fe management areas with deer, bears; ·lso small-game. Craggy Gardens and ·loan Mountain, famous for purple ·hododendron; Appalachian Trail, Trout, ·ass, and perch fishing. Hiking horse- ·ack riding, swimming. Scenic roads nd trails. **Facilities:** 28 camp and pic- ·ic sites, 23 picnic only; 9 swimming ·ites. Resorts and cabins available. **Near- ·y towns:** Brevard, Burnsville, Canton, ·lot Springs, Lenoir, Marion, and ·Vaynesville

·HIO

·Vayne National Forest (106,129 acres)

Ironton and Athens, Ohio (ranger ·tations). Highways: US 21, 23, 33, 35, ·0, 52; Ohio 75, 141, 124, 7, 37. **At- ·ractions:** Particularly beautiful fall ·oloring of hardwoods. Nearby are ·istoric Marietta, Gallipolis, Blen- ·erhasset's Island, and Amesville 'Coonskin Library.'' Old charcoal fur- ·aces. Small-game, fishing on numerous ·treams and lakes. Horseback riding, ·uto tours, scenic lookout points. **Facil- ·ties:** 1 camp and picnic site, 3 picnic ·nly; 1 swimming site. Overnight ac- ·ommodations at numerous motels,

tourist homes, and hotels along the main highways and at the larger towns. **Near- by towns:** Athens, Ironton, Jackson, Marietta. Forest Supervisor's office: Bed- ford, Indiana

OREGON

Deschutes National Forest (1,659,368 acres)

Bend, Oregon. Highways: US 126, 97, 26, 20. **Attractions:** Beautiful southern Cascade Range. Snow-clad peaks, ice caves, waterfalls, and over 300 lakes; lava caves; Deschutes River; Newberry Crater; scenic Century Drive; Bend Forest Service Nursery; historic Wil- lamette Military Road; Mount Jefferson Wild Area and Three Sisters Wilderness Area. Sections of Oregon Skyline Trail from Mount Jefferson to Mount Thielsen. Mount Washington and Diamond Peak Wild Areas, and Lava Cast Forest Geological Area in a ponderosa pine setting. Rainbow trout fishing, deer. Scenic drives, saddle and pack trips, skiing. **Facilities:** 76 camp and picnic sites, 11 picnic only, 7 swimming sites; 1 winter sports area. Dude ranches, motels, and resorts. **Nearby towns:** Bend, Chemult, Redmond, and Sisters

Fremont National Forest (1,254,595 acres)

Lakeview, Oregon. Highways: US 395; Oregon 66, 31. **Attractions:** Indian paint- ings and writings. Protected herds of antelope; Oregon Desert; Gearhart Mountain Wild Area. Drier inland for- ests. Deer and birds, winter sports. Abert geologic fault east of Lake Abert, second second largest vertical fault in world. **Facilities:** 21 camp and picnic sites; 1 winter sports area. Motels. **Nearby towns:** Bly, Chemult, Klamath Falls, Lakeview, and Paisley

Malheur National Forest (1,410c548 acres

John Day, Oregon. Highways: US 26, 395. **Attractions:** Mountains, fishing streams, fossil beds of prehistoric plants and animals, extensive stands of ponderosa pine. Strawberry Mountain Wild Area. Steelhead and rainbow trout fishing; elk and deer. Cabin of Joaquin Miller. Scenic drives, saddle and pack trips. **Facilities:** 39 camp and picnic sites; 2 winter sports areas. Motels, cabins in and near the national forest. **Nearby towns:** Burns, Dayville, John Day, and Prairie City

Mount Hood National Forest (1,115,344 acres)

Portland, Oregon. Highways: US 30, 99E, 26. **Attractions:** Beautiful Mount Hood with Timberline Lodge; Multno- mah Falls; glaciers, lakes, hot springs, and flower-filled alpine meadows. Mount Hood and Mount Jefferson Wild Areas. Mount Hood Loop and Columbia Gorge scenic drives; Oregon Trail route. North

end of Oregon Skyline Trail, a segment of the Pacific Crest Trail system. Stream and lake fishing, swimming, saddle and pack trips, huckleberry picking, winter sports. **Facilities:** 110 camp and pic- nic sites, 8 picnic only; 7 winter sports areas. Timberline Lodge, Multnomah Falls Lodge, and other resorts in and near the national forest. **Nearby towns:** Gresham, Hood River, Maupin, Oregon City, and Portland

Ochoco National Forest (845,876 acres) Prineville, Oregon. Highways: US 26, 126, 97. 20. **Attractions:** Parklike ponderosa pine forest, many beaver colonies. Fort Watson and Camp Maury, frontier-day army posts; scenes of early- day range wars. Steins Pillar, geological landmark. Trout fishing, elk and deer, scenic drives. **Facilities:** 28 camp and picnic sites. Motels, cabins. **Nearby towns:** Bend, Burns, and Prineville

Rogue River National Forest (839,290 acres—partly in California)

Medford, Oregon. Highways: US 99, 199; Oregon 62, 66. **Attractions:** Beauti- ful Rogue River, lakes, trout streams, and waterfalls; extensive sugar pine and Douglas-fir forests; mammoth sugar pine roadside specimen. Mountain Lakes Wild Area. Table Rock, site of bloody war with Rogue River Indians. Rainbow and steelhead trout fishing, deer and migratory birds. Oregon Skyline Trail extends through national forest from Crater Lake almost to California line. Scenic drives, saddle and pack trips, skiing. **Facilities:** 47 camp and picnic sites, 3 picnic only, 1 swimming site; Onion Creek and Tomahawk Winter Sports Areas. Resorts, motels, cabins. **Nearby towns:** Ashland, Grants Pass, Klamath Falls, and Medord

Siskiyou National Forest (1,046,607 acres —partly in California)

Grants Pass, Oregon. Highways: US 99, 101, 199. **Attractions.** Beautiful Oregon coast, famous salmon fishing in lower Rogue River Gorge; early-day gold camps. Home of rare species, including Port-Orford-cedar, "Oregon myrtle," rock rhododendron, Brewer weeping spruce, and Saddler oak. Profuse growth of wild lilac, rhododendron, azaleas, and pitcher plants. Kalminopsis Wild Area. Cutthroat and steelhead trout and salmon fishing. Deer, bears, and cougars. Boat trips up the pristine Rogue, saddle and pack trips, scenic drives. **Facilities:** 18 camp and picnic sites, 2 picnic only. Resorts, outfitters, and cabins in and near the national forest. **Nearby towns:** Brooking, Gold Beach, Grants Pass, Port Orford, and Powers

Siuslaw National Forest (621,044 acres) Corvallis, Oregon. Highways: US 20, 99, 101; Oregon 34. **Attractions:** Heavy stands of Sitka spruce, western hemlock, cedar, and Douglas-fir; pitcher plants, rhododendron, azaleas. Bordered by Pacific Ocean; 34 miles of public beach, shoreline, and sand dunes, including Cape Perpetua Overlook. Marys Peak, ghighest in the Coast Range, with road to camp sites near summit. Ocean, lake, and stream fishing; deer, bears, cougars, and migratory birds. Swimming, boating, clam digging, scuba diving, scenic drives. **Facilities:** 23 camp and picnic sites, 4 picnic only. Resorts, motels. **Nearby towns:** Corvallis, Eugene, Florence, Mapleton, Reedsport, Tillamook, and Waldport

Umatilla National Forest (1,075,938 acres—partly in Washington)
Pendleton, Oregon. Highways: US 30, 395, 410; Oregon 11. **Attractions:** Skyline trip along summit of Blue Mountains on the Kendall-Skyline Forest Road. Spectacular views of Touchet and Wenaha River Canyons. Extensive stands of ponderosa pine. Oregon Trail route; hot sulfur springs. Stream fishing for steelhead and rainbow trout; elk, deer, pheasants, and other birds. Saddle and pack trips, scenic drives, skiing. **Facilities:** 44 camp and picnic sites; Tollgate-Spout Springs Winter Sports Area. Hotels, resorts, dude ranches. **Nearby towns:** La Grande and Pendleton, Oregon; Clarkston, Pomeroy, Waitsburg, and Walla Walla, Washington

Umpqua National Forest (978,704 acres)
Roseburg, Oregon. Highways: US 99; Oregon 42. **Attractions:** Spectacular North Umpqua Cataracts, Steamboat and Watson Falls, Umpqua River; a little Matterhorn, Mount Thielsen, rising above beautiful Diamond Lake. Unique stands of incense-cedar. Steelhead and rainbow trout fishing; deer, bears, cougars. Oregon Skyline Trail from Windigo Pass to Crater Lake. Scenic drives, saddle and pack trips, skiing. **Facitilities:** 39 camp and picnic sites, 1 picnic only, 4 swimming sites; Taft Mountain Winter Sports Area. Resorts, dude ranches, motels. **Nearby towns:** Canyonville, Cottage Grove

Wallowa-Whitman National Forests (2,285,207 acres—two national forests)
Baker, Oregon. Highways: US 26, 30; Oregon 7, 86, 82. **Attractions:** Snow-capped peaks; Wallowa and many other lakes; glaciers; alpine meadows and rare wild flowers; Minam River, famous fishing stream. Grand spectacle of Snake River and Imnaha Canyons from Grizzly Ridge Road and Hat Point. Blue and Wallow Mountains, Anthony Lakes, Eagle Cap Wilderness Area. Stream and lake trout fishing; elk, deer, and bears. Saddle and pack trips, scenic drives. **Facilities:** 40 camp and picnic sites, 2 picnic only; Little Alps Winter Sports Area. Resorts, dude ranches, motels. **Nearby towns:** Baker, Enterprise, Halfway, La Grande, and Union

Wilamette National Forest (1,666,036 acres)
Eugene, Oregon. Highways: US 126, 99, 20; Oregon 58, 22. **Attractions:** Most heavily timbered national forest in the United States. Snowcapped peaks, lakes, waterfalls, and hot springs; McKenzie Pass Highway and lava beds. Historic Willamette Military Road. Three Sisters Wilderness Area including extensive volcanic formations; Mount Jefferson, Mount Washington, and Diamond Peak Wild Areas. Sections of Oregon Skyline Trail from Mount Jefferson south to Maiden Peak. Stream and lake fishing, deer and bears. Scenic drives, saddle and pack trips, winter sports. **Facilities:** 69 camp and picnic sites, 2 winter sports areas. Motels, cabins, pack trip outfitters. **Nearby towns:** Albany, Eugene, Lebanon, and Salem

PENNSYLVANIA

Allegheny Nationa Forest (470,197 acres)
Warren, Pennsylvania. Highways: US 6, 62, 219. **Attractions:** Allegheny Plateau country; Hearts Content and Tionesta virgin timber stands; 260 miles of trout streams, 85 miles of bass fishing in Allegheny and Clarion Rivers, 32 acres of lake fishing in Twin Lakes and Beaver Meadows Pond; deer, turkeys, and bears; scenic drives. **Facilities:** 7 camp and picnic sites, 4 picnic only in Cook Forest and Allegheny State Parks. **Nearby towns:** Bradford, Kane, Ridgway, Sheffield, Tionesta, and Warren

SOUTH CAROLINA

Francis Marion National Forest (245,650 acres)
Columbia, South Carolina. Highways: US 17, 52; S.C. 41, 45. **Attractions:** Ruins and remnants of early colonial settlements and plantations. Many "Carolina bays," small lakes, believed to be caused by meteors; picturesque moss-hung oaks, flowering yucca, dogwood, redbud, and holly. Bass and other fishing; alligators, deer, turkeys, and quail. Boating. **Facilities:** 3 camp and picnic sites, 10 picnic only. Hotels and motels near the national forest. **Nearby towns:** Charleston, Georgetown, McClellanville, and Moncks Corner

Sumter National Forest (341,624 acres)
Columbia, South Carolina. Highways: US 25, 76, 123, 176, 221, 378; S.C. 28, 72, 107. **Attractionsl:** Piedmont and Blue Ridge Mountains rank growth of rhododendron and other flowering shrubs; Walhalla Trout Hatchery. Trout and some bass fishing; quail, scenic drives. **Facilities:** 20 picnicking, 2 camp and picnic sites, 2 swimming sites. Hotels and motels near the national forest. **Nearby towns:** Abbeville, Clinton, Edgefield, Greenwood, Newberry, Union, and Walhalla

SOUTH DAKOTA

Black Hills National Forest (1,045,44 acres—partly in Wyoming)
Custer, South Dakota. Highways: U 14, 16, 85, 385. **Attractions:** Spectacula canyons and waterfalls, crystal caves Historic gold rush area where famou early-day characters lived and wer buried, including Calamity Jane, Wil Bill Hickok, Deadwood Dick, an Preacher Smith; famous Homestak Mine. Harney Peak, highest east o Rocky Mountains. Mount Rushmor National Memorial. Lake and strean fishing; deer and elk. Boating, saddl trips, and scenic drives. **Facilities:** 2 camp and picnic sites, 45 picnic only 2 swimming sites, 1 winter sports area Motels and dude ranches in and nea the national forest. **Nearby towns:** Bell Fourche, Custer, Deadwood, Edgemon Hote Springs, and Rapid City, Sout Dakota; Newcastle and Sundance Wyoming

TENNESSEE

Cherokee National Forest (595,097 acres
Cleveland, Tennessee. Highways: U 411, 421, 11, 19E, 19W, 25, 64; Stat 68, 67, 70. **Attractions:** Rugged moun tain country cut by river gorges. Beaut ful scenery, mountains of rhododendro and laurel blooming in season. Lak and stream fishing, rainbow and broo trout. Small and big game, includin wild boar. Hiking, boating, swimming Ducktwon Cooper Basin, one of th Nation's worst examples of deforestatio through air pollution, with consequen erosion. **Facilities:** 17 camp and picni sites, 27 picnic only; 9 swimming sites Hotels and tourist cabins in nearby towns] **Nearby towns:** Cleveland, Erwin Etowah, Greeneville, Johnson City Madisonville, Mountain City, Newport Parksville, and Tellico Plains

TEXAS

Angelina National Forest (154,392 acres
Lufkin, Texas. Highways: US 59, 69 Texas 147. **Attractions:** Flat to rollin sandy hills with longleaf pine-heardwoo forest along river bottom. Angelina Rive and many overflow lakes, Boykin Lake Bass and cat fishing in rivers and lakes quail and doves. **Facilities:** 2 camp an picnic sites, 3 picnic only; 1 swimmin site. **Nearby towns:** Jasper, Lufkin an San Augustine

Davy Crockett National Forest (161,55 acres)
Lufkin, Texas. Highways: US 287 Texas 7, 94, 103. **Attractions:** Flat, shor leaf-loblolly pine woods; hardwoods i bottoms; timber management demon stration area at Ratcliff Lake. Bass an cat fishing in rivers and lakes; dee **Facilities:** 2 camp and picnic sites, picnic only; and 1 swimming site. Nea by towns: Alto, Crockett, Groveton

A young deer, antlers in velvet, wades in a national forest brook

Sabine National Forest (183,842 acres) Lufkin, Texas. Highways: US 96; Texas 21, 87. **Attractions:** Southern pine and hardwood forest, Sabine River and overflow lakes, Boles Field Fox Hunt Area. Bass and cat fishing in river and lakes; foxes. **Facilities:** 2 camp and picnic sites, 3 picnic only; 1 swimming site. **Nearby towns:** Center, Hemphill, Jasper, and San Augustine

Sam Houston National Forest (158,204 acres) Lufkin, Texas. Highways: US 59, 75, 190; Texas 105, 150. **Attractions:** Flat, shortleaf-loblolly pine woods, hardwoods in bottom, numerous lakes and small streams; part of "Big Thicket" area. Bass and cat fishing in rivers and lakes. **Facilities:** 2 camp and picnic sites, 3 picnic only; 1 swimming site. **Nearby towns:** Cleveland, Conroe, and Huntsville

UTAH

Ashley National Forest (1,282,829 acres) Vernal, Utah. Highways: US 30, 40; Utah 44. **Attractions:** East half of Uinta Range, Kings Peak, 13,498 feet, highest point in Utah; Red Gorge of the Green River, 1,500 feet deep; exposed geological formations a billion years old; site of Flaming Gorge dam scheduled for completion in 1962; High Uintas Wilderness Area, mostly above 10,000 feet; numerous scenic gorges, natural erosion formations. Lake and stream fishing; big-game, including deer, elk, and antelopes. Riding trails, wilderness pack trips. **Facilities:** 33 camp and picnic sites, 3 picnic only; 1 winter sports site. Resorts, motels, dude ranches. **Nearby towns:** Green River and Rock Springs, Wyoming; Duchesne, Manila, Roosevelt, and Vernal, Utah

Cache National Forest (651,909 acres —partly in Idaho) Longan, Utah. Highways: US 30S, 89, 91; Utah 39. **Attractions:** Rugged mountains, Bear River and Wasatch Ranges, Minnetonka Cave, Logan and Ogden Canyons, Monte Cristo Mountain. Bear Lake nearby. Fishing; deer and elk. Scenic drives, riding and hiking trails. **Facilities:** 46 camp and picnic sites, 17 picnic only; Beaver Mountain and Snow Basin Winter Sports Areas. **Nearby towns:** Brigham, Logan, and Ogden, Utah; Montpelier, Preston, and Soda Springs, Idaho

Dixie National Forest (1,839,547 acres) Cedar City, Utah. Highways: US 91, 89; Utah 14, 18, 24. **Attractions:** Red Canyon, Panguitch and Navajo Lakes, Pine Valley Mountains, Boulder Top Plateau and its many lakes not accessible by road. Table Cliff Point with vista into 4 States (Colorado, Arizona, Nevada, and Utah). Spectacularly colored cliffs. Deer, elk, and cougars; lake and stream fishing. **Facilities:** 13 camp and picnic sites, 8 picnic only; Cedar Canyon Winter Sports Area. Resorts, motels, dude ranches. **Nearby towns:** Cedar City, Enterprise, Escalante, Panguitch, Parowan, and St. George, Utah; Las Vegas, Nevada

Fishlake National Forest (1,415,673 acres) Richfield, Utah. Highways: US 50—6, 89, 91. Utah 10, 13, 24. **Attractions:** Beaver Mountains, Thousand Lake Mountain Scenic Area. Fish Lake, Petrifield Wood Scenic Area. Lake and stream fishing; big-game, including deer and elk. Scenic drives: Beaver Canyon, Wayne Wonderland, Fish Lake-Salina, Marysvale-Belknap, and others. **Facilities:** 24 camping and picnic sites, 5 picnic only. Resorts, hotels, and motels.

Nearby towns: Beaver, Delta, Fillmore, Kanosh, Loa, Monroe, Richfield

Manti-La Sal National Forest (1,237,128 acres—partly in Colorado) Price, Utah. Highways: US 89, 50—6, 160; Utah 10, 29, 31, 46, 95. **Attractions:** Wasatch Plateau; Skyline Road penetrates high alpine meadows and sylvan glades; unique geology, Indian hieroglyphics and cliff dwellings. World's largest aspen trees. La Sal and Abajo Mountains. Fishing; deer and elk. Scenic drives, riding and hiking trails, limited skiing. **Facilities:** 15 camp and picnic sites, 4 picnic only; Bluebell Flat Winter Sports Area. **Nearby towns:** Blanding, Ferron, Huntington, Manti, Moab, Monticello, Mount Pleasant

Uinta National Forest (774,721 acres) Provo, Utah. Highways: US 40, 50, 89, 91, 189. **Attractions:** Cool high mountains rising out of desert. Near Provo, deep canyons with spectacular waterfalls cutting through upthrust Wasatch limestone. Timpanogos Cave; Alpine Scenic Highway around Mount Timpanogos; Nebo Scenic Loop Road; maple, aspen, and oak make brilliant color landscapes in fall. Fishing in mountain streams; deer and elk; 6-mile hiking trail to top of 12,000-foot Mount Timpanogos. **Facilities:** 42 camp and picnic sites, 6 picnic only; 2 winter sports areas; 4 valley view overlook points. Hotesl, motels. **Nearby towns:** American Fork, Heber, Nephi, Provo, and Spanish Fork

Wasatch National Forest (827,441 acres —partly in Wyoming) Salt Lake City, Utah. Highways: US 30S, 40, 89, 91, 189; Utah 35, 150, 152, 210, 65, 36. **Attractions:** Big cool mountains on the city's doorstep; rugged back country; Wasatch, Uinta, Stansbury,

Onaqui Mountain Ranges, High Uintas Wilderness Area, with 12–13,000-foot peaks. Mirror Lake; Grandaddy Lakes; Bridger Lake; many others; picnic sites in Mill Creek and Big Cottonwood Canyons. Lake and stream fishing, deer and wlk. Boating, swimming; riding and hiking trails, wilderness trips, outstanding skiing, skating, and mountain climbing. **Facilities:** 51 camp and picnic sites, 20 picnic only; 4 winter sports areas including the famous developments at Alta and Brighton. Numerous resorts, motels, and dude ranches. **Nearby towns:** Heber, Kamas, Murray, Ogden, Provo, and Salt Lake City, Utah; Evanston, Wyoming.

VERMONT
Green Mountain National Forest 230,954 acres)

Rutland, Vermont. Highways: US 4, 7. **Attractions:** Rugged mountains, scenery, picturesque valleys, quaint New England villages. Green Mountain Range traversed by the "Long Trail." Champlain Valley and points of historic interest such as famous battleground of Revolutionary and French and Indian Wars. Winter sports; scenic drives; hiking and bridle trails. Big and small game; principal game species are deer, ruffed grouse, rabbits, and black bears. Fishing in some 400 miles of streams and 30 lakes and ponds. **Facilities:** 8 camp and picnic sites (including 5 Adirondack shelters on Long Trail), 2 picnic only, 1 swimming site; Mount Snow and Sugarbush Winter Sports areas. Summer resorts and famous New England inns, hotels, and cabins. **Nearby towns:** Brandon, Burlington, Manchester, Middlebury, Rochester, and Rutland

VIRGINIA
George Washington National Forest (1,002,167 acres—partly in West Virginia)

Harrisonburg, Virginia. Highways: US 50, 11, 220, 211, 33, 60, 29; Virginia 42, 259. **Attractions:** Rugged mountainous terrain with elevations up to 4,500 feet; Blue Ridge, Shenandoah, Allegheny, and Massanutten Ranges. Outstanding scenery: Crabtree Falls, limestone caverns, Lost River sinks, Devils Garden, Trout Run sinks, and other unusual geological sites. Duncan, Bald, High, Reddish, and Elliott Knobs, Shenandoah and Warm Springs Valleys. Civil War iron furnaces. Sherando Lake Camp Site, with 20-acre swimming and fishing lake. Trout and bass fishing, 208 miles of cold-water fishing streams. Black bears, deer, turkeys, grouse, and squirrels. Panoramic views, scenic drives, Blue Ridge Parkway and 391 miles of foot trails. **Facilities:** 9 camp and picnic sites, 7 picnic only; 2 swimming sites. Hotels, resorts, and numerous small cabins available. Many secondary roads. **Nearby towns:** Luray, Harrisonburg,

Staunton, and Winchester, Virginia; Franklin and Moorefield, West Virginia; Washington, D.C.

Jefferson National Forest (542,725 acres)

Roanoke, Virginia. Highways: US 11, 220, 21, 52, 23, 58. **Attractions:** Blue Ridge Mountains; Mount Rogers, 5,719 feet, highest in Virginia. Transitional zone between northern and southern flora; rhododendrons. Glenwood and Roaring Run Civil War iron furnaces; Appalachian Trail; Blue Ridge Parkway. More than 200 miles of fishing streams, 3 fishing lakes. Principal game species: White-tailed deer, grouse, squirrels, bears, raccoons, and elk. **Facilities:** 4 camp and picnic sites, 60 picnic only; 2 swimming sites. Resorts, hotels, and cabins. Network of good secondary roads. **Nearby towns:** Bristol, Bluefield, Lexington, Marion, Radford, Roanoke, and Wytheville

WASHINGTON
Colville National Forest (928,232 acres)

Colville, Washington. Highways: US 395; Washington 22, 6, 4, 3P. **Attractions:** Roosevelt Lake, 151 miles long, 82,000 cares, Grand Coulee Dam, largest masonry structure in the world. Scenic drives. Old misson near Kettle Falls. Water transportation from Roosevelt Lake to Arrow Lakes in Canada. Huckleberries and mushrooms. Lake and stream fishing: Thomas, Swan, Sullivan Lakes, and others. **Facilities:** 16 camp and picnic sites; 2 swimming sites. Chewelah Peak Winter Sports Area. Resorts and cabins. **Nearby towns:** Chewelah, Colville, and Republic, Washington; Grand Forks, British Columbia, Canada

Gifford Pinchot National Forest (1,263,380 acres)

Vancouver, Washington. Highways: US 99, 830. **Attractions:** Mount Adams, 12,300 feet, reached by scenic Evergreen Highway; Spirit Lake, many other lakes; snowcapped peaks; Mineral Springs. Wind River Forest Nursery. Goat Rocks and Mount Adams Wild Areas. Lake and stream trout fishing- deer and bears; historic Indian huckleberry fields. Cascade Crest Rrail extends through the national forest. Spectacular auto tours, saddle and pack trips, mountain climbing, winter sports. **Facilities:** 54 camp and picnic sites, 2 picnic only; 1 swimming site. Resorts, motels, cabins. **Nearby towns:** Castle Rock, Morton, Stevenson, Vancouver, and White Salmon

Mount Baker National Forest (1,818,283 acres)

Bellingham, Washington. Highways: US 99, Washington 1, 17A. **Attractions:** Superb mountain scenery; snowcapped peaks, including Glacier Peak; numerous glaciers; alpine lakes; heavy stands of Douglas-fir up to 200 feet in height.

North Cascade Wilderness Area. Moun Baker Recreation Area featuring bot summer and winter recreation. Segment of Cascade Crest Trail from Harts Pas to Glacier Peak. Steelhead and rainbo trout fishing; deer and bears, skiing saddle and pack trips, mountain climb ing. **Facilities:** 51 camp and picnic site 3 picnic only; Mount Baker and Moun Pilchuck Winter Sports Areas. Hotel resorts; experienced guides. **Nearb towns:** Bellingham, Darrington, Everet and Granite Falls

Okanogan National Forest (1,520,34 acres)

Okanogan, Washington. Highways: U 97; Washington 16. **Attractions:** Alpin meadows, snow peaks, and glaciers. Cas cade Crest Trail, a segment of th Pacific Crest Trail system, originates a Canadian boundary and extends south ward to Harts Pass. North Cascad Wilderness Area. Lake and stream fish ing, boating, saddle and pack trip mountain climbing, winter sports. **Faci ities:** 52 camp and picnic sites, 1 pic nic only, 2 swimming sites; Loup Wint Sports area. Dude ranches, motels. Nea by towns: Brewster, Okanoga Tonasket, and Twisp

Olympic National Forest (621,744 acre

Olympia, Washington. Highways: U 99, 410, 101. **Attractions:** Dense ra forests, big trees, spectacular sno peaks, scores of lakes and streams. Fis ing includes salmon and steelhead trou deer, bears, cougars, and elk. Scen drives; saddle and pack trips. **Facilitie** 14 camp and picnic sites, 2 picnic onl 2 swimming sites. Resorts, motels, du ranches. **Nearby towns:** Aberdee Olympia, Port Angeles, Quilcene, ar Shelton

Snoqualmie National Forest (1,207,8 acres)

Seattle, Washington. Highways: U 99, 10, 410, 2. **Attractions:** Snoqualm Falls, 250 feet high; scenic Chinook ar White Pass Highways; giant Dougla firs; snow peaks, lakes, fishing stream Sections of Cascade Crest Trail fro Cady Pass to Goat Rocks. Mather Mem rial Parkway, Goat Rocks Wild Are Stream and lake fishing, includir salmon and steelhead trout; black-taile and mule deer, bears, and elk. Scen drives, saddle and pack trips, skiin **Facilities:** 100 camp and picnic site Snoqualmie Pass and White Pass Wi ter Sports Areas. Motels and outfitter locally avialable. **Nearby towns:** C Elum, Everett, Seattle, Tacoma, ar Yakima

Wenatchee National Forest (1,728,08 acres)

Wenatchee, Washington. Highwa US 10, 2, 97. **Attractions:** Lake Chela 55 miles long, between precipito mountain ranges; lake bottom 389 fe elow sea level. Snowcapped peaks, kes, alpine meadows, rare wild flowers Tumwater Botanical Area; fishing reams; Lake Wenatchee. Stream and out fishing; deer and bears. Cascade rest Trail between Rainy Pass and lowout Mountain. Scenic drives, Lake helan boat trip, saddle and pack trips, inter sports. **Facilities:** 93 camp and icnic sites, 4 picnic only; 6 winter ports areas. Motels and dude ranches. **earby towns:** Cashmere, Chelan, Cle lum, Ellensburg, Leavenworth, and enatchee

VEST VIRGINIA

Monongahela National Forest (805,668 cres)

Elkins, West Virginia. Highways: US 3, 60, 219, 220, and 250. **Attractions:** ppalachian and Allegheny Mountains; pruce Knob, 4,860 feet, highest in West irginia; Blackwater Canyon and 60- oot falls; spectacular Seneca Rocks on istoric Seneca Indian Trail. Botanically urious Cranberry Glades; rhododen- rons in early July; unexplored limestone aves; beaver colonies. Parsons Forest Jursery, Smoke Hole rugged mountain cenery. Some 1,900 miles of trout and ass fishing streams; deer, turkeys, squir- els, bears, grouse, and other game. wimming, horseback riding, scenic rives. Manmade lakes at Spruce Knob, ummit, and Sherwood offer trout and ass fishing with good camp sites near- y. **Facilities:** 21 camp and picnic sites, 5 picnic only; 6 swimming sites. Tourist omes and motels. **Nearby towns:** harleston, Elkins, Lewisburg, Peters- urg

VISCONSIN

Chequamegon National Forest (827,027 cres)

Park Falls, Wisconsin. Highways: US , 8, 63; Wisconsin 13, 64, 70, 77, 182. **Attractions:** Hundreds of large and small akes. Pine, spruce, and balsam forests; xtensive jack pine plantations. Lake nd stream fishing, particularly for nuskellunge; deer and small game. Canoe travel on Flambeau and Chip- ewa Rivers; skiing. **Facilities:** 9 camp nd picnic sites, 14 picnic only; 5 swim- ning sites; 1 winter sports area. Resorts nd cabins. **Nearby towns:** Ashland, Eau Claire, Hayward, Medford, Park Falls, uperior, and Washburn

Nicolet National Forest (640,075 acres)

Park Falls, Wisconsin. Highways: US , 8, 63; Wisconsin 13, 64, 70, 77, 182. **Attractions:** Hundreds of large and small akes. Pine, spruce, and balsam forests; xtensive jack pine plantations. Lake nd stream fishing, particularly for nuskellunge, pike, bass, and trout. Deer, ears, grouse, and ducks. Swimming; oating; canoe trips; snowshoeing and kiing. **Facilities:** 19 camp and picnic

sites; 14 picnic only; 7 swimming sites. Sheltered Valley Ski Area. Numerous resorts and private cabins on private lands within and near the national forest. **Nearby towns:** Eagle River, Green Bay, Marinette, and Rhinelander

WYOMING

Bighorn National Forest (1,113,597 acres)

Sheridan, Wyoming. Highways: US 14, 16, 87. **Attractions:** Bighorn Moun- tains, snowcapped peaks, glaciers; more than 300 lakes. Curious prehistoric Indian Medicine Wheel on Medicine Mountain; Indian battlefields. Cloud Peak Wild Area. Fishing; elk, deer, bears, and ducks. Saddle and pack trips; scenic drives. **Facilities:** 60 camp and picnic sites, 14 picnic only. Motels and dude ranches in and near the national forest. **Nearby towns:** Buffalo, Greybull, Lovell, Sheridan, and Worland

Bridger National Forest (1,699,059 acres)

Kremmerer, Wyoming. Highways: US 26, 89, 189, 187, 30A. **Attractions:** Salt River, Wyoming, and Wind River Moun- tain Ranges, live glaciers, Bridger Wilder- ness Area; Gannett Peak, highest in Wyoming at 13,785 feet. Lots of remote country. Lake and stream fishing; bears, moose, elk, mountain sheep, and deer. Scenic drives: Pinedale Skyline Drive, Greys River Road. Wilderness trips. **Facilities:** 24 camp and picnic sites, 2 picnic only; 1 swimming site; Divide and Surveyor Park Winter Sports Areas. Resorts, hotels, cabins, and dude ranches. **Nearby towns:** Afton and Pine- dale

Medicine Bow National Forest (1,063,537 acres)

Laramine, Wyoming. Highways: US 30; Wyoming 120, 230. **Attractions:** Medicine Bow, Sierra Madre, Laramie, and Pole Mountains. Many lakes and fishing streams; numerous beaver colonies. Fishing; deer. Saddle and pack trips; scenic drives. **Facilities:** 23 camp and picnic sites, 25 picnic only; 3 winter sports areas. Motels and dude ranches in and near the national forest. **Nearby towns:** Cheyenne, Encampment, and Laramie

Shoshone National Forest (2,429,510 acres)

Cody, Wyoming. Highways: US 14, 20, 12, 287. **Attractions:** Rugged Absaroka Mountains and Beartooth Plateau, Wind River Range with per- petual snow; Gannett Peak, 13,785 feet, highest in Wyoming; largest glaciers in Rocky Mountains; hundreds of lakes. Glacier, Stratified, and North and South Absaroka Wilderness Areas; Popo Agie Wild Area. Fishing; Mountain sheep, ilk, moose, deer, antelopes, black and grizzly bears, and game birds. Saddle and pack trips. Scenic drives: Red Lodge –Cooke City Highway, Sunlight Basin

Road, Cody–Yellowstone Road, Togwotee Pass Road. **Facilities:** 34 camp and picnic sites, 2 picnic only; 1 winter sports area. Motels and dude ranches in and near the national forest. **Near- by towns:** Cody, Dubois, and Lander, Wyoming; Cooke City and Red Lodge, Montana

Teton National Forest (1,700,766 acres)

Jackson, Wyoming. Highways: US 98, 187, 26, 287; Wyoming 22, 1. **Attrac- tions:** Unspoiled scenic back country famous for big-game herds. Gros Ventre Slide; Gros Ventre, Teton, and Wind River Ranges; Continental Divide. Teton Wilderness Area; famous Fackson Hole country. Outstanding skiing; stream, lake fishing; moose, elk, deer, moun- tain sheep, grizzly bears. **Scenic drives:** Hoback Canyon, Snake River Canyon, Wind River Highway. **Facilities:** 4 camp and picnic sites, 7 picnic only; 1 swim- ming site; 3 winter sports areas includ- ing Jackson and Teton Pass Ski Runs. Resorts, dude ranches, cabins. **Nearby towns:** Dubois and Jackson, Wyoming; Rexburg, Idaho

Note.—General information about the recreation resources within a geographic region may be obtained from the- ap- propriate Regional Forester, Forest Service, at one of the following addresses:

1. Federal Building
   Missoula, Montana 59801

2. Federal Center
   Building 85
   Denver, Colorado 80225

3. 517 Gold Avenue SW.
   Albuquerque, New Mexico 87101

4. Forest Service Building
   Ogden, Utah 84403

5. 630 Sansome Street
   San Francisco, California 94111

6. 729 NE. Oregon Street
   Post Office Box 3623
   Portland, Oregon 97208

7. 6816 Market Street
   Upper Darby, Pennsylvania 19082

8. 50 Seventh Street NE.
   Atlanta Georgia 30323

9. 710 North Sixth Street
   Milwaukee, Wisconsin 53203

10. Fifth Street Office
    Building
    Post Office Box 1631
    Juneau, Alaska 99801

V

VASCULAR PLANT

Vascular plants, or tracheophytes, are green plants that have a specialized system for conducting fluids. The vascular plants belong to the subkingdom Embryophyta and include the psidophytes, club mosses, calamophytes, ferns, conifers, cycads, and flowering plants. They are often grouped in a single division—Tracheophyta. (*See under Plant: Plant Kingdom*)

In the higher plants, the translocation process is achieved in a special system of tubelike structures, the *xylem* (composed of elongated cells called *tracheids* that also form the woody part of the plant); and the *phloem* (a complex system of *sieve cells* usually accompanied by fibrous tissues and parenchyma cells).

The process by which fluids move from the roots of vascular plants to the surface cells, primarily in the leaves, where they are lost to the air by evaporation in a process known as transpiration is not fully understood. In trees attaining heights of 200 feet or more, the pulling force must be considerable, and that evaporation alone would supply this pull seems puzzling.
—G.A.B.

VEERY

Other Common Names— Tawny thrush, willow thrush, nightingale
Scientific Name—*Hylocichla fuscescens*
Family—Turdidae (thrushes, solitaires, and bluebirds)
Order—Passeriformes
Size—Length, 6½ to 7½ inches
Range—Breeds in the northern border of the United States and throughout southern Canada, southward in the Allegheny Mountains to North Carolina, and westward to the eastern valleys of the Rocky Mountains. Winters in the West Indies and northern South America

The veery is not a very large bird even for a thrush. The upper parts of the veery are cinnamon-brown, and although its underparts are spotted with the same color, it is indistinct at a distance.

The name veery is an imitation of its ringing calls. The veery has often been mistaken for the wood thrush, despite the difference that the wood thrush has distinct black spots on its breast.

There is no mistaking the veery's song, however. It is one of the most melodious of the northern woodlands and during the spring migration is frequently heard on still days in the forests and groves of the South. It begins singing shortly after its arrival in May and usually stops early in July. There have been many attempts to describe the veery's song, but the best description is a delicate, metallic *to-weel-ah, twil-ah, twil-ah*, accompanied by a fine trill.

Nesting usually takes place in June. The nest is always on the ground or very near it, normally at the foot of a tree or stump where it is damp, and in heavy growth of timber along the fringes of streams overgrown with thick shrubbery. The veery builds its nest where only slender shafts of sunlight brighten the forest floor. The nest is fairly large —sometimes as long as 10 inches. It is made of small weed stalks, slender twigs, leaves, and a mass of decayed leaf fragments. The inside of the nest is lined with strips of soft bark.

The veery feeds largely on insects— ants, ground beetles, and grasshoppers are especially sought. Sometimes it ventures to the open fields, probably in search of beetles, cutworms, and earthworms. It also eats the hairy cater-

The small veery inhabits the northern and mountainous forests of North America

pillars of the gypsy moth. In summer and fall, it also eats wild berries.

The veery arrives in the United States from its winter home in the tropics about the first of May. It then scatters throughout the northern United States and southern Canada. It is rarely seen or heard south of New York City and the Great Lakes, except in the mountains, until it returns during migration in the autumn.   —A. B., Jr.

VERDIN
Other Common Names—Goldtit, yellow-headed bushtit
Scientific Name—*Auriparus flaviceps*
Family—Paridae (titmice, verdins, and bushtits)
Order—Passeriformes
Size—Length, 4 to 4½ inches
Range—Desert scrub in parts of California, Nevada, Utah, Arizona, New Mexico, and Texas

Verdins are nervous birds, continually on the move through the thorny scrub and flaunting the yellow head and the rufous color at the bend of the wing. The forehead is often a deeper yellow

Verdin

or orange color. The rest of the plumage is an undistinguished gray.

The preferred habitat of the verdins is valley land where shrubs and bushes are thick. They are insect-eaters, and are especially fond of insect eggs. Other members of their family, with similar habits, are the chickadees and titmice.

Verdins build large nests, domed over at the top, out of thorny twigs. The side entrance is flexible and expands as the bird moves through it.

A similar bird, but one that is wholly a drab gray, is the common bushtit (*See Bushtit*). It has a wider range, from British Columbia south to Texas and Baja California. The nest of this species is a hanging bag that may be 10 inches long, and is made of spider webs, mosses, and lichens; it also has a side entrance.

Bushtits are more gregarious than verdins, and often live in flocks. They are more likely to inhabit woodlands than scrub thickets. There are several races of the common bushtit; one of these has cheek patches of brown, one of black, and two others of gray.   —G.B.S.

VERTEBRATE
The animals that possess a backbone of vertebrae that enclose a spinal cord are placed in the subphylum Vertebrata (Craniata) of the phylum Chordata. The chordates, named for the rodlike notochord, are a complex group of animals.

The vertebrates (lancelets, tunicates, lampreys, fishes, amphibians, reptiles, birds, and mammals) are more highly organized than other animals. Generally speaking, they have a skeleton of cartilage or bone, and a head, with a brain encased in a skull. Most of the sense organs are located in the brain. The trunk contains the organs of digestion, circulation, and respiration. Four limbs are present in all but a few families. The nervous system has many sensory endings, all of which connect to the spinal cord and the brain. A large muscle, the heart, pumps blood through arteries and veins, carrying the products of digestion and respiration, and removing wastes through kidneys. The digestive system has a number of specialized organs. (*See Classification of Animals and Plants; also Invertebrate*) —G.B.S.

VIOLET

Some Common Violets

To some people, a violet is a violet, and that is all there is to it. To others, there are blue violets and white ones and yellow ones, and that is quite simple. But as a matter of fact, there are three or four kinds of white violets that are quite easy to distinguish; also two or three kinds of yellow ones; several kinds of leafy-stemmed ones; and several kinds of stemless blue ones with leaves of unusual form, all of which are fairly easy to know. But the different kinds of heart-leaved stemless blue violets are hard to tell apart; it should cheer the amateur to know that even a professional botanist has trouble with them. But this need not prevent anyone from learning to recognize a few of the commonest and most distinct, such as those that are included here; and when we find a kind that we can not name, we can usually call it "just another stemless blue violet".

It is assumed that most people will care little about the identity of a violet that is not in bloom; and so the various kinds are distinguished largely by the color of the flowers and the shape, hairiness, and position of the leaves. Any plant species that has colored flowers may occasionally bear white ones; but if we find a number of white-flowered plants together, we can assume that the flowers are normally white.

It is impossible, of course, to pick out one leaf that is entirely representative of a particular species of stemless violet, because the leaves vary, not only among different individuals, and not only as the leaves of a tree vary, but also with the stage of development of the plant. The first leaves of any plant are likely to be smaller, and they are often hairier

and more rounded. The earliest leaves of a cut-leaved species may be undivided. The first to come out in *Viola lanceolata* are broader in proportion to their length, as are the later leaves of *V. primulifolia,* and so on. In the summer, after most of the flowers are gone, the leaves often grow very much larger as well as smoother. The aim has been to choose a well-developed leaf at the height of the blooming season. But the reader must allow for a certain amount of variation, and in case of doubt he should consult a book giving more details, for example, Gray's Manual.

Violets are closely related to pansies; in fact the botanist calls both *Viola.* Those who know that a sugar maple, a Norway maple, and a box elder all are kinds of maples or species of *Acer,* will enjoy knowing that pansies and violets all are species of *Viola.* Several kinds of pansies from the Old World have been introduced into this country and have gone wild in some places. The cultivated English violet, so popular in herb gardens for its very fragrant flowers and its easily spreading habit, is "just another stemless blue violet". Not all violets are fragrant; and pansies never are.

Violets are usually perennial, that is, each plant normally lives through a number of years. Its leaves die every year, just as the leaves of most of our common trees do; if it has a stem above ground, that dies too; but the plant lives through the winter in the form of an underground stem full of stored food that the leaves have made and sent down before their death. It is the presence of this store of ready-made food that enables violets to put out their new leaves and flowers so early in the spring. Most of us do not notice the leaves of violets after the flowers are gone; but they remain through the summer and often late in the fall, doing the work for the following spring. Pansies are potentially perennial too; but they degenerate so quickly that they are cultivated as

annuals, that is, new plants are grown from seeds each year.

Besides making food, violet plants are doing another very important kind of work after the spring flowers are past. They are producing seeds, of course; and they are still blooming, too, but most people do not realize this. The fact is, most violets have two different kinds of flowers. In the spring the plant produces the ordinary flowers that everyone knows—flowers with showy petals. One of these petals (the lower one) has a tubular projection, or spur pointing backward from the base. The length of this spur is an important feature in recognizing certain kinds of violets. Two of the stamens have nectar-bearing appendages projecting into the spur. The color of the petals (assisted by the fragrance, when present) attracts insects, mostly bees, which come to the flower and take the nectar. Incidentally, while doing this, the bees cross-pollinate the flowers.

After the showy flowers are gone, the plant produces flowers that look exactly like young buds, for they have no petals and they never open at all. They are self-pollinated and self-fertilized in the bud without any help from insects; for this reason they are called *cleistogamous* flowers (uniting while closed). They are often (in the stemless violets) formed close to the ground, sometimes hidden under the leaves. Fortunately for the plant, these flowers produce many more seeds than the showy ones (*See under Seed*). And so there is usually no harm in picking the spring flowers of violets, if one does not pull up the whole plant or take too many leaves, for seeds will be produced anyway. But there is one exception: the bird-foot violet; we should not pick its showy flowers, because it does not produce any other kind (*See Wildflower*).

The capsules in which the seeds are formed (after pollination and fertilization) split lengthwise when they are ripe, into three boat-shaped divisions, each of which has along the middle a

California golden violet

thickened "keel" on the outside, and a row of seeds on the inside. The margins or sides of the division are thin; and as they dry and shrink, they come together and pinch the seeds, shooting them off to a distance from the plant—sometimes as far as nine feet, it is said. —H.M.R.

California Golden Violet
Other Common Names—Yellow pansy, Johnny-jump-up
Scientific Name—*Viola pedunculata*
Family—Violaceae (violet family)
Range—California Coast Ranges and southern Sierra Nevada from Napa and Tulare counties to San Diego County and adjacent Baja California
Habitat—Grassy hillsides, Upper Sonoran Zone

Time of Blooming — February to May

The yellow pansy, sometimes called Johnny-jump-up, is among the first spring flowers to bloom. Its petals are golden yellow on the face but the two upper ones are reddish-brown on the back. Its leaves are round-pointed and it grows on low hills near the coast. In the redwoods there is a violet called western heart's-ease with petals of purple and white. The petals of the pine violet are yellow on the face and purple on the back. Its leaves are divided like the palm leaf, and it occurs under tall pines in the high mountains.

Common blue violet

Common Blue Violet
Other Common Names — Marsh blue violet
Scientific Name — *Viola cucullata*
Family — Violaceae (violet family)
Range — Newfoundland to Thunder Bay District, Ontario and Minnesota, south to Nova Scotia, New England, Long Island, Virginia, upland to Georgia, Tennessee, Arkansas, and Nebraska
Habitat — Wet meadows, springy swamps, bogs, and similar places
Time of Blooming — April to July

A violet is a flower that almost everyone knows whether it is blue, white, or yellow. But when one tries to identify the 49 species that occur in the northeastern United States, not to mention the additional 35 others that occur in the South and West, one has quite a piece of detective work on his hands. Two very common blue violets that bloom at the same time are the marsh blue and the meadow blue. The lower petal of each has tiny hairlike projections known as a "beard." This prevents water from rolling into and diluting the nectar; also it acts as a foothold for visiting insects. The marsh blue violet hairs have a knob at the end of each hair while those of the meadow blue violet do not.

The seeds of the numerous species of violet are eaten by upland gamebirds such as the ground dove and mourning dove, the ruffed grouse, the bobwhite and valley quail, and the wild turkey. The wild turkey also enjoys the tuberous roots of this plant. The seeds are also known to be eaten by juncos, among the songbirds. Pine mice and white-footed mice eat the seeds, too. The whole plant is eaten by the cottontail rabbit.

VIREO

There are 13 species of vireos in North America. All resemble the red-eyed vireo, *Vireo olivaceus*, in silhouette and in behavior, but differ in such field marks as eye-rings, wing bars, whisker marks, and the color of their heads and underparts.

The black-capped vireo, *Vireo atricapilla*, is limited to Kansas, Oklahoma, and Texas. The gray vireo, *Vireo vicinior*, occurs in California and east to

The pensile nest of the red-eyed vireo is ornamented with bits of insects' cocoons

Texas. The yellow-green vireo, *Vireo fla-voviridus,* is Mexican, rarely straying across the border into California. The black-whiskered vireo, *Vireo altioquus,* is West Indian, but also breeds in South Florida.

The white-eyed vireo, *Vireo griseus,* breeds in eastern United States and winters along the Gulf Coast and in Central America. Hutton's vireo, *Vireo huttoni,* brownish and with an interrupted eye-ring, is a western species, from British Columbia south through California, Arizona, and western Texas. Bell's vireo, *Vireo bellii,* a light gray bird with no conspicuous field marks, ranges from central California eastward to Illinois, and south to Texas. The

yellow-throated vireo, *Vireo flavifrons,* breeds from Manitoba and Maine south to central Florida and Texas.

The solitary vireo, *Vireo solitarius,* has a grayish-blue head and was once known as the blue-headed vireo; its range is from Nova Scotia to British Columbia, south to the Gulf of Mexico and Baja California. The Philadelphia vireo, *Vireo philadelphicus,* is one of the few that is without wing bars; it is a northern bird, nesting from British Columbia to Maine, northern Michigan, and North Dakota. The warbling vireo, *Vireo gilvus,* also lacking wing bars, occurs in summer from Nova Scotia and British Columbia south to North Carolina, Texas, and Mexico. —G.B.S.

In a nest woven tightly to the crotch of a limb, a red-eyed vireo feeds her young

Red-eyed Vireo
Other Common Names—Preacher bird
Scientific Name—*Vireo olivaceus*
Family—Vireonidae (vireos)
Order—Passeriformes
Size—Length, 6 inches
Range—British Columbia to Nova Scotia, south to Oregon, Montana, Colorado, Texas, and central Florida; winters in South America

This is the most abundant and widely distributed vireo. It is equally at home in the forests' solitude or among the shade trees of towns and cities where it seems perfectly oblivious to the passerby. It also comes to lawns and orchards where it gleans the foliage for the insects that constitute the greater portion of its diet.

The red-eye vireo's persistence as an insect-eater is only equalled by its persistence as a songster—a characteristic that has caused it to be called preacher bird. All day long with slight interruptions it warbles its simple song. When the noonday heat brings a hush over the forest the red-eye warbles on, and even dark skies and gloomy weather offer no hindrance to its unceasing notes. The song is somewhat broken and uneven in delivery and there are many pauses between the flutelike phrasings. The call note is a petulant *whang* or *wang*.

The nest is a model of artistry—a miniature basket suspended from a small fork, woven of strips of bark, paper, and plant down, and lined with finer materials. Three to four white eggs, marked at the larger end with brownish-black, are laid.

Solitary Vireo
Other Common Names—Blue-headed vireo
Scientific Name—*Vireo solitarius*
Family—Vireonidae (vireos)
Order—Passeriformes
Size—Length, 5 to 6 inches
Range—Nests from central British Co-

Solitary vireo

lumbia east to Newfoundland and Nova Scotia, south to southern Baja California and Central America. Winters from Arizona and South Carolina south to Baja California, Mexico, and Cuba

The solitary vireo is a handsome bird for, like the yellowthroat, it has departed from the ashen grays and plain olive drabs that are the common vireo colors, and has taken on a coat of olive-green that, accentuated by white wing bars, makes it stand out prominently among its relatives.

This species is the first of the vireos to return in the spring and it lingers latest in autumn. It is a bird of the woods and does not come about homes like the red-eyed vireo and the warbling vireo. It is, however, a gentle and confiding bird, and now and then manifests marked traits of tameness.

The song of the solitary vireo is typical vireo music and may be described as having some resemblance to the combined songs of the red-eyed vireo, the Philadelphia vireo and the yellow-throated vireo.

Vireos play a very important part in helping to keep down the number of insect pests, for 91 percent of their food has been found to consist of insects.

The nest of the solitary vireo is suspended from a small forked branch and consists of pine needles, plant down, and other materials, neatly interwoven into a compact cup. From three to four white eggs, sparingly speckled with brown or black, are laid.

Warbling Vireo
Other Common Names—Warbling greenlet
Scientific Name—*Vireo gilvus*
Family—Vireonidae (vireos)
Order—Passeriformes
Size—Length, 5 to 6 inches
Range—Nests from northern British Columbia across southern Canada to Ontario, northern Minnesota, northern Michigan, to southern Maine and Nova Scotia south to western North Carolina, Alabama, Louisiana, and Texas to Baja California. Winters in Mexico and Central America

This little vireo has especially endeared itself to bird lovers on account of its unusually attractive song which is strikingly different from that of the red-eyed vireo. Instead of the halting, broken recitative of the latter, the warbling vireo pours forth a sprightly, rippling melody composed of sweet and silvery notes. It seems to speak of sunny hours and the happy days of spring, for there is an unmistakable note of joyousness

Warbling vireo

in its song. It usually arrives in late April, and even more than the red-eyed vireo seems to court the society of man, for its favorite haunts are roadside elms and the trees of lawns and parks. It is not so commonly seen in thick woodlands. High up in the trees it sings, usually invisible except to those who diligently hunt for it.

It is of immense service to man on account of the great number of injurious insects it destroys. Its food consists largely of caterpillars and other leaf-eating insects.

The nest is suspended from the forks of branches and is made of plant fibers and grasses, compactly and neatly woven together and lined with finer material. The eggs are three to four, white, and speckled at the larger end with brown or black.

White-Eyed Vireo
Other   Common   Names—White-eyed greenlet
Scientific Name— *Vireo griseus*
Family—Vireonidae (vireos)
Order—Passeriformes
Size—Length, 4½ to 5½ inches
Range—Nests from Nebraska, Indiana, Iowa, southern Wisconsin, and New York, south to southern Florida and Mexico. Winters from southern Texas

White-eyed vireo

and southern Louisiana to Central America and Cuba

This active, bright olive-green little vireo is a bird of very decided ways. It has departed somewhat from the mild manners and conventional habits of its relatives that love the shade trees of woodland, lawn, and village streets. The white-eyed vireo's favorite haunts are thickets and briar patches and deep tangles of undergrowth bordering streams or bodies of water. It seldom lives far from such situations, and with saucy impertinence, resents the presence of those who would seek to intrude upon its tangled retreats. All such are greeted with a sharp petulant *click* that is followed by a jerky song. This has been variously interpreted by the syllables, *chick-a-ree, chick,* and by the phrases, *Chick-ty-beaver-limber stick,* and *ginger beer, quick.* The white-eyed vireo is more often heard than seen, for its notes ring out from the dense thickets which it seldom leaves. Its song continues through the summer heat until well near the time for the southward flight. The white-eyed vireo is nowhere abundant, and usually not more than one pair inhabits a thicket. The food of this species consists largely of insects.

Yellow-throated Vireo
Other Common Names—Yellow-throated greenlet
Scientific Name—*Vireo flavifrons*
Family—Vireonidae (vireos)
Order—Passeriformes
Size—Length, 5 to 6 inches
Range—Nests from southern Manitoba to north-central Minnesota, central Wisconsin, central Michigan, to Ontario and Quebec, south to Maine and New Hampshire, west to eastern North Dakota, Nebraska, Kansas, and Oklahoma south to eastern Texas, the Gulf Coast, and central Florida. Winters in Mexico and south to Panama and northern South America, Isle of Pines, and the Bahamas

Yellow-throated vireo

This handsome vireo usually lives in the tops of the taller trees of open woodlands. It lives near the habitations of man and frequents the shade trees of lawns and village streets. Its conspicuous mark is its bright yellow breast that, even at a distance, at once serves to set it apart from other members of the family. Its movements are slow and sedate and it easily may be observed as it feeds among the tall tree-tops on insects that constitute the greater portion of its diet. Its usefulness as a protector of both forests and orchards is unquestioned, for it consumes large numbers of plant lice; tent, gypsy, and tussock caterpillars; and also many kinds of moths. It also eats common houseflies and mosquitoes, as well as larvae, beetles, and leafhoppers.

The song of the yellow-throated vireo is more vigorous than that of most members of the family and consists of two or three questioning notes followed by similar more emphatic ones that would make the bird appear to ask and then answer its own question.

The nest, beautiful and artistic, is made of plant fibers and strips of bark, is lined with fine materials and covered externally with lichens. It is suspended from a forked branch from 10 to 30 feet above the ground. From three to five creamy white eggs, thickly speckled with reddish-brown, are laid.

VISION (*See under Animal: Color Vision of Animals*)

VOLE

Small, furry mammals resembling mice, voles differ from them in having shorter ears and tails (*See also Mouse*). They are quite common and very prolific, with 3 to 10 young in a litter and as many as 17 litters in a year. However, they are shy and often nocturnal, and seldom seen. The damage they do to grain crops and to saplings of orchard trees and nursery stock, as well as their runways through the grass, are ample evidence of their presence.

There are about 30 species of voles in North America. Many are of limited distribution, others, such as the pine vole, *Pitymys pinetorum,* and the sagebrush vole, *Lagurus curtatus,* are limited by their adaptation to one type of environment. The heather vole, *Phenacomys intermedius,* of western conifer forests, is one of the few voles that nests in trees. —G.B.S.

Meadow Vole
Other Common Names—Field mouse, meadow mouse

The meadow vole is a major source of food for many predatory birds and mammals

Scientific Name— *Microtus pennsylvanicus*
Family—Cricetidae (mice, rats, voles, and lemmings)
Order—Rodentia
Size—Body length, 5 to 7 inches; tail, 1¼ to 2½ inches; weight, up to 4 ounces
Range—North America, from the limit of vegetation in the Arctic south to North Carolina, north-central Tennessee, and central Illinois; west to Nebraska, northern New Mexico in the Rocky Mountains, northeastern Utah and Idaho, and eastern Washington. Absent from the coastal area of British Columbia and western Alaska

Meadow voles of one sub-species or another usually live throughout North America wherever there are grassy areas. One pair of these small mammals may raise several litters of young a year. Each litter may contain from 3 to 10 young, and these offspring, in turn,

have left the nest and may be raising families of their own in a matter of weeks. Fortunately for man, carnivores from grizzlies to weasels relish meadow voles, and bobcats, hawks, foxes, and owls thrive on a steady diet of them.

A network of little runways through grassy fields and meadows is a sure sign of meadow mice. Active throughout the year, they usually feed at night. In summer they cut grass, clover, alfalfa, and grain to eat; in winter they tunnel under the snow to gnaw the bark of trees and shrubs. Their nests of dry grasses may be placed underground to avoid cold weather, but are often on the surface. By cutting timothy and grain, and girdling the bases of fruit trees, meadow mice have become serious agricultural pests where their natural predators have been destroyed.

Population "explosions" are known to occur with this species. On one such occasion in 1907-08 its multiplying millions destroyed a 20,000-acre tract of alfalfa in Nevada. The total damage to crops in that area alone was estimated at no less than $250,000. Such plagues can be attributed largely to man's intervention, resulting in an uneven balance of nature (*See Balance of Nature; and under Predation*).

VULTURE
Turkey Vulture
Other Common Names—Carrion crow, turkey buzzard
Scientific Name—*Cathartes aura*
Family—Cathartidae (American vultures)
Order—Falconiformes
Size—Length, 30 to 31 inches
Range—Breeds across southern Canada, south through the United States, and through Mexico and South America to the Falkland Islands. Winters from the Ohio Valley and southern New Jersey southward

Turkey vultures look big and black against the sky. It is there that they are usually seen, soaring in wide circles without flapping a wing. In flight they are among the most majestic of all birds. Vultures soar much like glider planes. Their weight is supported by thermals, which are rising columns of air warmed and set in motion by the sun. They seldom leave their roosts until the sun is well up; then they circle to keep within the thermal currents.

When vultures are in the air, the best way to identify them is to look at their wings. The wings have a spread of nearly six feet and are held slanted upward. They very seldom flap. The thicker, forward part looks very black, while the flight feathers extending back appear gray. Vultures spend much of their time soaring above farm and ranch lands and can be seen from coast to coast and from southern Canada south to the southern tip of South America.

At close range, it is easy to see where this vulture gets the name turkey, for it looks like one. Its wrinkled head is completely unfeathered and is red with blue markings. Its plumage is a dark brown-black and its size that of a young domestic turkey. But here the resemblance stops, for its bill is not the seed-eating kind of a fowl. Instead, it is long and ends in a hook for tearing flesh.

Vultures are meat-eaters, but lack the strong curved talons of the hawks and owls. Their feet are weak and it is impossible for them to pounce and kill. They usually feed on animals that are already dead, for they are scavengers—nature's garbage collectors. When one bird descends to feed, others, always alert, appear to share in the feast. Freshly killed or carrion, as long as the

A comparison of the flight patterns of the turkey vulture and the black vulture reveal the marks of identification of these similar birds

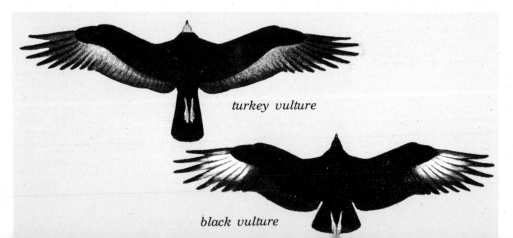

turkey vulture

black vulture

R·BRUCE HORSFALL

The turkey vulture is a large, ungainly bird that spends much of its time in the air

Young black vultures have wrinkly, black facial skin characteristic of this species

animal is dead, it is food for the vulture.

Strong headlights blind and confuse many creatures that roam at night and make them helpless victims of speeding cars. Every morning, cottontails, jackrabbits, opossums, skunks, and sometimes deer lie dead along roads. These are food for the turkey vultures. Usually they are eaten on the spot, for their feet are poorly adapted for removing it. They are able, however, to carry small pieces to their young.

Turkey vultures nest in secluded places, usually in a hollow stump or log. The birds do not build a nest but lay their two eggs—cream-white and marked with chocolate-brown—on the floor of the spot selected. The eggs take from 30 to 40 days to hatch, and it may be 8 to 10 weeks before the young are able to fly.

Although vultures nest and hunt independently, they often congregate at night in roosts of a hundred or more birds. These may be located in dead trees in a remote part of some woods, or in a swamp where man is unlikely to disturb them. Each morning they fly off in various directions to seek out creatures that have died in the countryside, especially birds and mammals. Occa-

sionally, dead fishes, thrown up on the shore, are eaten.

The turkey vulture performs a valuable service as scavenger of fields and roadsides. It must be credited with fulfilling an important function in nature's plan of interdependence among all living things (*See also under Condor*).

Vultures are often called buzzards, but this is incorrect. The word buzzard properly applies to Old World buteos or broad-winged, soaring hawks (*See Buteo*).

In the South the range of the turkey vulture overlaps that of the black vulture. The black vulture, *Corygyps atratus*, is a somewhat smaller bird and less adept at soaring. It frequently flaps its wings. Its tail is much shorter than the turkey vulture's—scarcely long enough to cover the trailing feet as the bird flies. Its wing pattern is quite different—a large white patch near the end of each wing is distinctive when seen from underneath. Black vultures also have black heads. (Young turkey vultures have black heads, too, and are often confused with the black vulture.) Black vultures live from Maryland and west Texas south to southern South America.   —A.B., Jr.

W

Small-flowered prairie rocket

WALKINGSTICK
Other Common Names—Stick insect, leaf insect
Scientific Name— *Diapheromera femorata*
Family—Phasmatidae (walkingsticks)
Order—Orthoptera
Size—Length, to three inches
Range—Northern United States and Southern Canada

The long, thin body of the walkingstick insect looks like a dead twig; under natural conditions, where the animal creeps slowly along a branch or over dead leaves, it is not readily noticed. Its movements are halting and deliberate, and it becomes motionless when danger approaches. If this defensive action fails, it can eject a foul-smelling liquid that often discourages predators.

It feeds upon plant material, living and dead. The eggs are dropped at random as the female walks along. Young walkingsticks are green, but adults are brown.

One of the most remarkable abilities of this insect is that of regenerating legs that have been lost. Few other insects, and none of the higher animals, can do this.

Four other species of walking-stick, all similar to the one described, live in the southern United States.   —G.B.S.

WALLFLOWER
Small-flowered prairie rocket
Other Common Names—Western wallflower, blister cress
Scientific Name—*Erysimum inconspicuum*
Family—Cruciferae (mustard family)
Range—British Columbia to northern California east to Idaho
Habitat—Open hillsides, Transition and Upper Sonoran Zones
Time of Blooming—March to August

The wallflower makes its home in many places. It occurs along the seacoast, in the high mountains up to 12,000 feet, and on the islands of San Miguel and Santa Rosa off the coast of California. It rarely exceeds 2½ feet in height and the large flowers are deep yellow or cream color. The plant looks much like the common yellow mustard. The seedpods of the western wallflower are four-sided. The seed has no commercial value, as does that of its relative, the common yellow mustard. Large fields of mustard are raised near Lompoc, California, and tons of the seed are sold for use in medicine and in cooking.

The wallflower of gardens is *Cherianthus cheiri* of southern Europe, also in the family Cruciferae. It is an old favorite of American gardeners because of its early spring bloom, and its many forms and colors.

WALNUT
Black Walnut
Other Common Names — American walnut, eastern black walnut
Scientific Name — *Juglans nigra*
Family — Juglandaceae (walnut family)
Range — Western Massachusetts south to extreme northwestern Florida and eastern Texas, west through southern Wisconsin and Minnesota to eastern Nebraska, Kansas, Oklahoma, and Texas. Absent in the Coastal Plain
Habitat — Rich soils, most often in level woodlands
Leaves — Compound, 1 to 2 feet long with 13 to 23 narrow pointed leaflets. They are yellowish-green with finely toothed edges and sometimes hang straight down from the stem
Bark — Rough, dark, and of mixed gray and reddish or yellowish-brown color. The stout winter twigs have prominent pale leaf scars (in three U-shaped clusters) and blunt, heart-shaped buds
Flowers — Male catkins two to four inches long, from late April to June. Female "spikes" very inconspicuous
Fruit — About two inches in diameter, round, hard, and green, with a pebbly or granular surface; usually in clusters of two to three. Inside the thick husk is a much grooved blackish nut with rich, edible meat

Black walnut is so well known as a wood used for furniture, gunstocks, and special paneling, and for its nuts that are a familiar flavoring in baking and pastry that little need be said of the practical uses of this attractive, stalwart tree. Less familiar is the old-time use of the crushed and boiled husks of the nuts in making dye (a potentiality that is soon revealed if one spends a few minutes opening and shelling these fruits). The herbalists claim that this same juice is helpful in curing certain forms of dermatitis.

Many people who may take pride in Black walnut as paneling in their homes or as stocks for their rifles would fail to recognize the growing tree. It is strong-looking with rather irregular, but crisply contoured branches free from twigs and clutter, the compound leaves of yellow-green color bunching at the ends of the twigs. It casts a dense but dappled shade and, as the warmer months draw to a close, the ground beneath it is increasingly strewn with the round, ball-like nuts. If these are not collected, their husks gradually rot as they lie on the damp ground and the ripened nuts within are more easily available to squirrels and other rodents that feed upon them.

There are a total of five or six native species of walnut in the United States beside the imported English or Persian walnut that is raised in orchards on the West Coast and produces most of our commercially sold walnut crop. Several of these native walnut trees are of moderate to small size and occur in the Southwest, usually along the banks of streams. The two larger ones are the black walnut and a species called butternut, *Juglans cinerea*. This tree has a somewhat narrower range than the black, occurring over a similar area of the country but extending further north into southeastern Canada.

Butternut, or white walnut, has rather blunt, thick leaflets on its compound leaves. The undersides of these are covered with a soft, yellow-brown fuzz. Its fruits are football-shaped, have a sticky surface covered with fine bristles, and also contain an edible nut of elongate

Black walnut (left) is similar to butternut (right), but their leaves differ

shape. The bark is pale gray with wide fissures that give it a striped appearance and the tree generally has a broad, spreading form with rather irregular branching. The sap of this tree can be made into a fairly good quality of sugar syrup.

Maximum size for the black walnut is usually attained in richer soils in the middle Atlantic States and the upper Mississippi Valley where it may grow to 150 feet high and up to 6 feet in diameter. The top height for the butternut is nearer to a 100 feet with trunks to 4 feet in diameter but the average size for both trees is well below these dimensions.

Also in the Juglandaceae, or walnut family, are the hickories. Many of these are woodland trees of no great stature or importance, but the kernels of the hard-shelled nuts are of value to wildlife. Mockernut, bitternut, and broom hickories are in this category. All of them have the typical hickory leaves, compound and with five to fifteen leaflets, and all produce fruit in the form of nuts. The only economically important nut tree in this genus is the pecan, a large, showy tree of the rich river bottoms from southern Indiana to Alabama, and now cultivated more widely (*See also under Hickory; Pecan*). —M.H.B.

Both male and female walruses have tusks that give them a ferocious appearance

WALRUS

Other Common Names—Atlantic walrus
Scientific Name— *Odobenus rosmarus*
Family—Odobenidae (walrus)
Order—Pinnipedia
Size—Male: body length, 10 to 12 feet; weight, over 2,000 pounds. Female: about one-third smaller
Range—Arctic Ocean, extreme North Atlantic, and Hudson Bay; a similar subspecies, the Pacific walrus, in Alaskan waters

A mightly sea mammal, usually traveling in herds, the walrus is probably the noisiest marine mammal of the Arctic. It is armed with magnificent ivory tusks and its coarse, hairless skin is wrinkled and warty like the bark of an ancient gnarled oak. The walrus was known to the early Scandinavian seaman as Hvalras or the whalehorse. At that time walruses ranged over most of the open waters of the arctic seas, its choice of a homeland the shore ice bordering the frozen lands far from human habitation. It never ranges south of the ice fields, nor has it ever been found in the Antarctic. Despite its regal and formidable appearance, the walrus is an inoffensive, peace-loving creature. Those handsome gleaming tusks were not acquired as weapons of offense, though they may be used to inflict terrific havoc in defense. It neither hunts warm-blooded animals nor does it take a toll of fishes. The tusks are used by it to dig its daily bread on the ocean floor: clams and shell-fishes which are swallowed whole and crushed by action of the stomach and innumerable pebbles. After the meat is digested, the empty shells, pebbles, and sand are then ejected.

Family life of the walrus is sociable.

Bulls, cows, and calves mingle together in one somewhat quarrelsome family. The discord is not so much in competition over the females as a dislike of being disturbed while asleep. If one is accidentally nudged by another, like a spoiled child it must retaliate and failing to accost the culprit it slaps its most convenient neighbor which in turn, lets out a roar and passes it on until the whole colony is in a turmoil.

Maternal instinct is strongly developed in the parent walrus. A cow will sell its life dearly for the safety of its calf, and once aroused will charge any suspicious stranger in the vicinity. Both male and female walruses have tusks and prize individuals may carry 38-inch ivories, each weighing as much as 11 pounds. Some of the giant bulls may weigh 3,000 pounds and measure 11 feet in length.   —G.G.G.

WARBLER

Warblers, a group of 113 small, mostly colorful bird species are members of a typically American family, the Parulidae. They are more properly labelled wood warblers to avoid confusion with the Old World warblers.

These little sprites are the delight of the amateur bird-watcher who thrills to the spectacular spring migrations, mostly east of the Rocky Mountains. Most of them winter in Middle America, and in mid-April they advance northward *en masse,* up either side of the Gulf of Mexico, or right across it; by mid-May they have reached the 40th parallel and if weather has held them up at all, are likely to be piled up in great "waves" that animate the newly-tasselled oaks excitingly. It is then possible to see twenty or so species in an early morning's walk.

Fifty-two of the 113 species occur in the contiguous United States, although one region enjoys more than about 15 as summer resident species. Being insectivorous, all the northern species are migratory. The eastern deciduous forest region is richest in warblers, the northern evergreen forest is almost as rich, and the western forests are poorest.

A few species are of very extensive occurrence, others suprisingly restricted. Noteworthy in the first group is the yellow warbler, *Dendroica petechia,* which occurs in summer from northern South America to Alaska and Labrador. The Kirtland's warbler, *Dendroica kirtlandii,* however, occurs as a nesting bird only in young jack pine which is between five and eighteen feet in height in a few counties of northern Michigan, in an area only 80 by 60 miles at most.

Like any other large group of species, the warblers illustrate the evolutionary principle of adaptive radiation (*See also Sparrow*). Some are ground dwellers, some brush birds, some inhabitants of tree tops. In a recent study of this group, Robert M. Mengel of the University of Kansas Museum of National History, suggested that about one out of four of our warbler species were differentiated during the Pleistocene Epoch, when ice advances split off population segments. These disjunct groups evolved at different rates while isolated. When warm interglacial periods reversed the trend, these differentiated warbler populations reinvaded the ice-free lands as soon as suitable vegetation had established itself. Since the Pleistocene, which covers the last million years or so, had four major glacial periods, and three interglacial warmings (not including the present which may also be an interglacial period), there have been at least four major evolutionary "experiments" in the northern half of North America during this span of years.

The spruce forest habitat that James Bond describes below is a rather uniform environment. Its trees are mostly spire-shaped. One may wonder, therefore, how the dozen or more species of this northern coniferous forest get along together. There is a rule in biology that no two species with similar requirements can long occupy the same area.

One usually soon displaces the other.

This question interested Robert H. MacArthur while he was a graduate student at Yale University some years ago. His analysis of the interrelationships of a group of closely associated warblers was a brilliant combination of field observation and the theoretical approach.

He began by objectifying the environment. The spruce forest, he saw, is not a mere jumble of needle-leaved boughs, but is composed of trees, each of which is a cone. Further, he thought, the five warblers that live in a mature spruce forest must have a measurable relationship to the conical trees. Some could seek insects low down, some high, some in between; some could work up and down inside the cone; some up and down the surface (on the outside); some could work radially, from the trunk to the tips of the horizontal boughs and back. These were the physical possibilities, geometrically expressed.

And sure enough, by dint of close observation, MacArthur found that the warbler species were keeping out of each others' way by specializing on various portions of the tree.

This minimizes competition to each species' advantage and allows maximum survival for the population. The birds actually occupy different portions of the available space instead of competing for living space at random; they even concentrate their nesting within different periods of time; and also feed on different insects, or different stages of the same insects, to some extent. Two of these warblers: the bay-breasted and the Cape May—can actually respond to insect outbreaks by increasing their clutch size!

Two other students, Millicent and Robert Ficken of Cornell University, have pointed out that warblers which forage for food near the ground have songs of lower pitch; those that feed high up in trees have higher-pitched songs; and those that feed at intermediate heights have songs of intermediate pitch. This is another bit of adaptive specialization, since birds that live near the ground in dense cover, or in a noisy environment—such as a streamside thicket may well be—have need of a lower-pitched voice, since this carries farther. The dwellers of the shadowy thickets are, moreover, usually dull-colored, and may need a louder voice to identify one another more easily, and thus minimize conflict.   —R.C.C.

Recommended Reading

The Living Bird—Cornell Laboratory of Ornithology, Ithaca, New York.

Wood Warblers

In North America most warblers summer in the Canadian Zone where, in suitable localities, as many species may be seen in a day as during a good warbler "wave" in May. Ship Harbor, on Mount Desert Island in Maine, is such a spot, and there, in early June, one finds in quick succession the redstart, magnolia, black-throated green, myrtle, parula, chestnut-sided, Nashville, Canada, and black-and-white. In the high spruce woods we hear the lisping songs of the Cape May, bay-breast, and Blackburnian, in the alder swales the rapid chippering of the Wilson's and Tennessee, and in the open sphagnum bog nearby we shall surely see the yellowthroat and yellow palm warbler. All of these species nest within a mile of Ship Harbor, while others are found not far away—the yellow warbler in the villages, the northern waterthrush about some beaver flowage, the ovenbird and black-throated blue in the deciduous woods of the interior and, finally, the blackpoll in the low spruce of the Duck Islands, less than five miles distant.

At such localities as Ship Harbor it is interesting and instructive to search for warbler nests. The discomfort involved in exploring the mosquito-infested woods and swamps is immediately forgotten when one is discovered. We are now able to study the birds intimately, but care should be taken not to disturb the nest or the surrounding foliage, for this might cause the parents to desert the nest or it might attract the attention of a marauder. Small and well hidden, the nests are difficult to find at first. With experience, we become familiar with the characteristics of the site and construction of the nest of each particular species, and then, more and more often, we are able to go directly to the right spot.

North American warblers may be divided roughly into two groups—those that nest on the ground and those that nest in trees or bushes. The former are for the most part of Central American origin, whereas most of the latter were apparently derived from the West Indies. Thus the tree-nesting *Dendroica* winter largely in the Antilles, although some pass on to South America, whereas the ground-nesting *Vermivora* winter in Central America. Incidentally, so far as is known, all resident Antillean warblers nest above the ground, whereas most of the Central and South American species nest on the ground.

There can be little doubt that the wood warblers, a family comprising some 115 species and entirely confined to the New World, originated in Middle America, since all the 25 genera are found there either as indigenous species or as winter residents. On the other hand, only six genera breed in South America and of these, *Dendroica* has merely a toehold on that continent. As many as 16 genera, including 54 species, breed in North America.

The relationship of the family lies with the nine-primaried finches and tanagers rather than with the ten-primaried Old World warblers, which are akin to the thrushes. The resemblance is thus purely superficial although the Sylviidae fill the same ecological niche in Europe as do the Parulidae in North America. As a general rule Old World warblers are dull in color but superlative songsters, whereas our wood warblers are brightly colored but poor singers. The Sylviidae are represented in the New World mainly by the kinglets and gnatcatchers, which, however, are not typical of this family.

It is important to learn the songs of our warblers. These range from the weak, inarticulate notes of the bay-breast to the loud, ringing melody of the yellow-throated warbler. But once these songs are learned, they are not easily forgotten, although an occasional variation will be confusing. One will notice that the *wichity* of our Pennsylvania yellowthroats becomes *wichawichity* in Maine. There is a more striking difference between the songs of the blackpoll warbler on its breeding grounds in southeastern Canada as compared with those of transients in the Philadelphia region. Future field studies may show that most of the latter are individuals that nest in northern Canada as compared with those of transients in the Philadelphia region. Those that breed in the White Mountains possess a third type of song.

In addition to the familiar territorial songs, some warblers (e.g. the prothonotary, ovenbird and yellowthroat) have "whisper" songs. These are sung by the males during the nesting season and perhaps play some part in courtship. They differ completely from the normal songs and are always very soft and rather canarylike in character.

Again, certain species (e.g. the waterthrushes, ovenbird and yellowthroat) utter what are known as flight songs—rapturous outpourings of notes emitted for the most part above the treetops during the night. In character they are usually a mixture of the territorial and whisper songs.

In New England, warbler singing is at its height during the first half of June, that is to say during the incubation period. By late July the woods are virtually silent and the autumnal migration has begun. Now is the time that the true warbler addict is afield, for you have to be very discerning to

A female MacGillivray's warbler, like her mate, has conspicuous white eye markings

identify the young in their first fall plumage, and even the adults of many species are different in appearance from what they were during the spring months. For it must be remembered that all our warblers undergo two molts a year, a prenuptial molt when there is a new growth of body feathers, and a postnuptial, complete molt after the nesting season. As a general rule, where the sexes differ in nuptial plumage, the adult male resembles more or less the adult female in fall plumage, a notable exception being the black-throated blue warbler; but where the sexes are similar in spring they are also virtually alike in autumn. In most cases the young bird has acquired by its first spring the appearance of its parents, but the male redstart does not attain his gaudy reddish-orange coloring until just before his second breeding season.

By late autumn almost all of our warblers are in the tropics, although a few hardy species remain with us throughout the year. The pine warbler winters almost entirely in the southeastern United States, while numerous myrtle warblers brave the northern winter, particularly in places where there are bayberry bushes which offer an abundance of food, for warblers are not entirely dependent on insects, seeds being frequently eaten in the West Indies.

The migrations of several species are very extended. The blackpoll warbler, for example, breeds as far north as Alaska and winters in northern South America, flying directly across the Caribbean Sea. The cerulean warbler has been found in northwestern Bolivia, the Connecticut warbler in southwestern Brazil. Comparatively little is known concerning the migration route of the latter, since there are as yet no records of transients from the Antilles or Central America.

Warblers, like the majority of our birds, are essentially night migrants, spending the daylight hours feeding and resting. However, over the Caribbean Sea they are often forced to fly by day. Flocks of these little birds have frequently been seen struggling against a stiff breeze north of Cuba or over the Caribbean Sea. Always they were within a few feet of the water to avoid the full force of the trade wind. Yet there can be no doubt that the great majority reach their destination.

The hurricane season coincides with the autumnal migration and could cause great havoc among the migrating hosts, but one wonders if birds sense the approach of such storms, causing them to delay their flights. A springtime ice storm in more northern climes will sometimes overtake a "wave" of warblers, thousands of which will be killed. This may result in a temporary, local scarcity of these birds.

The winter homes of our warblers are often quite circumscribed. Thus, Kirtland's warbler, which breeds in Michigan, winters only in the Bahama Islands, Bachman's warbler only in the western half of Cuba and on the Isle of Pines. The western palm warbler is the most abundant bird in Cuba during this season, although it is very rare in Puerto Rico and unknown from the Lesser Antilles. On the other hand, the redstart and black-and-white warbler have a very extensive winter range.

The term "winter resident" is not strictly correct, since most of our warblers reach their wintering grounds in late summer and some even in early summer. One naturalist has had the opportunity of awaiting their arrival in the West Indies. The first to appear are the Austral Zone species, those that breed in the southeastern United States. For as soon as their broods are fledged warblers return to their ancestral homes, where they live together, apparently in perfect harmony. It is a very different matter on their nesting grounds, where every individual male requires a territory from which all other males of the species are excluded. In winter, warblers *chip* constantly but rarely sing, although a black-and-white warbler was heard in full song in Port-au-Prince, Haiti, one Christmas Day, and snatches of their song have been heard on other occasions during this season. By early spring the birds become more restless and then sing rather frequently.

It is sometimes easier to determine the status of a bird on its wintering grounds than in its breeding range. Thus it would appear that Bachman's warbler is even rarer than Kirtland's warbler, and that the Cape May warbler is far more numerous than is generally realized.

At one time wood warblers were considered "our most beautiful, most abundant, and least-known birds," but the last statement is not true at the present time. All of the species that breed in North America, north of Mexico, have received considerable attention from field ornithologists. Their songs are known and their nests and eggs have been described. The only possible exception is the so-called Sutton's warbler, *Dendroica potomac*, of West Virginia; but in the opinion of most orithogists, this bird is merely a hybird between the yellow-throated and parula warblers. In this case, it would appear likely that a yellow-throated warbler, on finding none of its kind, mated with the parula, West Virginia being outside the normal breeding range of the former species.

It is a pity that many of our ornithologists who have visited tropical America were intent only on obtaining specimens and cared little about the living bird. For this reason not much is known about warblers south of the United States, particularly in Central and South America, other than what can be learned from skins, which information is of value mainly to taxonomists.

The largest and most widespread of the tropical genera of wood warblers is *Basileuterus*, a rather heterogeneous group. In addition there are numerous "species" of yellowthroats (*Geothlypis*), and also the gayly colored *Myiobori* of the Temperate and Subtropical Zones, with their Tropical Zone representatives, the beautiful red-breasted chats (not to be confused with our yellow-breasted chat, the largest and most aberrant member of the family). None of the above are found high up in trees.

Perhaps the most notable of tropical warblers inhabit Central America. These include the sweet-voiced red warbler, or *oreja de plata*, an aboreal species of the pine and spruce forests of the Mexican highlands, and the lovely Irazu warbler, a dweller of the mountaintops of Costa Rica and Chiriqui, and the most southern member of our genus *Vermivora*.

Several North American species breed in Central America and in the West Indies. The bird we know as Sennett's warbler, closely related to the parula, ranges as far south as Argentina. However, the yellow warblers are the most widespread of the family, nesting from northern Canada and Alaska south to northern South America and the Galapagos Islands. The males of some of the southern subspecies have rufous caps while others have the entire head rufous. On the mainland, south of the Mexican plateau, they are confined to the coastal mangrove swamps.   —J.B.

Audubon's Warbler

Other Common Names — Western yellow-rumped warbler
Scientific Name — *Dendroica auduboni*
Family — Parulidae (wood warblers)
Order — Passeriformes
Size — Length, 4¾ to 5¼ inches
Range — Breeds throughout most of the West — west of the Great Plains and north to central British Columbia and Saskatchewan. Winters from southern British Columbia, Nevada, and Utah, south to California and New Mexico, and in the lower Rio Grande Valley of Texas

In winter the Audubon's warbler is probably one of the three commonest birds in California. The Gambel's sparrow and the linnet are the other two. The Audubon's warbler flits from every roadside, showing a white patch on the wings and a yellow spot at the base of the tail when it flies. That yellow spot is the Audubon's warbler's badge of identity. These warblers can be seen in city parks, suburban gardens, on telephone wires, or on the ground. Their loud *tsip* note, bright rump, and pattern of white on the tail attract attention. They are constantly on the move — active all day long like small flycatchers, snapping up gnats, wasps, and flies. They even are seen around sand dunes and the sea drift along the beaches.

Instead of going north in the spring, they have only to climb the mountains.

Audubon's warbler, male (above); female (middle); young (below)

However, a great many of them do go north to the western Canadian provinces and then south again in the autumn. Many songbirds have this vertical migration. It is more of a drifting back and forth from the mountains to the lowlands—*altitudinal* rather than *latitudinal* migration.

On reaching his nesting territory, the male takes his post in an evergreen and sings. It is a pleasant song—a succession of notes followed by a loose trill on a lower pitch. Like most birds he sings to attract a mate and to tell other male Audubon's warblers that this is his territory. Should another male trespass, he is quickly chased away. The song is a challenge, but should a female appear, it becomes a love song. The male has lost his drab winter plumage and now sports his black, gold, and blue-gray colors.

The nest is usually in an evergreen, anywhere from 4 to 60 feet from the ground. It might be out on a limb or near the trunk. It is a well-built, nicely cupped nest consisting of fine twigs, rootlets, strips of bark, and grasses and is lined with hair or feathers. If the nest is located high in the mountains at timberline, white ptarmigan feathers might be used; at lower levels, the dark feathers of the sooty grouse are often used. The males of many birds help with the nest-building and egg-brooding, but not the Audubon's warbler. The male sings and follows his mate about, but he does not help her.

There are usually four eggs in the nest. They are white, or pale green, or blue-white spotted with brown. When they hatch the male does help a little in providing food. In less than two weeks the streaked nestlings are able to follow their parents around. The little family groups can often be seen later in the summer traveling over the mountainsides above timberline. By September there are often great numbers on the move over the rugged slopes.   —A.B. Jr.

Black-and-white Warbler
Other Common Names—Black-and-white creeper, creeping warbler
Scientific Name—*Mniotilta varia*
Family—Parulidae (wood warblers)
Order—Passeriformes
Size—Length, 5 to 5½ inches
Range—Nests from British Columbia and Saskatchewan east to Newfoundland. In the United States from Montana and South Dakota south to central Texas, east to Louisiana, Mississippi, Alabama, Georgia, and North and South Carolina. Winters from Baja California, southern Texas, and central Florida south to Mexico, Central America, the Bahamas, and West Indies

Allan Brooks

Black-and-white warbler

The black-and-white warbler is among the first of the warbler family to arrive in spring, when croplands are just beginning to show a tinge of green.

Those who experience difficulty in learning to distinguish the different species of wood warblers need have no trouble in identifying this conspicuously marked and very peculiar member of the family. Its habits are more akin to those of a true creeper than of a warbler. It climbs in a nervous, jerky fashion, creeping about tree trunks and limbs, or over logs or fallen trees, often hanging from the under surface of branches with the greatest agility and ease. It progresses by a series of sidewise movements that seem not to get it to any particular destination, for apparently it has none, as it is constantly flitting from tree to tree making the briefest tours of inspection. Its call note is a faint, sharp *pit* or *psip* while the slender thread of song that it essays may be represented by the syllables *see-see-see-see.*

The nest is on the ground at the base of a stump or rock, and is made of grasses, strips of bark and lined with long hair or rootlets. From four to five eggs, white and speckled with brown, are laid.

Chestnut-sided warbler

Chestnut-sided Warbler
Other Common Names—Bloody-side warbler, golden-crowned flycatcher
Scientific Name—*Dendroica pensylvanica*
Family—Parulidae (wood warblers)
Order—Passeriformes
Size—Length, five inches
Range—Breeds throughout the northern United States and southern Canada as far west as Saskatchewan and Utah and south to New Mexico; also in the uplands of Tennessee and the Carolinas. Winters in Mexico and Central America

One of the most common members of the warbler family in the eastern United States is the chestnut-sided warbler. The male is a trim little bird with an olive-green back and a bright yellow crown; its underparts are lighter, and its sides are marked by deep chestnut. That is the way the male looks in spring. In fall and winter the plumage is quite different. The upper parts are a light olive-green, sometimes with faint streaks on the back. The deep chestnut color of the sides has been reduced to a few spots or patches.

The chestnut-sided warbler lives in woodlands that have been cut over and grown up in bushes. Its nest is usually placed in a small tree or bush 2½ to 3½ feet above the ground. The nest is made of strips of bark and soft, dead leaf

Black-throated green warblers

go to Central America by way of the Gulf of Mexico. Only a comparatively small number travel to Florida and the Bahama Islands.   —A.B., Jr.

Black-throated Green Warbler
Other Common Names—Evergreen warbler, green black-throat
Scientific Name—*Dendroica virens*
Family—Parulidae (wood warblers)
Order—Passeriformes
Size—Length, 4½ to 5¼ inches
Range—Nests from western to eastern Canada, Labrador, Newfoundland, and Nova Scotia and from Minnesota, Wisconsin, and Michigan south to Ohio, Pennsylvania, and northern New Jersey, southward in mountains to Alabama and northern Georgia. Winters from southern Texas and southern Florida south through eastern Mexico, Central America, Panama, and Greater Antilles

Among the great army of migrating warblers that comes streaming northward in the spring, this species is one of the most abundant. It is associated in the mind of bird lovers with joyous spring days when it may be seen flitting about through the tender green foliage of woodlands and orchards searching for the insects that make up the major part of its diet. Its bright olive-green back and bright yellow cheeks, together with its velvety black throat and breast and white belly, and the large amount of white in its tail, make a striking color combination that serves well for purposes of identification.

During migration it occurs almost anywhere trees grow, but its breeding haunts are preferably evergreens.

Its call note is a rather loud *tsip* or *chip,* and its song a highly modulated trill, though not so clear-toned as in the case of many other warblers.

The nest is in coniferous trees, of twigs and mosses, lined with rootlets and grasses. From four to five white eggs, speckled at the larger end with umber or brown, are laid.

stems, or similar materials. It is lined with tendrils and rootlets.

Four or five eggs are laid. They are white with light and dark brown markings, some distinct, others more or less obscure. The spots and blotches form a wreath around the larger end.

The chestnut-sided warbler feeds almost exclusively on insects. These include caterpillars, plant lice, ants, leafhoppers, and small bark beetles. Sometimes they take short flights in the air after winged insects.

The song of the chestnut-sided warbler is cheerful and strong and resembles the words *I wish, I wish, I wish to see Miss Beecher.*

All birds that depend on insects for survival, as do the chestnut-sided warblers, are necessarily highly migratory. By the middle of September nearly all of them have left their summer homes, which extend across the southern Canadian provinces from Saskatchewan eastward, and southward as far as New Mexico, Tennessee, and the highlands of the Carolinas. Most of the migrants

Myrtle Warbler

Other Common Names — Myrtle bird, yellow-rump, yellow-crowned warbler
Scientific Name — *Dendroica coronata*
Family — Parulidae (wood warblers)
Order — Passeriformes
Size — Length, 5 to 6 inches
Range — Nests from Alaska and Yukon south to British Columbia and eastward to Labrador and Newfoundland, south to Minnesota, Michigan, northeastern New York, Massachusetts, and Maine. Winters from Kansas, southern Great Lakes region, and southern New England south to Mexico and Central America; along Pacific Coast from northwestern Oregon south to Baja California

This is among the largest and hardiest of the warblers, and is to some extent gregarious, flocking in loose companies during the winter. Its movements during this time are largely determined by the weather and the food supply. Depending less upon insect life for food than most members of the family, it often braves the snow and cold, provided a plentiful supply of wild berries is available.

In the southern states it is one of the most abundant winter visitants and may be seen flocking over the plantations, among thickets and in scraggly fields, as well as among the stunted vegetation along the seabeaches. In regions where bay or myrtle berries are plentiful, it usually dwells in considerable numbers; likewise in cedar thickets, as it is very fond of these two kinds of berries.

Its call note is very characteristic and consists of a sharp *tchip* or *tchep*. In spring and early summer it sings a sprightly song somewhat like that of the junco.

The nest is in evergreens, of fibers lined with grasses. From four to five grayish-white eggs, speckled with brown, are laid.

Palm Warbler

Other Common Names — Yellow redpoll, wagtail warbler, yellow tip-up

Myrtle warbler

Scientific Name — *Dendroica palmarum*
Family — Parulidae (wood warblers)
Order — Passeriformes
Size — Length, 5 inches
Range — In Canada from southwestern Mackenzie, northern and central Alberta, Saskatchewan, Manitoba, Ontario, southern Quebec, Newfoundland, and Nova Scotia south to northeastern British Columbia. In United States from northeastern Minnesota, central Michigan, Maine. In winter from Louisiana, Mississippi, Tennessee, and North Carolina south to the Yucatan Peninsula, northern Honduras, Greater Antilles, Bahamas, Bermuda, Puerto Rico, Hispaniola, and the Virgin Islands

The habits of this warbler resemble those of the yellow palm warbler, a similar subspecies, from which it differs with respect to range and coloration. The whitish belly of this bird serves to distinguish it from the yellow palm warbler which is uniformly bright yellow underneath.

Yellow Palm Warbler
Other Common Names—None
Scientific *Name*—*Dendroica palmarum hypochrysea*
Family—Parulidae (wood warblers)
Order—Passeriformes
Size—Length, 5 inches
Range—Breeds from eastern and southern Ontario, central and southern Quebec and ·southern Newfoundland, south to central eastern New Hampshire, northern and eastern Maine, New Brunswick, and Nova Scotia. Winters from central and southeastern Louisiana, northern Mississippi, central southern and northern Tennessee and North Carolina south to the Gulf Coast, central Florida and also occurs casually north along the Atlantic Coast to Pennsylvania, New Jersey, and Connecticut

Although a wood warbler this bird seems to have departed widely from the time-honored habits of the family. It apparently has little use for woodlands and not very much for trees. Most of its time is spent on or close to the ground after the habit of some sparrows. It also constantly wags its tail like a titlark. In its winter home in the South it may be seen flitting about the streets of towns and villages.

The nest, on or near the ground, is built of coarse grasses lined with fine material. From four to five eggs, buffy white with brown markings, are laid.

Parula Warbler
Other Common Names—Blue yellow-backed warbler, blue yellowback
Scientific Name—*Parula americana*
Family—Parulidae (wood warblers)
Order—Passeriformes
Size—Length, 4½ to 4¾ inches
Range—Nests from Manitoba eastward across Canada to Ontario, Quebec, and Nova Scotia, south to eastern Texas, Louisiana, Mississippi, Alabama, and Florida. Winters in Mexico, Central

Parula warbler, male ; female (below)

America, Nicaragua, and Costa Rica, also from Florida to Bahamas

Bird lovers of the South usually associate this dainty little warbler with cypress swamps where, with advancing spring, its slender chippering trill is one of the characteristic notes. Its *chipper-ze-ze-ze* seems to blend well with the spirit of the languorous southern spring, with the fragrance of yellow jasmine, the budding of swamp maples, and the gently swaying Spanish moss about which it flits and clings and in which it builds its nest (*See under Epiphyte*).

In the northern United States and Canada lives a subspecies, the northern parula warbler. This bird differs slightly from the southern form in having more black color across the breast, while the throat of the male is not quite so yellow. The northern parula warbler, except during migration, also usually lives in low, wet woodlands, for it invariably builds its nest of *Usnea*, a lichen that grows only in such places.

Few birds have shown finer instinct for utilizing nesting sites that nature bountifully provides than this little warbler. In the South the omnipresent *Tillsandia* and in the North the ever-abundant *Usnea* are the materials generally used as the foundation for nests (*See under Lichen*).

The nest is from 3 to 30 feet from the ground. From four to five white eggs, marked with brown about larger end, are laid.

Pine Warbler

Other Common Names—Pine-creeping warbler, pine creeper
Scientific Name—*Dendroica pinus*
Family—Parulidae (wood warblers)
Order—Passeriformes
Size—Length, 5 to 5½ inches
Range—Nests across southern Canada from Alberta to Ontario and Quebec, and from central Maine south to southeastern Texas, the Gulf Coast, Florida, and the Bahamas. Winters from Arkansas, Tennessee, and North Carolina south over southern part of its nesting range

Few birds have been more appropriately named than this little member of the family of wood warblers, for it rarely, if ever, lives outside of pine woods. Bird lovers who spend the winters in southern states may have splendid opportunities to become acquainted with this plainly colored little warbler. It often may be seen in small companies, and on warm, sunny days its song, which consists of sweet, clear, trilling notes, may be heard above the sighing of the wind through the pines.

Pine warbler, male ; female (below)

At such times its notes seem to blend with, and become a part of, the music of the murmuring pine tops, so aptly does the bird seem to fit in with its environment. So closely indeed is it associated with the pines, about which it clings and creeps from top to bottom, that its plumage becomes dingy and soiled from the pine resin.

The nest is in pines, and made of plant fibers, strips of bark, and leaves. From four to five white eggs, marked with speckled brown toward the larger end, are laid.

Prothonotary Warbler

Other Common Names—Golden warbler, golden swamp warbler
Scientific Name—*Protonotaria eitrea*
Family—Parulidae (wood warblers)
Order—Passeriformes
Size—Length, 5½ inches
Range—Nests from Minnesota, Wis-

Prothonotary warbler

willow-bordered streams of more northern states, its radiant form glows like a golden flame as it flits restlessly about in search of its food. It may light on some half-decayed, moss-covered log near a stagnant pool; again it may be seen nimbly climbing tree trunks for short distances, much after the fashion of the brown creeper. The song of the prothonotary warbler, when heard at some distance, is described as bearing a close resemblance to the *peet peet* of the solitary sandpiper. However, this resemblance mostly disappears when it is heard at close range, for then it has a piercing penetrating quality which is quite remarkable. This warbler is somewhat local in distribution and follows large watercourses in its migrations.

The nest is usually close to the ground, in a hole in a stub or stump, often in an old woodpecker's nest cavity. It is lined with rootlets, fine twigs, and feathers or plant down. From five to seven white eggs, thickly and coarsely marked with brown spots, are laid.

consin, Michigan, and southern Ontario, south through central New York, New Jersey to Florida and Gulf Coast, west to eastern Nebraska, Kansas, Oklahoma, and western Texas. Winters in Mexico and south to Central America and northern South America

The exquisite beauty of this warbler can be appreciated only by those who know it in its favorite haunts. It inhabits low, swampy woodlands and seldom strays far from water. Whether seen in the dark recesses of southern cypress swamps, in the verdant depths of bay and myrtle thickets, or along the

Yellow Warbler

Other Common Names—Summer warbler, yellow titmouse, summer yellowbird
Scientific Name—*Dendroica petchia*
Family—Parulidae (wood warblers)
Order—Passeriformes
Size—Length, 5 inches
Range—Breeds in Alaska and thoughout Canada and the United States. Winters from Mexico to Brazil and Peru

Of the vast hordes of wood warblers that sweep north from the tropics into the United States and Canada each spring, none is better known or more widely distributed than the yellow warbler, or summer yellowbird. These warblers enter the Gulf states and California later than most of their kin, along toward the middle of April, but by the first of May some of them have reached the northern edge of the United States.

To many people the yellow warbler is a wild canary, a name which more adequately fits the goldfinch. Others, more discriminating, call it the summer yellowbird, distinguishing it from the goldfinch, which has black wings and a black tail. It appears to be yellow all over, but at close range the male shows long red streaks on its breast.

The breeding range of this little bird is enormous—from the Florida Keys and Mexico north to the limit of willow trees in Canada and Alaska—between five and six million square miles of the North American continent. Of course, there are great expanses of forest country where very few live, for they are not woodland birds. The history of the yellow warbler in many places is very similar to that of the house wren. They lived together along the streams and the willow bottoms, but when man changed the face of the countryside, the wrens and the yellow warblers found the new habitat with its fruit trees and garden shrubbery ideal for their purposes. They became birds of the farms and villages.

The male yellow warbler's *tsee-tsee-tsee-tsiweesee* is pleasing and cheerful. He sings most persistently during courtship and while his mate is building the nest. He sometimes helps, other times not. The nest is usually wedged into an upright crotch in a bush about two or three feet from the ground, but in some places where undergrowth is scanty, they nest as high as 60 feet in large trees. They are beautifully constructed, deeper than wide, quite compact, and of the same silvery color as some oriole's nests. The thin fibers stripped from the stalks of dead plants contribute to this effect, as does the plant down embedded in the walls. Four or five eggs are laid. They are blue-white with brown spots.

Normally, one brood is raised each year, but on rare occasions, there are two. These are perhaps birds that met with ill fortune in their first attempts. The young are fed almost entirely on

Yellow warblers

insects. Whenever the caterpillars, of which the yellow warbler is fond, are plentiful, they form about two-thirds of its food. It feeds on the small caterpillars of the gypsy moth and the brown-tail moth, also cankerworms and other measuring worms, tent caterpillars, small bark beetles, boring beetles, weevils, flies, plant lice, grasshoppers, spiders, and myriapods.

Summer yellowbird is indeed a descriptive name, as the species disappears with the first hint of fall. By late July or early August, migration is in full swing. Migrants reach Central and South America before the month of August is over.   —A.B., Jr.

WASP

Wasps and Their Relatives

Although we may not be always well disposed toward the wasps and their relatives, the ants and the bees, we cannot fail to be impressed by their remarkable adaptations to various ways of life. Many Hymenoptera are social insects, forming cooperative communities that store food and have a complicated economic life. Among the wasps, only a few species are social; most wasps are solitary.

In the United States alone some entomologists (those who study insects) say there are more than 1,000 species of solitary wasps and about 50 social species. Every one of these species has its own distinct behavior and its own complex chain of habits. The solitary wasps differ from the social in having only two sexes, male and female. Each female builds her own nest and provides the food for her young. There is no cooperation among the solitary wasps. Some build their nests in burrows hollowed out in the ground, others in trees or in the stems of plants, and some build mud nests. The social wasps are born into a community and the young stay on in the nest and help with further broods. Two common wasps, one a social insect and the other solitary, will serve as an introduction to the wasp clan.

The Blue Mud Dauber

In the spring and early summer a graceful, thread-waisted wasp, the blue mud dauber, *Sceliphron cementarium* with shining black body and black wings is often seen at the edges of pools and in other damp places, nervously gathering in her jaws particles of mud for her nest. The mud is mixed with saliva and formed into a ball by the wasp's jaws. The nests made of these mud pellets are attached beneath the rafters of barns or sheds or other sheltered places about buildings. Each nest consists of several tubular cells made by placing ring upon ring of mud. In many nests the successive ridges show plainly where the little architect added each new layer of mud.

After the mud dauber has finished each tube she leaves one end open and flies away to hunt for spiders. The spiders are stung and paralyzed and carried to the mud cell and placed within it. Supplying each cell with spiders sometimes takes the female two or more days. She then lays an egg in the cell with this stock of provisions and seals the opening with more mud. The larvae or grubs that hatch from the eggs devour the spiders, undergo pupation, and finally gnaw their way out of the cells as winged adults.

A Common Social Wasp

The large, gray paper nests found hanging in trees and from the eves of houses are the nests of a social wasp, *Vespa maculata*, commonly known as the white-faced or bald-faced hornet. These wasps and their relatives the yellow jackets (*see Yellow Jacket*), were the first and orginal papermakers. They use paper made by collecting bits of weatherworn wood and chewing it into a pulp mixed with saliva. The nest is built from the roof downward and the outside covering consists of many layers of paper with air pockets between. The entrance is at the bottom, below rows upon rows of cells. Each member of the colony lives boxed up in its private cell from egghood to adult emergence and the huge nests of *Vespa maculata* contain many thousands of cells.

A colony of *Vespa maculata* is started in the spring by a single female, the queen. Roused from hibernation into activity by the warmth of early spring, each queen seeks a likely situation for her nest. First she makes a few paper cells and deposits an egg in each. When the eggs hatch, the larvae are fed on insects that have been previously masticated by the queen.

From egg to adult requires about ten

days. As soon as the larvae pupate and emerge as adult workers, the queen confines her activities to egg laying and the workers take up the tasks of enlarging the nest and feeding the larvae as they hatch from the eggs. When an adult emerges from a cell the little compartment is cleaned and made ready for another egg.

The adult wasps live mainly upon fruit and the nectar of flowers but the larvae are fed morsels of insects. After a worker has fed a grub it taps the grub's head and a drop of slightly sweet liquid is given out from the salivary glands, which the worker promptly licks up. Thus the worker is provided with a certain kind of food it needs and at the same time is bribed to continue feeding the grub.

The worker wasps are imperfectly developed females. The difference between workers and females seems to be brought about by feeding. Throughout the summer all the eggs laid by the queen produce workers, but late in the season fully developed males and females are produced. The queens and workers are provided with stings but the males are stingless. The sting is a modification of the ovipositor, or egg layer. With the approach of winter all the members of the colony die, except the fertilized females, or queens, which hibernate and start new colonies the following year. (*See also under Bee; Insect; Sawfly; and under Pigeon Horntail*)

Clustering Wasps

To artists and scientists—and to the germ of artist and scientist in everyone —there are few more alluring places

Each generation of clustering wasps returns to the same cluster site every year

than Jackson Hole, Wyoming, with its massive Tetons and other surrounding mountains.

Even the wildlife and vegetation seem conceived on a grand scale: a white pelican on the turbulent waters of the Snake River, a moose cow and her calf pushing through a dense growth of fireweed, or the clustering wasp of Jackson Hole. Despite its unusual habits, surprisingly little has been discovered about this digger wasp, *Steniola obliqua*. It occurs widely in the western United States and a number of brief reports had been published on its clustering behavior, but virtually nothing was known of its nesting behavior or the significance of its clusters. During the 1950's, a team of scientists decided to investigate the habits of the clustering wasps at Jackson Hole, following a report of unusually high populations of the wasps in that area.

Wasps prey on many kinds of insects and need undisturbed sites for nesting. Where nature is in balance—where there are suitable hosts for the native insect population, and suitable niches in which to nest—the wasp fauna flourishes.

The Jackson Hole Biological Research Station near the outlet of Jackson Lake is maintained by the University of Wyoming and by the New York Zoological Society. Everyone there was familiar with the clustering wasps and with the fact that one branch of a lodgepole pine at the station served for several summers as a clustering point for these insects. Each evening, as the rays of the declining sun slanted through the pines, the wasps formed their cluster, and each morning, between 8 and 9 o'clock, they departed.

During the day they were seen only rarely, chiefly on the flowers of fleabane. In this particular genus of wasps, the tongue is greatly prolonged, by means of which they can take nectar from flowers with deep corollas, usually penetrated only by bees.

Some clusters of the wasps occurred along the Snake River on pine trees as high as six feet, others on sunflower heads and other herbs close to the ground. All were in protected woodland patches along the river.

At night and on rainy days the clusters were always intact—and in the same places—but on sunny days the wasps departed, not only from the clusters, but from the surrounding woodlands. The nesting sites of the wasps were at some distance from their clustering sites.

No information had been available on whether the sexes clustered separately or together, although the investigators found that neither alternative was completely true. Each cluster contained many males and many females, but within it the females clumped together in certain parts, especially on the inside. The slightly larger males covered much of the outside of the cluster of insects. One entire cluster collected by the investigators in mid-July and placed in the refrigerator so that the number of each sex could be counted while the wasps were too chilled to object, contained 162 wasps, of which 91 were females and 71 males.

Later it was discovered that all clusters contained a higher percentage of females, and by mid-August only a few males with tattered wings remained in a cluster. The investigators believed that, doubtless, early in the summer, the clusters contain mostly males, for in most digger wasps the males emerge first and reach the end of their lifespan well before the females.

What could be the function of these clusters, so unusual for wasps? The well-known clusters of the honeybee are formed in the winter and serve to conserve heat. But these wasps do not need to keep warm at night. Like most cold-blooded animals they simply enter a state of quiescence induced by chilling, then recover promptly in the morning. In fact, the temperature inside a large cluster is only a degree or two higher

A female blue mud dauber stocks her nest with the bodies of paralyzed spiders

than the outside temperature.

Some believe that the clusters serve a purely social function. They provide a type of overnight rest center for this gregarious creature following its nuptial union—sort of a honeymoon-hotel variation.

Shortly before sunset the males begin to gather at the clustering site, but they do not actually settle down for some time. As the females begin to arrive, each is joined by a male. The two descend close to the ground together and them proceed in a strikingly undulating fight, finally landing on the ground, mating, and then separating and rejoining the growing swarm at the clustering site.

At times dozens of pairs could be seen performing this ritual together. As darkness descends, the wasps become less active, and gradually they settle into a compact, inert cluster. The males tend to be more restless than the females—perhaps waiting for a few last females to come in—and when they finally settle down are, therefore, mostly on the outside of the cluster.

In the morning, about two hours after

Odontocynips nebulosa Kieffer
A GALL WASP

Prosevania punctata (Brulle)
AN EVANIID

Formica exsectoides Forel
THE ALLEGHENY MOUND ANT

WASPS AND

Pelecinus polyturator (Drury)
A PELECINE WASP

Chrysis nitidula Fabricius
A CUCKOO WASP

Vespula maculata (Linne)
THE WHITE FACED HORNET

Eumenes fraternus Say
A POTTER WASP

Sphecius speciosus (Drury)
THE CICADA KILLER

Dasymutilla occidentalis Linne
THE COW-KILLER ANT

Tiphia inornata Say
A TIPHINE WASP

Vespa crabro Christ
THE IMPORTED EUROPEAN H

Agapostemon radiatus (Say)
A GREEN BEE

Campsomeris quadrinotata (Fabricius)
A SCOLIID

Sceliphron caementarium (Drury)
A MUD-DAUBER

Bembix spinolae Lepeleti
A DIGGER WASP

RELATIVES

Diprion similis (Hartig)
THE IMPORTED PINE SAWFLY

Apanteles congregatus (Say)
A BRACONID

opa virginica Linne
CARPENTER BEE

Bombus terricola Kirby
A BUMBLE BEE

Itoplectis conquisitor (Say)
AN ICHNEUMONID

Megarhyssa macrurus (Linne)
AN ICHNEUMONID

Psyllaephagus trioziphagus (Howard)
AN ENCYRTID

Tremex columba (Linne)
THE PIGEON HORN-TAIL, A SAWFLY

Thyreodon atricolor (Olivier)
AN ICHNEUMONID

Brachymeria ovata (Say)
A CHALCID

Ooencyrtus kuwanai (Howard)
A TANAOSTIGMATID WASP

Pseudotorymus lazulellus (Ashmead)
A TORYMID

Perilampus ruficornus (Fabricius)
A PERILAMPID

sunrise, the wasps awaken, one by one, finally flying off to take nectar from flowers and then off to the nesting areas.

It was several days before the investigators discovered the nesting sites. They found them scattered near the banks of the Snake River, primarily in small patches of earthy sand or gravel which apparently had been deposited during periods of flooding.

The nests in riverside sand or gravel were absurdly shallow—only a couple of inches deep. There the females reared their larvae, feeding them from day to day on flies. The soil in the nesting areas was dry and powdery and on warm days became quite hot at the depth of the nest cells.

Some nests had apparently been dug out by mammals feeding on the wasp larvae. It was surprising to the investigators that most of the larvae managed to survive in such an uncongenial environment.

Another curious fact discovered was this wasps selection of food for its larvae. Its choice is a stout-bodied, hairy fly, usually known as the bee fly. Most digger wasps related to *Steniolia* capture almost any kind of fly. But the investigators, after examining many *Steniolia* nest found nothing in them but bee flies gathered by the adult wasps as provender for the wasp larvae after hatching. Apparently these wasps are individualists in food selection as well as in many other ways.

How far from the clustering place does the female nest? Do individual wasps return to the same cluster each night? These questions were answered by the investigators by marking all individuals in certain clusters. They found to their surprise that some of the marked wasps appeared in other clusters up to a mile away, while the original clusters soon contained many unmarked individuals.

In general, the females of a given cluster tended to nest within a radius of 100 yards of the clustering point, but this was not always true. Late in the season there seemed to be a tendency for the clusters to break up into smaller ones closer to the nesting sites.

If individuals do not necessarily return to the same cluster night after night, why is it, asked the investigators, that certain branches of trees and certain herbs have clusters night after night for most of the summer as does the lodgepole pine at the Jackson Hole Biological Research Station? Since the wasps live for only one season, the question arose as to what factors induce successive generations to return to the same branch of the pine trees each year.

Presumably this branch has some unusually fine properties, for the wasps cannot "remember" the branch when in fact it was their parents that inhabited it the previous season. The investigators were at a loss to discover what these properties might be. There seemed to be many, many branches that were alike. It was possible that the wasps lay down an odor that attracts the clusters each evening. But would such an odor persist for the entire year? One finds a parallel in the monarch butterflies that select certain trees in which they roost, year after year (*See under Butterfly Migration*). And what of the clusters on annual plants, which are simply not there the next year?

The investigators concluded that these were questions that might be answered only by further intensive studies of the fascinating clustering wasps.   —H.E.

Recommended Reading

Field Book of Insects—F. E. Lutz. G. P. Putman's Sons, New York.
The Social Wasps—William M. Savin. *Natural History*, Jan.-Feb., 1925.
Solitary Wasps—G. and E. Peckham. Wisconsin State Bulletin.
Wasp Studies Afield—P. and N. Rau. Princeton University Press, Princeton, New Jersey.
Wasps That Hunt Spiders—William M. Savin. *Natural History*, May-June, 1922.
Ways of the Six-footed—Anna B. Comstock. Comstock Publishing Company, Ithaca, New York.

WATER

Water—Lifeblood of the Earth

The road north of the town was the best one for bird walks. The north road led to the river, and to the brooks and swamps that were some of the best birding spots in the country.

It was on the river that the ducks stopped, spring and fall. It was in the lush woodlands along the brooks that the barred owls could be heard hooting at dusk. The best list of warblers could be got there in May (*see under Warbler*), and there the greatest number of birds stayed through the summer to nest. The wet places, or at least the well-watered places away from the river, were quite good, too. Dry hillsides had their birds, but not so many as the glade.

An Experiment

The soil is alive and birds and other animals depend on it. Soil alone will not sustain life without the help of water (*See under Soil*).

As a concrete proof of this, try an experiment. Dig up two large pieces of earth, each a foot square. Put these into separate pails and put on a shelf in a room. The soil in one pail is to be sprinkled frequently, and the soil in the other left exposed to the dry air of the room. After a time green shoots begin to appear—grass, clover, a small fern, and several larger plants. It is fascinating to see these thing grow. They were in the soil, of course, but water was needed to bring them to life. The soil in the other bucket dried out, cracked, and life died.

The soil of the world would hardly produce a thing without water. There would be no birds, nor men either.

1500 Cubic Miles of Water

Fortunately, most of America has plenty of water—sometimes a little too much in some places, but there are reasons for that, too. At any rate, it is said that 1,500 cubic miles of water fall on the United States every year.

Simple mathematics will show that such an amount could cover the country 2½ feet deep. Of course it falls over a period of twelve months, not all at once.

Where does all this water come from? Some of it comes from the ocean which covers three-fifths of the earth's surface; moreover, the depth of these waters runs to five miles or more in some places. They are tremendous reservoirs.

Much of the water also comes from the land itself—there are lakes, rivers, and even puddles, which hold water. Some of this standing water evaporates, makes clouds, and then drops back to the earth again as rain or snow (*See under Cloud; Frost; and under Sun*). Another great source of water to the land is the moisture given off by leaves and other vegetation. This process is called transpiration, which is the sending off of vapors as through a porous substance or the tissues of plants

The Water Cycle, or Hydrologic Cycle

Summing up the hydrologic cycle briefly, it is:

1. The water leaves the earth by evaporation and transpiration.
2. The vapor forms clouds.
3. The vapor in the clouds condenses into rain, snow, or hail, and falls back to earth. This cycle never ends. It has been going on for countless ages.

But what happens to the water when it reaches the earth? Does it immediately start back again into the sky? Some of it does, but some of it evaporates from the surface of the ground soon after it has dropped. Some moisture even evaporates from the raindrops while they are still falling. But most of the water has a more complicated cycle.

1. Some of the water runs off the surface, trickling first into the little brooks, then into the rivers and finally into the ocean.
2. Some of the water soaks into the soil:
(a) Part of this is immediately absorbed by plant roots.

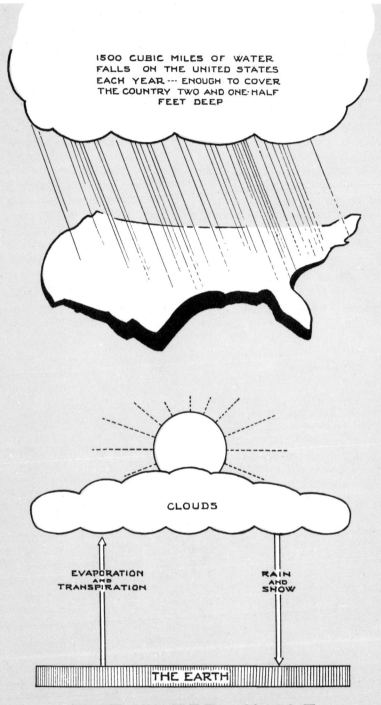

THE WATER CYCLE

(b) Part soaks through or infiltrates into the subsoil and porous rocks where it forms a sort of underground reservoir where the water is stored (the upper level of this is called the water table). This underground water finds its way eventually to plant roots or comes to the surface as bubbling springs or feeds into pools and lakes in the hollows.

It has been said that in some places out of every six raindrops, three evaporate immediately or are soaked up right away by plants and later transpired; two run off the surface and one is held in pools above ground or below the surface for later use.

Journey of a Raindrop

When a drop of water starts to the sea, it should not run a race; its journey should be a slow one—an obstacle race, at best. It is best that the rain be checked in its fall by the leaves and vegetation, then allowed to sink slowly into the soil, clear and clean, finding its way slowly to the underground streams and pools. If it is not picked up by a root, then it may find its way to a clear spring. The spring may bubble forth and reach a brook, and if the banks of the stream are healthy and the soil held together with a good luxuriant growth of plants, the water will remain clear and flow without cutting away the land. Perhaps the brook will meet a beaver pond (*See under Beaver*). There the water will be slowed up until it finds its way through the cracks and crevices of the dam. And so the stream flows on, around the bends down through the farming country to the big river and the ocean.

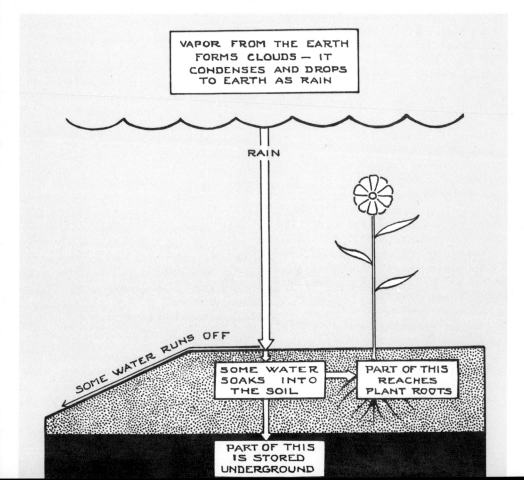

Some of the things that will slow a raindrop in its journey are:

Soil	Roots
Leaves	Beaver ponds
Grass	Plants along the stream
Stones	Bends in the river
Pebbles	Swamps
Rotting logs	Lakes

The more slowly the water travels the more good it does along the way, the more it is used by plants and animals before it is returned to the atmosphere. This balance between absorption (sinking in) and runoff was developed by nature through millions of years.

Journey of a Raindrop – 20th Century

The early settlers in the eastern United States found crystal-clear streams, luxuriant forests, lush marshes, and healthy grasslands. Wildlife was everywhere abundant. In the South and many other parts of the country, the same streams that now run red or brown with mud were clear enough to drink. A great change has taken place because of erosion or a wearing away of the land. The main causes of erosion are:

1. Careless lumbering
2. Fire
3. Overgrazing of livestock
4. Improper plowing
5. One-crop farming

The cutting of forests off the slopes leaves the soil unprotected so that the rain easily washes it from the rocks.

Fires kill the life in the topsoil, burn the spongelike humus, and make it easy for the soil particles to wash away during the rains.

Too many cows or sheep on an acre destroy the ground cover and pack the soil so that the rain cannot seep through but trickles off the surface, washing the soil with it. The paths of these grazing animals often wear into deep gullies.

Improper plowing, that is, plowing up and down hill instead of across the slopes, results in great erosion through-out the farming area. The rainwater washes down through the furrows, taking the soil along to the bottom of the hill.

One-crop farming, which means growing the same crop year after year on the same plot of land, soon exhausts the humus from the soil so that it easily washes away. Humus in soil makes it spongelike; gone, it is like rock powder.

The journey of many a raindrop is far different today than it was when the land was unspoiled. Instead of being checked by the grass and leaves, and allowed to sink slowly into the soil to maintain the underground water supply, the raindrop is joined by an army of others and they all trickle into the nearest small rivulet, which perhaps has started cutting its banks and is wearing a deep gully. The greater the rush of water, the more difficult it is for the plant roots to hold the soil against the cutting force. Farther down the line, where the beaver pond used to be, there is nothing to stop the rushing progress, for the beavers in that area have been trapped out long ago. A score of little streams joins the main body of water as it makes its way toward the sea. The swamplands, which offered pockets for the surplus water to retreat into, have been drained, so that by the time the now swollen, muddy creek reaches the big river it finds a great flood. The high waters from numerous smaller creeks have arrived at the same place at the same time. Houses in the lowlands are swept away and lives lost. When the water recedes, a week or two later, a heavy coating of mud and silt covers the fields where crops had been planted.

Too Little Water

Too much water can do a great deal of damage, but so can too little. These same streams that the raindrop traversed in its helter-skelter scramble to the ocean often present a vastly different aspect late in the summer. The beds of

Fires kill soil organisms and burn humus causing severe erosion damage in forests

Improper plowing and one-crop farming has destroyed millions of farm acres

the little streams are quite dry, for no water has been held back. Not receiving its proper supply, the underground water table has been lowered to such an extent that it no longer feeds a sufficient amount of water into the springs and streams to tide them through the hotter months. As a result of this lowered underground water level, soil in many places has become quite powdery, not fit for many plants to grow in. Dry soil means sick and stunted plantlife, which, in turn, results in scant animal life— the insects, mammals, birds, and even man, too, for he also depends on the earth for his living. He will always be dependent on it even though he may sustain his life with chemically made pills and tablets.

Wildlife Needs Water

Geese, ducks, and other birds live on the plants and smaller animals that thrive in the water of swamps, marshes, streams, and ponds. When the water balance is upset, many of these plants and animals die. This may be one of the reasons why ducks and geese reached such a low level in the United States in the 1930's (*See Waterfowl*).

Fish would also be affected because they, too, feed on the plant and animal life in the water, and the birds, like the kingfisher and the great blue heron which eat fishes, would become scarcer, too. Another and even greater menace than silt from erosion to life in the rivers is pollution from cities and towns. Almost everything in nature is interdependent. Nothing can live by itself. Animals cannot live without the soil, nor can the soil thrive without the animals; and without water the soil cannot produce plantlife nor support animal life.

"An ounce of prevention is worth a pound of cure," is an adage that applies to land as well as man. It takes only a short while to destroy an inch of topsoil, but it might take centuries to replace it.

The Beaver—Nature's Conservationist

The beaver practiced land and water conservation long before man ever thought about it. This large, flat-tailed rodent is not only a master woodsman but it stores water, thus evening up the flow and preventing floods and droughts and, in time, building up many rich meadows (*See under Beaver*).

Beavers build ponds by first building a dam across a waterway. They use their teeth instead of a hatchet to cut down small saplings and branches for the dam. Near the center of the pond a beaver house is built. The pond continues to grow until sometimes it covers several acres. At first, many trees that are standing in the flooded area die, and it would seem to many people that it is a pity that this should happen. However, after several years the beavers desert the pond, and the dam falls to pieces. When the waters go down, a rich black soil is exposed. This is soil that would have washed down into the big streams and would have been lost except for the dam that held it back. In due time a growth of sedges, and later, bushes, covers the bed where the pond used to be. Deer and other animals come to feed there and birdlife is abundant. The stream is about the same size it was before the beavers came but instead of rushing through hastily in the spring and becoming dry in the summer, the water meanders slowly across the beaver meadow, held back by the rich growth.   —R.T.P.

Water Table

[Editor's Note: The following material was written by the late Jay N. Darling, one of America's most ardent conservationists. Darling, Chief of the United States Biological Survey (now called the Fish and Wildlife Service), during the 1930's and 1940's stirred all Americans with his often poignant, humorous, and frequently hard-hitting newspaper cartoons depicting America's waste of its natural resources. He twice won the

Pulitzer Prize for his editorializing cartoons. Darling received the Audubon Medal in 1960 (*see Audubon Medal*) for his distinguished service to conservation.]

Asked to name the three things he would rather have more than anything else in the world, man would probably first say *riches* and the other two, *more riches*, which shows how little man knows what's good for him. If he had no air he would die in a few seconds, if he had no water he would die of thirst in a few days, and if there were no land he could have no food and would slowly die of starvation. But all three of these working together in the sunshine produce everything the richest man in the world can possess: food, clothing, forests, and all the living creatures on earth. Leave out any one of the three and the other two are powerless to keep us alive.

This is the story of water and how man, by his carelessness, is in danger of losing one of the most important sources of supply on which he (and all life) depends, namely, the groundwater storage, commonly called the *water table*.

Ordinarily, when we think of the part water plays in our lives we think first of rivers, lakes, and oceans and perhaps rain and the city waterworks. Few ever think of the vast amount of underground moisture stored away deep in the soil which scientists call "the most instantaneous and effective of all freshwater reservoirs." The reason we never think of it is because it is invisible and hardly anyone ever sees it except perhaps at the bottom of a well. Probably the simplest way to define the groundwater table is to say it is the underground water supply to which people dig when they need a well. Only those who have ever had to dig a well with a spade and shovel know how important it is to have that water table not too far down in the ground.

In earlier days, before cities and towns had public waterworks and started piping water to their homes, most people had their own wells or patronized the town pump. One of the first things the early pioneers always looked for before choosing a piece of farmland or establishing a settlement was to see how deep down in the earth they would have to dig to get water. Many a large city in the United States owes its beginning to the fact that the groundwater table could be easily reached without too much digging by hand with the spade and shovel. It never seemed to have occurred to anyone at the time that this same underground water supply might have other very important influences on their lives, the climate, vegetation, and wildlife.

It was a long time after that (let us say about fifty years) when things began to happen which jogged everyone's memory about the forgotten underground water table. Farmers who still depended on their old dug wells for their water supply found that their wells had gone dry.

Springs that used to flow from the ground at the bottom of a hill in the pasture and furnish fresh water for the cattle and horses stopped flowing altogether, except in very wet weather.

Little creeks and rivers that used to have plenty of water in them the year round were dried up in the summertime instead of furnishing a good place to go fishing and swimming. Of course, the fishes that had once lived in the little rivers and creeks had no place to go and wait until the water came back when the fall rains came, so they died and there were no parent fishes to raise new families of little fishes to take their places when they were gone.

When the springs also went dry and the water in the creeks ceased to flow in the summer, the birds and fur-bearing animals—particularly those that live near water, like the beaver, mink, marten, muskrat, and the ducks, sandpipers, and killdeer—had to move away in search of new homes where water and food supplies had not disappeared so mysteriously. Since new living quarters not already occupied were hard to find, the wildlife forced out by a water shortage simply disappeared; there was no increase in neighboring areas.

And something else very important seemed to be wrong. Everyone could remember when the summer farm crops and pastures in the earlier days could go without much rain for several weeks without being completely destroyed. Now they could no longer stand a drought nearly so well. Some years the crops were so poor it hardly paid to harvest the grain. The cattle lacked water and the pastures burned up from lack of moisture, and even the local summer showers that used to fill the cisterns seemed to have joined the general conspiracy and became less and less frequent.

All these changes had come about so gradually that no one tried to discover the reasons until conditions got worse and worse and finally so bad that something had to be done about it or else the people, like the birds and other animals, would have to move away. In some sections of the West many of them did, and lost their farms. Land became unsalable where conditions were very bad. Most everyone said it was all because the climate had changed and there was not enough rain anymore. No one—at least, not many—thought that the groundwater table could have anything to do with the changed conditions.

Then a group of scientists, who started to study the situation and its causes, remembered the old water table that used to be near the surface of the ground, sometimes not more than 12 or 15 feet deep on the average. That same

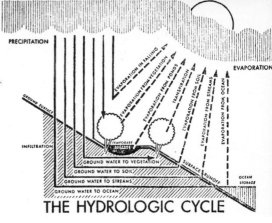

THE HYDROLOGIC CYCLE

The underground water table is supplied with water only from the atmosphere in the form of rain or snow

water table was now much lower, sometimes twice its original depth, and in one state in the Middle West, it had fallen to 59 feet, where once it had been only 8 to 10 feet below the surface of the ground. Nearly everywhere in the United States the water table had fallen considerably since the days of the pioneers.

Small wonder that the farmer's wells had gone dry. And because natural springs were only places where the underground water table came so near the surface that it bubbled forth out of the ground naturally the springs went dry too when the water table dropped. And if the springs no longer flowed into the little creeks and from the creeks into the rivers, it was easy to see why the streams dried up (or nearly so) in midsummer. And if there was less water on the ground, naturally the air became drier from lack of evaporation.

The same group of scientists reasoned that if the old water table was double the distance from the surface, and roots had to be twice as long to reach the moisture, it was to be expected that the plants might get twice as thirsty in dry seasons. Of course, corn, oats, and wheat have very shallow roots and no one thought that they ever depended directly for their moisture on their roots reaching the water table; yet in the neighboring fields where the native deep-rooted vegetation had never been disturbed, the plants remained green

Jack's River cascades through Chattachoochee National Forest, Georgia

long after the short-rooted domestic crops had perished from the drought.

Many theories were explored and not all of the supposed causes have yet been sufficiently proved to satisfy the scientific investigators. There are, however, some established facts which can be given that are known to have played a large part in lowering the water table. The most important ones are as follows:

The underground water table gets its supply from only one source and that is the moisture that falls on the surface of the land in rain or melted snows. If the water from rains or melted snow runs off the surface of the land too fast it does not have a chance to soak into the ground. Anything that speeds the run-off, therefore, robs the underground water table of its normal supply. This moisture must make its way slowly down into the soil until it comes to a stratum of rock or impervious clay and can go no farther. There it is held in storage for the many uses that nature requires. As moisture thus absorbed increases in quantity, the surface of the water table rises just as the surface of the water rises in a tub when more water is added. If it falls it is a sign that the new supply of moisture has for some reason been prevented from working its way down through the soil.

At first, it was thought that the falling water table had been caused by a decrease in the general rainfall, which of course would have been a very simple explanation. But examination of records over a period of several wet years showed that the water table had continued to fall even in periods of heavy rainfall and only a little less rapidly than in a dry cycle of years.

There was a time not many years ago when rains and melting snows were held on the surface of the land in marshes, ponds, and shallow lakes. In those pools the water stayed often the year round and had plenty of time to soak into the soil and replenish the water table.

Millions of acres of these marshes and sloughs, and even some of the shallow lakes, have been drained off through man-made drainage ditches in order to make more dry land for farming. That is one thing we know lowered the water table (*See Swamps and Marshes*).

Forests and underbrush, with their thick carpet of old leaves and decaying logs and deep matted roots, once occupied much more of the land than now, and rain and snow falling in the great natural forests were held in the spongy blanket of vegetation until the moisture slowly seeped down into the ground to join the underground water supply. When we cleared the forests and underbrush from the land we destroyed another of nature's methods of retarding the run-off of surface waters. The water was gone before it had time to soak into the ground.

Our prairies and meadows, when our pioneers first saw them, were waist high with a heavy growth of native grasses that caught the snows and rains and held the water in their matted roots almost as effectively as did the forests. When we mowed those fields or plowed them for planting, or when our sheep and cattle grazed them down close to the ground, they no longer held back the moisture until it had time to seep into the earth.

Now, just as though lowering the groundwater table was not enough of a calamity in itself to convict man of criminal carelessness, he seems to be guilty of a double crime, for by the same acts with which he destroyed his own habitat, he robbed wildlife—songbirds, fishes, wild ducks and geese, and fur-bearing animals of their natural homes. Their breeding grounds were destroyed, their food and water supplies were just as badly affected as man's living conditions. No matter how carefully we protect wildlife from human molestation, they cannot multiply when their natural homes are destroyed.

There is much more to the story. For example, the part that trees and deep-rooted vegetation play not only in holding the water on the surface until it soaks into the ground, but how the same vegetation serves as nature's pump to bring up the same water again from the ground and literally pour it back into the air through the pores in the leaves. Scientists have measured the amount of water an average-sized tree will pump up and give off into the air on a dry, windy day, if its roots can reach the underground water. Impossible as it sounds, a tree will bring up from the ground and give off through its leaves more water, and faster, than a man with a 3-gallon bucket can carry water by ladder to the top of the tree, working a full eight-hour day. A whole forest of trees working together could imaginably have a startling effect on the content of moisture in the air, and atmosphere heavily charged with moisture is a promising condition for a local summer shower (*See under Tree*).

If this analysis of the importance of the groundwater table seems too fanciful for ready belief, there are several experimental areas on which the above mentioned principles applicable to restoration of the ground water table have been successfuly applied.

For example, an area of more than 80 square miles north of Minot, North Dakota, and a semiarid area of approximately a million acres in northern Nevada can be cited as suitable subjects for study because of their wide variation in geographic location and environmental conditions. In both cases the ground water table had fallen to a dangerously low level, springs had dried up, wells had gone completely dry, vegetation had been practically eliminated. Both of these broad stretches of land had been famous hardly 50 years ago for the prolific amount of wildlife— ducks, prairie chickens, antelopes, deer, muskrats, sage grouse, and songbirds that made their homes there before man

had destroyed their natural environment. By 1934 all wildlife had either perished or moved out and man was on the way.

In one area the primary cause was overdrainage of surface waters. In the other case, it was overgrazing, which left no vegetation to hold the winter snows or sparse spring rains. Taking a tip from nature, the water from the rains and snows was held where it fell on these areas. Check dams were built to hold back the run-off, drainage ditches were stopped up and the water retained until it had time to soak into the ground. Vegetation began to appear around the small water-soaked spots and then spread over the entire acreage. From that time on nature took over the job of holding back the natural precipitation and storing it underground. In less than 10 years from the time these corrective measures were applied both areas were pretty well back to normal; soil erosion had been stopped entirely, springs were flowing again, vegetation was luxuriant, the birds and mammals—prairie chickens, ducks, sage grouse, and antelope—had returned in great numbers to live and multiply. Productive life was again possible for both wildlife and man.   —J.N.D.

Water Pollution and its Control

The beauty of Henry David Thoreau's quiet Massachusetts pond played no small part in providing that physical environment which, together with his views on society, produced his famous book, *Walden*. Yet, the quiet beauty of Walden Pond and the other great ponds of Massachusetts was preserved by the very government against which Thoreau's individualism had rebelled. Early statutes, enacted while the colony was still young, protected these fresh-water bodies by holding them open for "fishing and fowling" and providing ordinances against polluting them by dead carcasses or other similar acts harmful to fishes.

In the same year that Thoreau wrote of his experiences on the Concord and Merrimack rivers (1849), John Snow in London demonstrated that polluted water could transmit cholera, and Lemuel Shattuck started his classic sanitary survey of Massachusetts. These surveys resulted in a philosophy upon which rest modern public health practice. Said Shattuck: "It is the duty of the State to extend its guardian care, that those who cannot or will not protect themselves, may nevertheless be protected; and that those who can and desire to do it, may have the means of doing it more easily." Following this spirit, Massachusetts organized the first state health department in 1869, and set the pattern for similar departments throughout the nation.

For nearly one hundred years, and principally during the last sixty, dependence has been placed on these departments of government, their successors, and their local and federal government counterparts to combat hazards to men, animals, and nature, resulting from the pollution of waters. While Thoreau the individualist may not have agreed with this action, Thoreau the naturalist could not have withheld his support.

Pollution Grows with the Nation

City life of the 20th Century is a new experience for mankind and its future cannot be clearly envisioned. Looking back, however, three stages of pollution characterize the growth of cities.
1. From the revolutionary period until the mid-eighteen hundreds, pollution from man, beast, and industry was deposited in the streets and on the ground until, as one writer described, "it dried up and blew away." Storms were the great "washers of cities" and periodically each rain would carry the filth away to the nearby streams or other waterways.
3. By the time the 19th Century drew to a close, nearly every city of any size

had constructed a sewer system, and household conveniences were becoming more common. While sewers were beneficial, they also created problems, since they concentrated pollution, initially widespread throughout a city, at the places where the sewers discharged into rivers, lakes, or other watercourses. As these same waterways were usually used for sources of water supply, a recirculation pattern was established between waste discharges and water intakes which produced explosive epidemics of waterborne disease.
2. The new science of bacteriology, based on Pasteur's findings in the 1870's, together with the new technology of water and sewage treatment which began to develop rapidly after 1900, made it possible for society to attempt for the first time to control waterborne epidemics and pollution. Epidemic control made great strides by 1925 owing to the development of modern water filtration processes and chlorine disinfection. Progress in the construction of works to reduce pollution moved much slower and, as a consequence, the nation continued to be burdened with an ever-increasing volume of water pollution.

Today, the nation's standard of living takes for granted kitchens with garbage grinders and dishwashers, bathrooms and double plumbing, utility rooms with washers, basement drains, lawn watering and car washing, and 24-hour continuous water service and waste-water collection systems. An average of 22 billion gallons of water each day is used in cities and carried away in sewers after use. The same 22 billion gallons, carrying with it all the waste products resulting from the use of the modern conveniences, flows through underground sewers to thousands of municipal treatment works. While tremendous gains have been made in applying known sewage treatment technology to these wastes, modern society develops new problems even faster.

As cities grew and prospered, so did industry. By 1900 industry was using between 10 to 15 billion gallons of water per day. Between 1900 and 1960, industrial production expanded another eight times. Well over one-half of this increase occurred from 1940 to 1955.

By 1960 industry as a whole needed 12,175 billion gallons of water each year, and new technological developments lean heavily on water as an industrial raw material. For example, to produce 10,000 gallons of gasoline each 24 hours requires the following:

Natural gas (150 lb pressure)— 20,000,000 cu. ft.
Absorption oil recirculation per day— 150,000 gallons
Steam—60,000 lbs.
Electricity—20 kilowatt-hours
Direct labor—42 man-hours
WATER—200,000 GALLONS

Today, the composite waste products of man's accumulated cultures—through the coal age, the steel age, the chemical and the atomic age—are discharged to rivers, lakes, estuaries, and oceans. Older problems such as acid drainage from coal mines, salt brines from oil wells, and wastes from the food and paper industries join together with new and different pollutants from the chemical industry and radioactive wastes to produce a growing combination of old and new problems.

The Future—and Immediate Goals

The most recent predictions about water and water pollution control are those made by the United States Senate. Its Committee on National Water Resources concluded that by 1980 the nation's population will be 252 million, an increase of 3.6 million per year. By the year 2000 the country will contain about 350 million people. Industry will be two-and-a-half times greater than in 1960. Total water requirements will zoom from 300 billion gallons each day in 1954 to 559 billion by 1980 and will be about 888 billion by the year 2000.

Allowing for the best kind of control over municipal sewage and industrial waste that we can depend on with presently known treatment methods, it is quite clear now that the task of keeping our rivers and lakes clean will be our number-one future water problem.

In past years pollution control was largely a public health problem. The basic need to protect public health is more important than ever, but today it is recognized as equally necessary to protect our natural heritage of fish, aquatic life, and wildlife; to make possible water-based recreation; and to satisfy the needs of our cities and national economy. Today, the major role of pollution control is to make possible the full use of our resources.

The immediate task confronting us is to build, as soon as we can, treatment works for municipal sewage and industrial wastes. To meet the present backlog of needs for municipal treatment works alone, over 6,000 projects will have to be undertaken. Until research provides new technology to treat more completely the wastes of our civilization, some water storage reservoirs will be needed to provide additional water to carry away treated wastes and restore water values.

Science and Water

The study of water is complicated and draws heavily on many fields of science. It requires knowledge of fluid mechanics, hydrology, and sanitary and chemical engineering; the chemist's knowledge of the composition and character of water, how it reacts with the basic elements and natural and man-made compounds, and of the means to separate water from all the material it may dissolve or carry in suspension; the biologist's view of the great varieties of life within water and the effect of water on all forms of life, within water and the effect of water on all forms of life, within and out of water. More recently, it requires the physicist's understanding of the relation between water and radioactivity.

Unlike flood control, which requires knowledge of rivers when their flows are high, water quality management or pollution control is concerned primarily with conditions during the dry season and low streamflow periods. In addition, information is needed about the quality characteristics of streams. This includes chemical information, such as the amount of oxygen dissolved in water. It is this relatively small amount of oxygen that gives life to waters. If oxygen is absent, waters become dull, foul, and incapable of supporting useful plant and animal life and serving human needs.

Biological knowledge is a relatively new means of managing water quality, but one of the most important. It deals with the relation of fish, shellfish, and the minute organisms comprising this food chain, to the water environment (*See Food Chain*).

Increasing the Water Resource through Water Reuse

Imagine a single shirt. Each day it is used, soiled, and placed in the laundry basket. Each morning, however, it is back on the dressing table, cleaned, ironed, ready again to be used. Imagine, too, that this one shirt would magically serve for office, dress, or sport; and would turn to any desired color at the will of the owner. This would certainly be a multipurpose shirt, and the one shirt, through repeated use, would give the same effect as owning many shirts. Like the shirt, if the dirtied water could be cleansed after use and then returned to the nation's waterways, it would be the same as having a clean shirt waiting to be used again each day. In this way, water that has been made clean can be used again and again by anybody, for various purposes.

The Cleaning Process—Sewage and Industrial Waste Treatment

The technology of cleaning the waters of cities is fairly well developed. In general, 80 to 90 percent of the organic wastes (which can be reduced to non-offensive substances in the presence of oxygen) can effectively be decomposed by municipal sewage treatment works. In many cases, the waterways into which the treated wastes are discharged can satisfactorily absorb the task of treating the balance of the waste products.

At some places—and the number of places is increasing—the ability to remove in excess of 90 percent of the organic waste matter is not enough. Chicago, for example, still returns wastes (the undecomposed 10 percent) equal to nearly one million persons to the Illinois River waterway.

Municipal treatment works have developed many refinements during the past twenty years. However, the basic process—a half-century old—has not changed. As used, dirty water comes into a plant; large rectangular or round tanks hold the water quietly for several hours. During this period, the force of gravity is used to settle solids. These are collected at the bottom of the tanks. The partly cleansed water then is transferred to tanks or stone filters, where large numbers of organisms decompose the organic wastes. Subsequently, added settling basins and sometimes disinfection with chlorine essentially complete the treatment process. Cleaning the water used by over one-third of a million factories and industrial establishments is less complicated in some ways than renewing the waste waters of cities; and more complicated in other ways.

Industries use much more water than cities— 125 billion gallons each day compared to 22 billion gallons. But over 94 percent of this water is used for cooling purposes—in power plants, condensers, and for other industrial purposes such as making steam. This water is returned to the waterways without carrying waste products and needs little or no cleansing. It does carry heat, however, and this constitutes an increasing problem.

The safe disposal of industrial wastes is a major problem in many areas

The remaining water is used to perform the thousands of industrial processes in the nation's factories (process water); to clean up machinery, floors, and plants during and after the workday (clean-up water); and to provide drinking for industrial employees and for water to care for their needs in washrooms, showers, cafeterias, and lunchrooms (sanitary water).

After the many things possible are accomplished to reduce the amount of waste water and waste material within the plant, the remaining waste water must be processed in an industrial waste treatment plant. For most organic materials, the treatment process is much like that used by cities. However, because of the great variety of substances resulting from industrial operations, many different methods must be used, each one tailored to meet the conditions of the individual factory.

Today's First Team—Treatment and Dilution

Early in the 20th Century it was considered satisfactory to discharge wastes to a river or stream if a calculated volume of dilution water was available. Before World War II there was general agreement that all cities should have at least "primary" treatment, thereby removing about 35 percent of the pollution load and leaving the balance to be purified by the stream. Industries were generally to follow this requirement as well. In addition, where cities, towns, and factories were located on small bodies of water, that provided insufficient dilution water, treatment demands were correspondingly higher—up to about 90 percent treatment of the waste water.

Since World War II the nation's growth, the very large increase in water use, and the increased demand for high quality water to support public health, fish, wildlife, and outdoor recreation have forced the adoption of a new policy about treating waste water. In December of 1960 the National Conference on Water Pollution called by President Eisenhower expressed its view that, "the goal of pollution abatement is to protect and enhance the capacity of the nation's water resource to serve the widest possible range of human neeeds, and that this goal can be approached only by accepting the positive policy of keeping waters as clean as possible as opposed to the negative policy of attempting to use the full capacity of water for waste assimilation." This view was reviewed by the federal Water Pollution Control Advisory Board, appointed by the President, and adopted as its policy on February 3, 1961.

This policy recognizes that the nation's water resources have to be much cleaner than ever before if they are to support the nation's growing economy, and health and welfare goals.

In 1961 Congress amended the federal water pollution control act and provided that agencies like the United States Army Corps of Engineers, Bureau of Reclamation, and Soil Conservation Service could store waters in federally-constructed reservoirs for regulated release when needed. Such releases help to control pollution by providing for

Reservoirs that regulate water flow in dry seasons help reduce water pollution

additional dilution of *treated* municipal and industrial waste materials.

This combination of methods—treatment and dilution—represents the last major step that can be taken without significantly new knowledge. The next steps that need to be taken will be discussed in the section on research.

Silt from the Land—Waste from the Cities

Two problems are attracting increasing attention as water becomes more completely used by more people for a wider variety of purposes. These result from sediment coming from the land and the washings from the growing metropolitan and urban centers.

Siltation is a major factor affecting water quality. The principal source of silt is the erosion of land, although in certain locations industrial operations such as mining and gravel washing contribute considerably to the sediment load of water courses. Excessive unnatural erosion may be caused by timber harvest, agricultural practices, irrigation, road and highway construction, grazing, and land clearing for various purposes. Siltation from these activities is controllable or, at least, can be minimized by reasonable practices.

Most of the concern with pollution from urbanized areas has been centered about pollution created by discharges from city and industrial sewers. To these must be added pollutional material washed off the streets of the nation's cities. Chemical residues deposited by millions of automobiles, oil drippings, ash coming from home and industrial chimneys, salts used to melt ice, fertilizers and poisons washed off untold acres of lawns and gardens—all make additions to waterways into which waters from cities drain. Antilitter programs can be and are of great help in keeping our rivers and beaches not only useful, but pleasant as well.

Dollars for Pollution Control—Whose Dollars? How Many?

Water pollution, like smallpox and polio, is preventable. Why, then, does the nation continue to be troubled by it? The answers lie partly in the nation's history; partly in the speed of the nation's growth and technological progress; and partly in irresponsibility.

Given a choice, cities have preferred to spend public money for roads and highways, public buildings, schools, and water supplies, rather than controlling pollution. Industries preferred to spend their corporate moneys for new factories or mines rather than for nonproductive waste treatment works.

Each citizen preferred to spend his money on things he could use directly for himself and his family, rather than for a more distant and obscure purpose like a sewage treatment plant.

In 1956 Congress decided that progress was simply not adequate in the face of a mounting problem. A new law was passed authorizing the federal government to share the cost of municipal waste treatment with cities. This help, at the rate of $50,000,000 per year, increased the amount of annual construction to $350,000,000 by 1960.

By 1961 Congress increased the amount of assistance to cities by appropriating $80,000,000 in that year. This aid boosted city spending to well over $400,000,000 each year, and for the first time there is hope that treatment works to control pollution will pull even with needs. The present plan called for $90,000,000 in aid during 1962 and $100,000,000 each year thereafter until 1967.

The record of sharing costs has been extremely successful. For every federal dollar of aid, local communities have spent about five dollars.

The costs of needed facilities for controlling industrial pollution, estimated to be $600,000,000 per year, are still to be paid by industry. To some extent, it is proper and expected that these costs will be paid by all the people in the price of products that they purchase. However, unless more progress is made by industry in this aspect of the work, Congress may be expected to consider ways to stimulate these efforts.

It can be seen how the first team—the combination of sewage and industrial waste treatment and proper use of reservoir water to dilute *treated* wastes—is moving to attack the water pollution problem. But these efforts alone, even today, are not good enough for some problems that have already started to appear.

Research—Geared to the Jet Age

The basic science on which a large part of treatment technology rests is old—of early 20th Century vintage. It is not able to cope with problems resulting from pollution by persistent chemicals such as detergents and insecticides (*see Detergent; and under Insecticide*), which in one case were traced for one thousand miles in the Missisippi. It has not yet provided the answers for dissolved solids like chlorides, nitrates, and phosphates, and elements such as sodium, boron, and fluorides, which build up in the process of reusing water; radioactivity; and the final residue of organic pollution that remains following sewage treatment. Beyond this, there are problems of virus and other disease-causing organisms for which more information is needed.

Whether new knowledge can be developed rapidly enough to meet these mounting situations without restricting the use of the nation's water resources is a question that cannot be answered now. The rapidity of events and the decades of inadequate research cannot be overcome at once.

Events during the early 1960's indicate that there is developing a rapidly growing ground swell of understanding on the urgent need for a very large effort. University research, research grants, fellowship, and contracts with private industry for research on specialized problems are contributing their share to the research task. Regional water pollution control laboratories now being established by the federal government are expected to make significant contributions.

Administration and Law—Tools of Society

The protection of natural resources, including the control of water pollution, President Kennedy said, "is not a task that should or can be done by the federal government alone. Only through the fullest participation and cooperation of state and local governments and private industry can it be done wisely and effectively."

The responsibility for controlling water pollution and for improving water quality management operations is widely shared by all levels of government. Local governments—cities, towns, counties, metropolitan and sanitary districts, and other local forms—have the fundamental responsibility to plan, construct, and operate the actual works needed to cleanse waste water. In each local town, city, or district, by pulling together to develop "clean water" programs, citizens can make their best contribution to the national cleanup campaign.

State governments, through their water pollution control authorities, carry out the policies established by the state legislature, make river basin studies, and develop plans to control pollution. While there is usually one state agency principally responsible for pollution control activities, many parts of state government have an interest in the work. These include the fish and game departments, health, agriculture, and mines departments, and water resources and forestry agencies.

The federal government works generally to give support to the states. The federal water pollution control act places primary responsibility on the states for control efforts. In addition to research and training, comprehensive river basin planning for water-quality management and the collection of information about water in the nation's river basins, the United States Department of Health, Education, and Welfare provides financial assistance to cities and helps to enforce pollution control on interstate or navigable waters throughout the nation. This department cooperates fully with the United States Fish and Wildlife Service, the National Park Service, the Forest Service, the United States Corps of Engineers, and other agencies to insure that all those having a stake in clean water are represented and their aims supported.

These diverse but combined efforts make up the total, cooperative effort to keep the nation's water resources clean and healthy for all its needs. All depend on the individual citizen assuming his own share of the responsibility for preventing pollution,

The natural beauty of the land cannot be measured in dollars, and only a full understanding of the effects of man's selfish interests can safeguard it for the future

helping to pay the costs, participating in government, expressing his views, and exercising his rights and privileges in a free society (*See also Air Pollution; and under Oil Pollution*).   —L.B.D.

Recommended Reading

The Columbia River Basin Project For Water Supply and Water Quality Management: Introductory Report—U.S. Department of Health Education, and Welfare, Public Health Service, Region IX, Portland, Oregon.
Public Health Engineering—Earle B. Phelps. John Wiley & Sons, Inc., New York.
Public Health Service Bulletins: *Clean Water: A Challenge to the Nation* (No. 816); *The Living Waters* (No. 382); *Proceedings: The National Conference on Water Pollution,* 1961; *Protecting Our Water Resources: The Federal Water Pollution Program* (No. 950): *The Struggle For Clean Water: A Series For Teachers*—U.S. Department of Health, Education, and Welfare, Public Health Servie. U.S. Government Printing Office, Washington 25, D.C.
A Primer on Water—Luna B. Leopold and Walter B. Langbein. U.S. Department of the Interior, Geological Survey, U.S. Government Printing Office, Washington 25, D.C.
Water Supply and Waste-Water Disposal—Gordon M. Fair and John C. Geyer. John Wiley & Sons, Inc., New York.

Watershed
What is a Watershed?

Watershed is a new term to many people. The increasing use of soil and water conservation measures for watershed protection and flood prevention is bringing the term into more common use. Its definition is almost as simple as the well-known phrase "water runs downhill."

The drainboard that carries rinse water into one's kitchen sink can be compared to a watershed.

On the land, water that does not evaporate or soak into the soil usually drains into ditches, streams, marshes, or lakes. The land area from which the water drains to a given point is a watershed.

When a small child, one probably had a favorite mud puddle in which he liked to play. The part of the yard from

Diagram of a small rural watershed

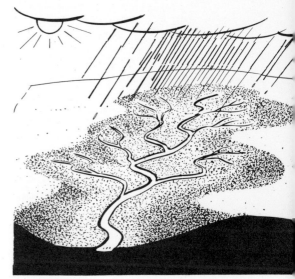

Drainage pattern of a small watershed

which the water drained into his puddle was its watershed.

Possibly a small stream ran by his house. It may have been dry most of the year or it may have flowed continuously. Water from a few acres drained into that little stream. Those few acres were its watershed. This small stream and others like it ran into a larger one. The small streams and the land they drained were the watershed of the larger stream into which they flowed.

Small-and medium-sized watersheds make up the larger one. The Mississippi

New River meanders through Jefferson National forest, Virginia

River, for example, drains a watershed of about 1,243,000 square miles. That watershed is made up of thousands of smaller ones.

So, wherever one lives he is in a watershed. It can be just one's own backyard or the area drained by a small creek or a large river.

A watershed may include farm or ranch land. It may include hills or mountains or both. Some of it may be rough, rocky or marshy land suited only to timber and wildlife. Some of it may be covered with towns, suburban developments, or industrial plants.

People who live in the watershed are a part of the watershed community. So are the birds, fishes, and other animals. All depend on the watershed, and they, in turn, influence what happens there— whether it is good or bad. What happens in one's small watershed also affects all the larger ones below.

Why a watershed is important

Water may be a friend or it may be an enemy. If it runs off the land too fast, it cuts gullies and carries off topsoil which should be kept on the farm to produce food and clothing. This soil along with other debris that the water carries into streams and lakes may spoil fishing. It may also reduce the amount of water the stream or lake can hold and thus decrease the water supply for one's town and his bathroom. Such sediment carried downstream by runaway water may greatly increase the cost of cleaning and filtering the water one gets from the kitchen faucet. It can interfere with the hydroelectric plant that produces the home's electricity. This may make one's electric bills higher.

If too much water runs away too rapidly, it causes a flood that damages farms, ranches, crops, property, homes, highways, and utilities. It may take lives. Stream channels may be choked with sediment. Then the flood is more serious because the choked-up channels

are forced to carry less water. Sediment deposited in water reservoirs after heavy rains reduces the amount of water that can be stored for use in water-short areas. When water does these things it is an enemy.

But water can be slowed down and used to advantage when needed soil and water conservation practices and other flood-prevention measures are established throughout a watershed. Terraces, strip-cropping, more grass and legumes in crop rotations, and improved pastures are practices that make more water soak into the soil for use of crops, pastures, or range. Conservation irrigations systems waste less water and thus leave more for other irrigators to use and help produce better crops. Later some water will go into streams, lakes, or underground storage to be used in other ways. It does not carry sediment to clog streams and water supplies. Thus, more water is available for the many uses people make of it. Then water is a friend.

Recommended Reading

Land – The Yearbook of Agriculture, 1958.
Soil – The Yearbook of Agriculture, 1957.
Water – The Yearbook of Agriculture, 1955. United States Government Printing Office, Washington, D.C.
Water for the World – Elizabeth S. Helfman. Longmans, Green & Company, New York.
Water and the Cycle of Life – Joseph A. Cocannoner. The Devin-Adair Company, New York.
A Primer on Water – Luna B. Leopold and Walter B. Langheim. United States Government Printing Office, Washington, D.C.
Water: A Study of its Properties, its Constitution, its Circulation on Earth and its Utitilization by Man – Sir Cyril S. Fox. Philosophical Library, New York.
Clean Water: A Challenge to the Nation; Highlights and Recommendations of the National Conference on Water Pollution. U.S. Department of Health, Education and Welfare, Washington 25, D.C. (Public Health Service Pub. No. 816).
Our Growing Water Problems – R. G. Lynch. Rev. 1959. Write to National Wildlife Federation, 232 Carroll St., N.W., Washington, D.C.
Water: 1955 Yearbook of Agriculture. United States Government Printing Office Washington 25, D.C.

Upstream watershed projects combine land conservation measures such as strip farming and contour plowing with small flood-retarding dams that discharge excess runoff at a safe rate. The average watershed project of 60,000 acres has six such dams

Water for America—Edward H. Graham and William R. Van Dersal. Oxford University Press, New York.
Water, Land, and People—Bernard Frank and Anthony Netboy. Alfred A. Knopf, Inc., New York.

WATERFOWL

Of the many species and families of birds that live on or near the water, the one that has received the name of waterfowl is the Anatidae. It is composed of the swans, geese, and ducks, generally plump, edible birds of large or moderate size, of world-wide distribution, and well known everywhere.

All of the nearly 150 species in this group share a number of important characteristics. All are compact of body, long-necked, and short-legged. The feet are always webbed. The bill is typically short and straight, often high at the bridge, and usually with laminations along the edges, useful for cutting leafblades and roots of aquatic plants. An exception is the bill of the mergansers, or fish-eating ducks, which is long and thin, with the laminations modified into rows of toothlike projections.

Most waterfowl are vegetarians, feeding on seeds, roots, grass, underwater vegetation, and the like. Many of the sea ducks, and some of the geese, feed on marine invertebrates, including clams and mussels. Mergansers live almost exclusively on fishes.

All waterfowl have a direct and powerful flight, with rapidly beating wings. None of them soar or glide, except for brief moments when coming in for a landing. Of the entire group, only the river ducks, or dabbling ducks are able to spring upward from the surface of the water and into flight; the others, or so-called sea ducks, taxi along the surface, paddling with the feet and beating with the wings until they rise from the surface.

Swans and geese are believed to mate for life or for the life of either partner. Some of the ducks may follow this pattern, but most of them appear to mate only for one season, while in a few species the males are polygamous (See under Duck). The eggs are numerous, clutches varying with the species from 10 to 20. The nests, on the ground except for a comparative handful of species that nest in trees, are lined with downy feathers from the breast of the female. The cygnets (young of swans), goslings (young of geese), or ducklings are covered with down at hatching, and can swim on the next day.

Waterfowl have dense plumage. The body, or contour, feathers are kept in a water-repellant condition by oil from the preen gland, located just over the tail, which is worked into the feathers by the bill. The feathers form an outer waterproof covering, protecting the inner heavy coat of down that is worn next to the skin. The flight feathers of waterfowl are all shed, or molted, at once, usually just after the breeding season. To protect themselves while flightless, the birds must hide until the new ingrowing flight feathers allow them to become airborne once again.

Most waterfowl nest in the northern United States, Canada, and Alaska, moving south ahead of ice and snow, or to the open coastal waters. Small family groups merge, until sometimes huge flocks are formed. The characteristic flight formation is a wedge, with a leader "breaking trail" and setting up air currents by its passage that are utilized by the others (See under Goose).

Swans, geese, and tree ducks are usually placed together in the subfamily Anserinae. They are larger than most ducks, and have proportionately longer necks.

The rest of the ducks are in the subfamily Anatinae. This group is again divided into tribes of birds that are similar in appearance and habits.

The dipping, or dabbling, ducks are the freshwater birds of ponds and rivers. Males and females are often very different in plumage, but they share the same *speculum*, a band of brilliant feathers on the edge of each wing. They feed on vegetable matter and on aquatic animals which they seine from the mud, while tipping up from a swimming position on the surface. The mallard, pintail, black duck, widgeon, and teal are typical of this tribe.

The bay, or sea, ducks have less difference between the plumage of the sexes, and the speculum is dull in color, generally grayish. They dive beneath the surface to grub for aquatic vegetation or animal matter. The canvasback, redhead, ring-necked, and scaup ducks are in this tribe. Most of them nest on fresh water, but winter on salt-water bays.

The perching ducks are largely tropical. The colorful wood duck is the only perching duck in temperate North America. It is largely vegetarian, inhabits woodlands near swamps and lakes, and nests in natural cavities in large trees (*See Ducks: Wood Duck*).

Eider ducks form the next tribe. They are northern birds, diving for mussels, and wintering along the coasts south to Long Island and California.

Sea ducks are strong swimmers and divers, most of them nesting along arctic shores, a few breeding on freshwater lakes and rivers but wintering on the coasts. Mergansers, scoters, goldeneyes, old-squaws, and harlequin ducks are among the sea ducks.

The last group, that of the stiff-tailed ducks, is represented by the ruddy duck. These are diving birds, with short wings that give them a labored flight and short legs set far back that make them awkward on land.

The taking of waterfowl is regulated by law, to insure the continuance of the species. The greatest threat to waterfowl is no longer the unrestricted hunting that nearly wiped out several species near the turn of the century, but the destruction of the habitat of the birds that breed on the lakes and potholes

Pintail ducks

Snow geese live in safety at Tule Lake National Wildlife Refuge, California

of prairies, and the draining of their wintering marshes.   —G.B.S.

Waterfowl and the Future

There was a day when North America's waterfowl populations gathered in such legions along the two coasts of the continent, and in the great valleys that drain it southward, that they rose like a thundering cloud from the water when disturbed (*See Souris National Wildlife Refuge*).

There are now a very few places where really large numbers of ducks and geese can be seen. Although the numbers of the waterfowl are much reduced, they are still in sufficient supply for all of us to enjoy them if this natural resource is managed wisely.

Waterfowl are almost all produced in wetlands, and it is the decrease in wetland acreage on the North American continent that is responsible for the major decline in waterfowl numbers. In the United States alone there were once 127 million acres of wetlands—of marshes and swamps. Today the total wetland area is less than 80 million acres. More than a million acres of the best duck-producing areas on the continent—the prairie pothole country of the north central states—was drained for agricultural use between 1943 and 1961. During this same period American agriculture produced embarrassing surpluses of grain.

Until early in this century there were few limits on the killing of waterfowl and hunting was conducted during the autumn, winter, and spring. In 1918 the first federal regulations of waterfowl hunting limited the daily bag to 25 ducks and 8 geese and the open season to 100 days. As the number of hunters grew and productive waterfowl habitat declined, the hunting regulations were tightened until, today, the open season may be limited to something between 25 and 75 days, depending on the numbers of birds, and the daily bag limit may be between two and six birds.

The drought years of the 1930's reduced duck numbers drastically, since some 50 percent of all our ducks are produced in the pothole country of the northern prairie. Alarm over this decline allowed the United States Biological Survey, now the Fish and Wildlife Service, to ask for a special Migratory Bird Hunting Stamp (the Duck Stamp) in 1934. With the funds from the sale of such stamps to some 10 million waterfowl hunters, the Service embarked on a dramatic National Wildlife Refuge acquisition program. Some three million acres of wetlands were acquired to help stabilize the waterfowl population.

The 1940's were wet years and the ducks responded to improved conditions in the prairie and increased rapidly. The 1950's were dry years again, however, and a new decline set in. This drought continued into the early 1960's and it was obvious that the future of the duck population is tied not only to the ups and downs of rainfall cycles but to our ability to preserve a good nucleus of the prairie nesting species in refuges during dry years. When rain comes again, these birds can take advantage of the new habitats and quickly rebuild their populations.

This emphasizes the importance of hunting regulations and of waterfowl refuges. Through an extensive duck banding (see Bird: Birdbanding) program, the United States Fish and Wildlife Service has learned a great deal about the movements and population dynamics of North American waterfowl. It is only by continually refining this core of scientific information, and basing management and regulations on it, that the waterfowl resource can be intelligently managed.   —R.C.C.

Recommended Reading

North American Waterfowl—Albert M. Day. Stackpole Company, Harrisburg, Pennsylvania. Waterfowl Tomorrow—Joseph P. Linduska (editor). U.S. Government Printing Office, Washington, D.C.

WATER HOLE

In dry regions, a water hole is a spring or a collection basin where water is available to wildlife. It becomes a focal point for the animal species that live nearby and depend upon it as the only source of water in the dry season.
—G.B.S.

Animals at a Water Hole

In very dry weather animals will come to a water hole at almost any time of day. To see the greatest number of birds, mammals, reptiles, and insects, it is best to select a hiding place near the water hole at about noon. Then one needs only to wait awhile for the show to begin. Usually, in dry country of the southwestern United States one will not have long to wait. In wooded country there will probably be many squirrels, and they come very early for their drink. Jackrabbits, too, are often early visitors, but cottontails and swamp rabbits come later, often waiting until after sundown, especially if there is an early moon.

It is usually four or five o'clock in the afternoon before deer start to appear, and these are does, fawns, and the younger bucks. Old bucks are always later. If the moon if full, they may wait until two or three o'clock in the morning to appear. As for wild turkeys, it is very seldom that they come for water in the afternoon. They are early morning drinkers, usually going to water directly from their roosts. Other birds drink at almost any time, many of them drinking all through the day.

But the afternoon is still the best time to see wildlife at a water hole. One afternoon at a Texas water hole, 17 animals—8 birds, 2 rattlesnakes, and 1 coachwhip snake—all drank from a small dirt tank at the same time. The rattlers were not together, nor drinking at the same spot, and birds and other animals kept a respectful distance from them.

In the course of an entire afternoon hundreds of animals come for water—

birds, deer, wolves, coyotes, and bob-cats. Once a mother skunk with 10 half-grown "kittens," following behind her in single file, walked to a water hole and all lined up for a drink. Even an occasional turkey hen with her well-grown chicks will move to the water in that cautious way that a turkey uses in all its comings and goings.

One Texas water hole was formed by a good spring that flowed from some rocks, forming a large basin of water. Because no habitation was near, this pool made an ideal watering place for the many wild creatures that lived in the vicinity. On one side of the pool was a bluff, or cliff, which was pos-sibly 40 feet high; on the other side, there was a little sandy shore that led up to higher ground, which had scat-tered timber on it as far as the eye

could see. The cliff made an excellent observation point and a good place of concealment. One could see thousands of animals coming to drink, to prey upon others, or in turn, to be preyed upon (*See Predation*).

Whenever one could see the great golden eagle hanging like a speck high in the heavens, it was certain that some of the animals at the water hole would soon furnish a meal for her, or for her eaglets waiting with hungry mouths in a nest on a peak that was miles away. The eagle, with folded wings and the speed of light, would shoot down from the clouds to pounce upon some bird, beast, or reptile. With her strike would come the thrashing of a snake, the scat-tering of feathers from a bird, or the squealing of a rabbit in its death throes. The eagle would then fasten her talons

firmly around the victim and fly away to the cliffs where she had nested for many years (*See under Eagle*).

Sometimes, too, a wily coyote would entertain observers at the water hole with his showmanship, carrying on clever antics in full view, making a deliberate effort to attract attention. All the while his mate would be wiggling along on her belly through the grass and weeds, finally pouncing upon some unsuspecting rabbit.

The showman's act would then be over; the first coyote would dash off to share in the meal that its trickery had helped it to capture. The age-old drama—the survival of the fittest, the strong preying on the weak—was almost constantly enacted. Woe be it to anything that was crippled, or that was in a weakened condition! Before reaching the

life-giving water, its life would be snuffed out by a hungry animal that would then feed upon it.

Hawks found the water hole an ideal feeding ground, preying upon the numerous smaller birds that came there. The small birds, in turn, preyed upon insects, and the insects upon the weaker of their kind. Late in the evening, the great horned owl, gliding silently like a wraith on silent wings, would appear out of the shadows to seize a rat or a rabbit and fly to the top of an oak, there to enjoy its evening meal. The *paisano,* or roadrunner (*see Roadrunner*) would wait with great patience for a lizard, or for one of the small water snakes. When a lizard or snake ventured out on the sand, the roadrunner is ready for them. With one stab of its long beak, it would pierce the snake

FERGUSON

at the base of its skull, and soon the snake would disappear rapidly down the bird's gullet.

The "Timekeeper" also frequented this water hole. The name, given it by observers at the water hole, may not sound like an appropriate one for a snake, but for this particular snake there was none better. Timekeeper was a large rattlesnake, about six feet long, with 14 rattles and a button. It always appeared at the water hole at almost the same time of day. There was never more than four or five minutes variation in the time of its arrival. Down across the sand, its heavy body forming huge S's, it would push its way to the water, where it would drink thirstily sucking up water as a cow, or a deer does. After getting its fill, with an increase of girth around the middle, it would go back the way it had come, soon disappearing in the weeds and grasses. Although dozens of rattlesnakes came to this water hole, none of them was so impressive as Timekeeper. Sometimes, before it reached the open ground, the warning cries of the birds and the scolding of the squirrels were enough to signal to all animals that the snake was on its way.

Only once was this snake observed to coil for a strike. That happened when an oversized, broad-striped skunk, deliberately walked slowly in front of the snake. Coiling, the rattlesnake poised to strike. The skunk unperturbed, sauntered on its way with never a backward glance. The *whir-whir* of the rattles filled the air, giving out that blood-chilling sound that is frightening to both man and beast. Every animal, except the skunk, scurried for cover.

The whirring of the rattles continued. Still the skunk ambled along, as if no six-foot rattlesnake was going to scare it. Finally the snake's fear or anger subsided (fear or anger are the only things that will cause a rattlesnake to rattle), for it uncoiled itself, went to its regular drinking spot, and drank as usual. Then, as usual, it returned the way it had come. Soon activity at the water hole returned to normal. Small birds flitted about, squirrels barked and chattered, and crows called. All the other creatures—those that but a moment before had remained completely silent and concealed—reappeared. Some drank, others searched along the bank of the pool or in shallow water for prey, as the fearful sound of the big snake's rattles seemed forgotten.   —V.W.T.

WATER LILY
Fragrant Water Lily
Other Common Names—Pond Lily
Scientific Name—*Nymphaea odorata*
Family—Nymphaeaceae (water-lily family)
Range—Throughout most of central and northeastern United States and beyond
Habitat—Ponds, back waters, bog pools
Time of Blooming—June to September

This fragrant flower, with its waxy, white petals and large number of yellow stamens, has long been a favorite summer wild flower both with people and with insects. Look into the heart of this beautiful flower and many times it will appear to be spotted with black, but upon closer investigation it will be found that the black spots are insects. It has been stated that more insects visit the flowers of the water lilies than those of any other kind. They come to get pollen. Bees and beetles in particular are most often responsible for the water lily's cross-fertilization.

Those who have gathered water lilies have noticed the gelatinous material that surrounds the stems and undersides of the leaves. This is a modification to keep water out of the plant. The problem here is too much water, not too little.

The underside of the floating water-lily leaf often becomes the nursery for protozoa, sponges, snails, and many types of insects. Its thickened rootstalk

The undersides of water lily leaves are a habitat for a variety of pond creatures

is one of the favorite foods of the moose. Other deer feed upon its leaves.

During winter the water lily is withdrawn to the bottom of the pond or stream where the water is warmer. During the period when the fruit with its seeds are ripening, the flower, now with its petals decaying, is likewise submerged.

The seeds of this and other species of water lily are eaten frequently by ducks and in the Gulf region are important as duck food. In Florida the sandhill crane eats the stem, roots, and seeds to a considerable extent. Lily pads are a principal item of diet for the moose. Various parts of the plant are eaten by beavers, muskrats, and porcupines.

In some areas the thoughtless nature lover has almost or quite exterminated this sweet-scented water lily by gathering it too freely. The plant is now pro-tected by law in a number of states.

WATERTHRUSH
Louisiana Waterthrush
Other Common Names—Large-billed waterthrush, southern waterthrush, wagtail
Scientific Name—*Seiurus motacilla*
Family—Parulidae (wood warblers)
Order—Passeriformes
Size—Length, 6¼ inches
Range—Nests from eastern Nebraska to Minnesota, Wisconsin, and southern Michigan and Ontario, south to central New York, Vermont, New Hampshire, and Rhode Island, south to North and South Carolina, Georgia, Alabama, Mississippi, and Louisiana. Winters in Mexico, Cuba, the Bahamas, and Bermuda south into Central and South America

This wood warbler has the distinction of representing in its habits a cross be-

The Louisiana waterthrush nests under stream banks or in the roots of fallen trees

tween the water ouzel and a sandpiper. Although not aquatic like the water ouzel, it frequents the margins and boulder-strewn beds of tumbling brooks that flow through wooded hills. It also inhabits the borders of woodland streams that flow through the lowlands. In such secluded haunts it leads an active life and may be seen flitting from rock to rock or feeding along the oozy margins of quieter streams. Like a sandpiper it tilts and teeters, and seems to have an abundance of nervous energy. Its shy and suspicious disposition conforms to the character of its favorite haunts, for it might well seem to be an embodiment of the wild and elusive spirit of the woodland. When frightened it darts ahead in low flight, alighting on some limb by the stream, or on its margin or rocky bed. On being further disturbed it again takes flight and disappears in the dusky undergrowth of the woods by the stream's edge.

The nest is under a stream bank or the roots of a fallen tree and is built of twigs, rootlets, and leaves. From four to six white eggs, spotted with brown, are laid.

WAX MYRTLE

An eastern family of low, shrubby plants, the Myricaceae contains the wax myrtle, the bayberry, and the aromatic sweet fern. In each species, the fruit is coated with grains of wax. Only in the bayberry is the wax thick enough to warrant harvesting the berries for extraction of the wax for candles.

Plants in this family are able to grow in very poor soil. As they enrich the soil by the disintegration of their leaves into humus, other plants benefit by the process and crowd out these pioneers.
—G.B.S.

WAXWING
Cedar Waxwing
Other Common Names—Cherry bird, cedar bird, Canada robin
Scientific Name—*Bombycilla cedrorum*

Family—Bombycillidae (waxwings)
Order—Passeriformes
Size—Length, 6½ to 8 inches
Range—Breeds from Alaska, Alberta, Saskatchewan, Manitoba, Ontario, Cape Breton Island, and south to northwestern California, Oklahoma, and northern Georgia. Winters throughout most of the United States. Many waxwings also migrate as far south as Colombia and Venezuela

No bird is sleeker or softer looking than a cedar waxwing. It is not as brilliant as an oriole or a tanager, but its plumage is beautiful. The soft browns are set off by a jet-black mask, a tapering crest, and a yellow band on the tip of the tail. Often the ends of some of the wing feathers are tipped with little, shiny, scarlet scales like bits of red sealing wax. Only cedar waxwings have trimmings like these.

Cedar waxwings are unable to sing. Their sole note is a high, thin lisp.

Cedar waxwings are among the last birds to nest. A few of them nest in June, but most of them wait until July or even August. One nest with eggs was recorded as late as October 12. Where they nest is decided by how easily food is attainable nearby. The nesting places vary considerably—from five or six feet to the tops of high trees, both hardwoods and evergreens. The material that goes into the nest varies too, depending on what is readily available. Both the male and female build the nest—the male brings the materials and his mate adds it to the structure which she molds into shape.

The three to five pale blue eggs are dotted with small dark spots. As is often the rule when the two sexes resemble each other, the male and female both take turns on the eggs that hatch in about 14 days. Blueberries and wild cherries ripen in midsummer and the parents stuff their gullets with fruit until their throats swell. Then they return to the nest and produce them one by

Cedar waxwings from Audubon's Elephant Folio

one as they feed their young. As with the songbirds, the newly-hatched young do not distinguish one thing from another very well. Any sudden movement near the nest will make their mouths pop open. In fact, after 12 or 13 days they will mistake each other for their parents. If a young one rises to its feet or tries to climb out of the nest the rest of them crowd around and beg for food.

Wild cherries are especially favored by cedar waxwings. So are garden cherries, and it has earned the waxwing the name cherry bird. Although cedar waxwings will eat insects at times, the greater part of their food is made up of berries. On these they gorge themselves, but most small fruits are not very rich in calories, and great amounts must be eaten to afford proper nourishments.

When cedar waxwings are not eating berries, they often gather in small groups in the tops of trees. It is not unusual to see them dress one another's feathers, or pass a berry back and forth. Their migrations and movements are erratic. Although many of them stay through snowy winters in the North,

others will travel as far south as Colombia and are among the last of the birds to return in the spring, often in late May or early June.

The Bohemian waxwing, *Bombycilla garrula,* is half an inch to an inch longer than the cedar waxwing, and has white wing patches and reddish feathers under the tail. It is more northern in range, breeding in western Canada, Alaska, and Eurasia. Its wintering habits are irregular, but it has been reported from New England, the Midwestern states, the Pacific States, and in the Rocky Mountains south to Colorado. —A.B., Jr.

WEASEL
Long-tailed Weasel
Other Common Names—Ermine (in white phase)
Scientific Name—*Mustela frenata*
Family—Mustelidae (weasels, skunks, and allies)
Order—Carnivora
Size—Male: body length, 14 to 23 inches; tail, 4½ to 7 inches; weight, 7 to 14 ounces. Females smaller
Range—From central British Columbia, Alberta, and Saskatchewan, southwestern Manitoba, southeastern Ontario, southern Quebec, and New Brunswick, throughout all of the United States except the southwestern desert, Baja California, and extreme northwestern Mexico, south through Central America to South America

Weasels are the smallest and, for their size, most ferocious and bloodthirsty of all the carnivores. They have the distinction of having the widest range and the greatest number of species of the flesh-eating animals in America. They are widely distributed over both the eastern and western hemispheres but the group as a whole is essentially a northern one. In development, the extremes range from the least weasels, about 6 inches in length, to the black-footed ferret with an overall of 23 inches. They are all long, slender-bodied

The long-tailed weasel, or ermine, changes its coat from brown to white in winter

animals with short limbs. Weasels are extremely active both day and night. The northern species are the only representatives of the large order Carnivora that make a complete change from a brown summer coat to a snow-white robe. Thus, the northern brown weasel with its summer pelage becomes a snow-white ermine in its winter coat. The phenomena of this remarkable change takes place with the first fall of snow and occurs almost overnight. It is accomplished by molting and not by change in color of the hair. An unseasonable thaw in winter with dispersal of the snow leaves the weasel at a disadvantage on the bare ground in its white cloak for it cannot change back to its brown summer coat until time for its spring molt.

In addition to its hardy nature the common weasel is also a prolific breeder. The number of young in a litter may even reach eight. It is also a tireless and relentless hunter, with well-developed senses. The army of weasels is the staple force that keeps the ever multiplying hordes of rats and mice within reasonable bounds. It kills not only for food but out of sheer pleasure. When in the midst of any number of victims, it slays all and feeds on the warm blood drawn from the neck of its victims. Gruesome as this awful carnage may seem, it is nature's method of helping control the vast numbers of mice. Meadow voles for example, breed practically every month in the year and have four to six in a litter—the young mice themselves are ready to breed when about a month old (*See under Mouse; and under Vole*). —G.G.G.

WEATHER
Forecasting the Weather

The weather is of interest to all, either as the most common topic of conversation, as a source of pleasure or disappointment on a holiday, or, for many people, a serious concern that affects their very lives and their means of earning a living. Although no one can change the weather to suit his whims or needs, all of us could change our plans to suit the weather, if we knew what it was going to be. And though detailed weather forecasting for large areas calls for the cooperation of many highly trained scientists, it is perfectly possible for any of us, if we observe accurately and practice consistently, to forecast the weather for our local area with some accuracy. It is fun, too, for as weather detectives we gather clues by observing the clouds, the wind, the temperature, and the air pressure much in the same way that the famous detectives of fiction gather their clues, and, like them, we weave these clues together to see where they point.

During World War II, we saw in a dramatic way the importance of weather forcasting, for upon the knowledge of the "weather men" in the armed forces rested an important share of the credit for the success and safety of air movements and of invasions. All through man's earthbound history, weather forecasting has been vital to the farmer, the traveler, the shipper, and the sailor. It is many times more important now that man has taken to the air, for all who plan to pilot airplanes must early become acquainted with a knowledge of the processes that bring about the weather.

The atmosphere is an enormous but delicate mixture of the lightest things on earth, extending for about 600 miles above earth's surface. Long before the coming of man to our planet, it was at work. Changes in air temperature caused the rocks to expand and contract and hence to become cracked and broken. The gases in the atmosphere have decomposed these rock fragments and played a large part in turning them into the soil on which we depend for food. The air is like a vast ocean in which we live, and though we can do without food or water for several days,

Cumulus, or fair weather clouds

if the air is taken away from us for a few minutes we cannot live. Sixty-five percent of the human body consists of oxygen, the gas that makes up about one-fifth of the air, and we use it for every life process.

The atmosphere is important to us also because it absorbs many of the types of rays from the sun that would injure life, and because it absorbs and holds much of the heat from the sun, so that the earth is not unbearably hot by day nor unbearably cold by night. Sound waves are transmitted through the air, and smells travel through it. It is chiefly because of the local conditions of the atmosphere that make up climate, that we find different types of plants and animals in different parts of the earth, and it is even believed that the states of man's civilization are largely influenced by the climate in which he lives. And finally, the air is important because the phenomena of weather take place in the air and because of it.

In knowledge of the weather, clouds play a leading role. In every season, on almost every day, they have a beauty that can be as well appreciated in the city as in the country, and every day

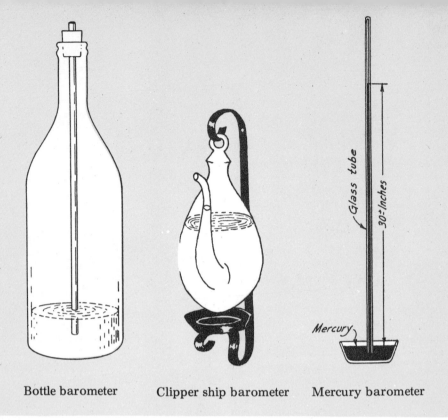

Bottle barometer   Clipper ship barometer   Mercury barometer

they furnish a clue to the coming weather. Clouds are formed of tiny droplets of water, condensed from the air when it is cooled, high above the earth's surface. The only equipment you need for studying the clouds are pictures from which to identify the different types, and a pair of dark glasses to cut out the sun's glare and enable you to see the cloud outlines more clearly (*See under Cloud*).

Forecasting Fair Weather

The most familiar type of cloud is probably the fair weather, or *cumulus,* cloud. It is a separate cloud, like a heap of white cotton in the sky, and, indeed, its name comes from the Latin word for *heap,* the same word that gave us *accumulate.* Occasionally one may see a single cumulus cloud floating in a bright blue sky, but they may be seen in rows parallel to the horizon. The base of a cumulus cloud is usually flat. They are characteristic of bright sunny days, with fair weather ahead, although on very hot, muggy days, when they are massed near the horizon, they some-

times bring showers in the afternoon.

A look at the wind direction may also help to reassure one that fair weather is in store, for a wind from a general westerly direction usually presages fair weather. (Winds are named from the direction *from* which they come; that is, a west wind blows *from* the west.) One can sometimes determine wind direction by seeing which way the wind is blowing leaves and branches, or a flag, and if one holds a handkerchief in his outstretched hand in an open place, it will blow away from the wind. But it is best to have a weather vane, and one can easily be constructed in the work shop. Set the weather vane high above the ground, where the wind is not likely to be affected by trees or houses.

The speed of the wind often gives us another clue to aid in our forecasts. In the middle of a period of fair weather the air is often very calm; and likewise, as we enter a period of good weather the speed of the wind is likely to decrease. Therefore, if one estimates its speed at perhaps three or four hour intervals, he can see whether it is lessening or increasing. To do this use the Beaufort scale of wind force. This scale gives a method of estimating the speed of the wind by observing its effects on surrounding objects.

As a period of fair weather approaches, the temperature is likely to fall. Therefore, one will wish to take periodic temperature readings. Temperatures are measured with a thermometer, a word coming from the Greek for *heat* and *measure*. The first satisfactory thermometer was made by a German scientist named Gabriel Fahrenheit, who lived over 200 years ago. Thermometers are inexpensive and easily purchased. A good thermometer shows very nearly the exact temperature of the air, if it is exposed to the wind, fully shaded, and removed from overly heated or overly cooled objects.

One property of air that we seldom think of is its weight. Although the air is light it extends so far upward that on the average over 14½ pounds of it rests on each square inch of the earth's surface. The air not only rests on our heads with this weight, but also presses on us from all sides, like a giant holding each of us in its grip. We do not feel uncomfortable, for the air in our lungs is resisting with almost equal force. We realize the great weight of the air only when we have "the wind knocked out" by falling with such violence that the air is driven from our lungs, when the weight of the air momentarily rests on us very noticeably.

The weight of the air varies in different places according to their altitudes, and it varies in one place from hour to hour and day to day. This change in air pressure is connected with weather changes: the pressure is greater before fair weather. Thus changes in air pressure are important in weather forecasting. But how do we go about detecting these changes? This is done with an instrument called the *barometer*. Although there are many types of barometers for sale, one can make one himself. Fill an empty beverage bottle about one-fifth full of water. Then run a piece of quarter-inch diameter glass tubing through a tight-fitting cork, and fit the cork tightly into the bottle. The tube should be long enough to reach down into the water. Set the bottom in a vertical position. As fair weather, with its greater air pressure, approaches, the weight of the air resting on the only opening to the bottle, the glass tube, will press down on the water in the tube and force the water level up in the bottle. As long as the water level stands high and continues to rise in the bottle, fair weather is approaching, and we say the barometer is rising. A string on the outside of the bottle will help to keep track of the fluctuations in water level. Occasionally one will need to add a little water to the bottle to offset the loss by evaporation. The clipper ship type of barometer, which may be purchased for a dollar or so, is patterned along the same principle. In fair weather the weight of the air pressing on the spout opening forces the water level higher up into the bottle.

If one wishes to be more accurate, and to avoid the necessary and complicating refilling of the bottle, he may decide to make a mercury barometer. Take a piece of clean glass tubing about one-quarter inch in diameter and about a yard long. Seal one end in a gas flame and leave the other end open. Fill the tube with mercury. Then, with a finger held tightly over the open end to prevent leakage, turn the tube upside down so that the sealed end is up, and set it in a small dish of mercury. Before filling the tube with mercury a scale of inches should be marked on it, beginning with the level of mercury in the dish. Before fair weather, when the air is heavy, it presses on the mercury in the dish with greater weight, thus forcing it to rise in the tube, and we say the barometer is rising. In fair weather the mercury will usually stand

30 inches high or over, but the important thing in foretelling fair weather is that the column of mercury continues to rise.

Imagine that one has observed these clues about the weather, and that all of them point to fair weather. The best way to keep track of them is on a chart, which might be made along these lines.
Apr. 5 10 A.M. Cumulus NW Moderate 70 Rising FAIR
Apr. 5 3 P.M. Cumulus NW Gentle 67 Rising FAIR

Forecasting Rainy Weather

But let us say that the clouds do not look like cumulus clouds, that the wind is from the east, that the temperature is rising more than normally as the day advances, that the barometer is not rising. In other words, that the signs do not point to fair weather, but if it is summer, to rain, and if it is winter, to snow. We may wish to attempt to forecast how soon the rain will come. In forecasting rainy weather one will also find certain clues, for there is a typical sequence of clouds that accompanies the approach, arrival, and departure of a rainy spell. As the rain approaches, the clouds become successively lower and cover more and more of the sky. After the rain they are usually succeeded by higher and higher types. Anywhere one may be he has a grandstand seat from which to watch this impressive parade. Keep in mind that in our latitude (30° to 60° N. Latitude) most of the weather comes from a general westerly direction, and watch the clouds of the western sky most closely.

First come the high clouds: the *cirrus* and *cirrostratus*, or if one wishes to use their popular names, the "feather clouds" and the "thin gray veil." The cirrus clouds often resemble great, delicate, white feather curls. Frail and wispy, they are sometimes called "tangleweb clouds." With their stream-ing filaments they ride highest of all the clouds, sometimes eight or ten miles above the earth, in a zone of subzero temperatures whose winds sweep and curl about them. They are made entirely of ice crystals, and move at speeds as great as 200 miles an hour. Usually they appear as the advanced guard of a storm, meaning rain in a day or so, and the coming end of the stretch of fair weather. Succeeding them comes the thin gray veil of cirrostratus clouds, sometimes covering the sky completely with a milky veil through which one can see the sun's outline. Usually they appear about 24 hours before the rain, so watch for them. Sometimes they are accompanied by a "mackerel sky" of *cirrocumulus* clouds, tiny high masses of white cloudlets arranged in groups or lines, making ripples of a delicate structure resembling fish scales.

Next come clouds lower than the cirrus types. The sky may be covered with a complete gray or white layer of clouds, called *altostratus*, lower and thicker than the gray veil of cirrostratus. They may be accompanied by a "dappled sky," or *altocumulus* clouds, large globular masses of white or gray clouds, arranged in groups or lines, sometimes so closely packed that their edges are confused, and only patches of sky show between them. They show that the rain is nearer, perhaps only several hours away.

Soon the sky cover becomes lower and thicker, and we have the *cumulostratus*. Next come the *nimbus*, or rain, clouds, those from which the rain or snow actually falls. After the storm the above clouds often appear in reverse order, the nimbus breaking up into scuds of broken sky cover, then into a dappled sky, to be followed perhaps by mackerel sky and by cirrostratus, and finally by cirrus. Soon cumulus clouds are again in the sky, and fair weather once more is due.

Before a rain the wind is generally

from an easterly direction, its speed is usually increasing, as is the temperature, and the barometer is falling. The air is steadily getting lighter as the storm approaches, and will soon be unable to force the water level far down in the glass tube of the bottle barometer. This means the water will rise in the tube, with the result that the level of the water outside of the tube will be seen to fall, and we say that the barometer is falling. If one has a clipper ship barometer, the water will not be held back in the spout by the lighter air of the approaching storm, and it will drip or fall from the open spout. If one has a mercury barometer, he will see the mercury in the tube lower, for the air pressure will not press down hard enough on the open dish of mercury to maintain the former level of the mercury in the tube. In all of these cases we say that the barometer is "falling." The important thing to notice in forecasting is whether the barometer is rising or falling. The rapidity of a storm's approach and its intensity are proportional to the amount of the barometer's "fall." Accuracy in forecasting comes with a knowledge of all the weather factors to be observed and their correct correlation.

One may wish to learn some weather proverbs, for many of them, made up long ago and handed down through the years, are trustworthy. One will want to see *why* they are true, and will want to make up some of one's own. There can be a "weather corner" in the classroom or in the home, or at camp, with wind scale, barometers, thermometer, a copy of the beautiful and useful United States Weather Bureau Cloud Chart, and daily weather charts to which one can add appropriate decorations. One may wish to announce forecasts by raising flags. A set of flags may be made of small squares (12 by 12 inches) of unbleached muslin and plain blue and black denim. The white flag indicates

a forecast of fair weather, the dark blue one indicates rain or snow. A black pennant above the square adds "and warmer" to one's forecast; when below the square it adds "and cooler."

The booklets and articles and textbooks in the *Recommended Reading* will give one a deeper insight into the "whys" of the weather, and hence add to the fun in it and to the accuracy of the forecasts. As time goes on in classroom or camp weather bureau, individuals or groups will pick up more and more knowledge that helps in forecasting. Some knowledge will be acquired because one needs it to make a particular forecast; some one will search for because questions will be raised by one's observations; some information will be found by children who have become interested in a certain phase of the subject. One will learn such things as how clouds stay up in the sky, why certain clouds precede a rainstorm, how raindrops are formed, how the beautiful crystals of snowflakes, no two alike, are built up, how to forecast a thunderstorm, what thunder and lightning are, why tornados occur in the Middle West. One may wish to study the history of the United States Weather Bureau and how it operates. One may be interested in the more intricate, but essential parts of meteorology, the cyclones and anticyclones, that bring alternating fair and rainy weather, and the cold fronts and warm fronts that produce them. Some of us may wish to use the United States Weather Bureau's daily weather maps. Such yet unsolved problems as the study of long-range forecasting may pique one's curiosity.

When young people become interested in this game of forecasting the weather, one will see fear of a thunderstorm give way to understanding of it and a wise prudence; the disappointment of postponing a picnic or trip is lessened when they themselves have forecasted the rain; one will see their understand-

1. Cirrus clouds

2. Cirrus clouds forming cobweb

3. Cirro-stratus clouds forming a veil

4. Cirro-cumulus clouds—mackerel sky

5. Alto-cumulus clouds—dappled sky

6. Alto-cumulus clouds—followed by rain

Sequence of cloud types before a storm

ing of nature grow as they become more familiar with the wind and clouds, the rain and snow, and the other phenomena that make up our daily weather.
—L.W.P.

Recommended Reading

All About the Weather—Ivan Ray Tannehill. Random House, New York.
Audubon Nature Bulletin—*How a Thunderstorm Grows,* (a flannel board story) National Audubon Society, New York.
Clouds, Air and Wind—Eric Sloane, Devin-Adair, New York.
Everyday Weather and how it Works—Herman Schneider. (For children) McGraw-Hill Book Company, New York.

Weather—P.E., Lehr, R.W., Burnett, and H.S. Zim. (A Golden Nature Guide) Golden Press, New York.
Weather—Merit Badge Library. Boy Scouts of America, U.S.A.
Weather Handbook—Lou Williams. Girl Scouts of America, U.S.A.
Weathercasting—by Charles and Ruth Laird. Prentice-Hall, Englewood Cliffs, New Jersey.
Weathercraft—A.F. Spilhaus. Viking Press, New York.
Eric Sloane's Weather Book—Eric Sloane. Devin-Adair, New York.
Wind, Storm, and Rain—The Story of Weather—Denning Miller. Coward-McCann, Inc., New York.

WEB (*See under Spider*)